365
DAYS OF
CROSSWORDS

 **SparkPool**

Published in 2024
First published in the UK by SparkPool Publishing
An imprint of Igloo Books Ltd
Cottage Farm, NN6 0BJ, UK
Owned by Bonnier Books
Sveavägen 56, Stockholm, Sweden
www.igloobooks.com

0324 001
2 4 6 8 10 9 7 5 3 1
ISBN 978-1-83771-459-9

Puzzle compilation, typesetting and design by:
Clarity Media Ltd, http://www.clarity-media.co.uk

Edited by Alexandra Chapman

Printed and manufactured in China

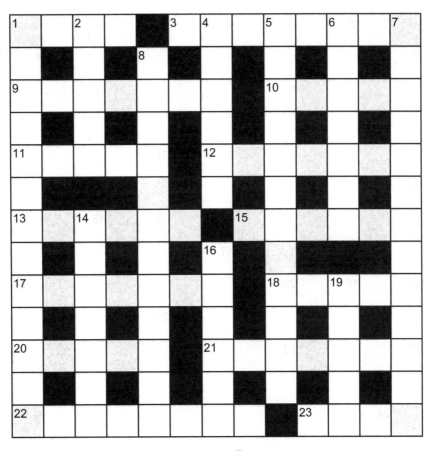

Across

1 Leave out (4)
3 British money (8)
9 Occurrence (7)
10 ___ acid: protein part (5)
11 Cinders (5)
12 Contempt (7)
13 Brief intervals (6)
15 State with confidence (6)
17 Goals (7)
18 Food blender (5)
20 African antelope (5)
21 Carried out incompetently (7)
22 Showed indifference (8)
23 Prestigious TV award (4)

Down

1 Excessively striving (13)
2 From Dublin (5)
4 Walks (6)
5 Re-evaluation (12)
6 Emulate (7)
7 In an amiable manner (4-9)
8 The management of a home (12)
14 Opposite of later (7)
16 In functioning condition (6)
19 Woody tissue (5)

CROSSWORD

Across

1   Luckily (11)
9   Inexperienced (of a person) (5)
10 Sticky yellowish substance (3)
11 Snarl (5)
12 Small shoot (5)
13 Spend wastefully (8)
16 Catch a conversation
    between others (8)
18 Response (5)
21 Where tennis is played (5)
22 Suitable (3)
23 Imbibe (5)
24 E.g. Plato (11)

Down

2   Sea creature with eight arms (7)
3   Catchphrase (7)
4   Sewing instrument (6)
5   Melodies (5)
6   Bring down (5)
7   Dictatorial (11)
8   Overstated (11)
14 Laugh unrestrainedly (5,2)
15 Exile; fugitive (7)
17 Changes; differs (6)
19 Piece of land (5)
20 Mountain cry (5)

CROSSWORD

Across

1 Heavy iron blocks (6)
7 Excessive or affected modesty (8)
8 Run steadily (3)
9 Circles a planet (6)
10 Destroy (4)
11 Standards (5)
13 Reptiles with scaly skin (7)
15 Self-important (7)
17 Uses a keyboard (5)
21 Female operatic star (4)
22 Trust or faith in (6)
23 Appropriate (3)
24 Young hares (8)
25 Spring suddenly (6)

Down

1 Be next to (6)
2 Good health; physical strength (6)
3 Go off (5)
4 Waterproof fabric (7)
5 Supplication (8)
6 Supplied or distributed (6)
12 Cartographer (8)
14 Mutters (7)
16 Thought; supposed (6)
18 Seabird (6)
19 Seat for two or more persons (6)
20 Grasp tightly (5)

PUZZLE 10

Across

1	Piece of software (11)
9	Item that unlocks a door (3)
10	Chocolate powder (5)
11	Rinse out with water (5)
12	Snow and rain mix (5)
13	E.g. Rudolph (8)
16	Friendly (8)
18	Water-filled ditches around castles (5)
20	County of SE England (5)
21	Tough problem (5)
22	Be in debt (3)
23	Celebrity (11)

Down

2	Recipient of money (5)
3	Lawful (5)
4	Laugh in a harsh way (6)
5	Mocking (7)
6	Compels (7)
7	Buildings of great height (11)
8	Everything that orbits the sun (5,6)
14	Projectile (7)
15	Mistake; blunder (4,3)
17	Make less tight (6)
18	Wall art (5)
19	Concerning (5)

Across

1 Trees with lobed leaves (6)
4 Devices that tell the time (6)
9 Started again (7)
10 Playful composition (7)
11 Large indefinite amount (5)
12 Rains heavily (5)
14 Rides the waves (5)
17 Type of fish (5)
19 Inhales open-mouthed when sleepy (5)
21 Apprehensive (7)
23 Young pilchard (7)
24 Stream (anag.) (6)
25 Official population count (6)

Down

1 Botch (4-2)
2 Essence of something (4)
3 Female ruler (7)
5 Enumerates (5)
6 Soldier (8)
7 Marsh plants (6)
8 Leader in a race (5,6)
13 Without warning (8)
15 Electronic retention of data (7)
16 Mineral used to make plaster of Paris (6)
18 Experiences the flavour of a food (6)
20 Strike firmly (5)
22 Exclamation of mild dismay (4)

Across

1	Crises (11)
9	Cup (3)
10	Position or point (5)
11	Levels; ranks (5)
12	Consumer (5)
13	Mythical sea creatures (8)
16	Be heavier than (8)
18	Choral musical composition (5)
20	___ Cooper: US rocker (5)
21	Observant (5)
22	Clothing needed for an activity (3)
23	Needless (11)

Down

2	Strength (5)
3	Stationery item for measuring distance (5)
4	Stimulate (6)
5	Outfit (7)
6	Native to a country (7)
7	Mimic (11)
8	Revive (11)
14	Inverts (anag.) (7)
15	Make public (7)
17	European country (6)
18	Tiny arachnids (5)
19	Buyer (5)

CROSSWORD

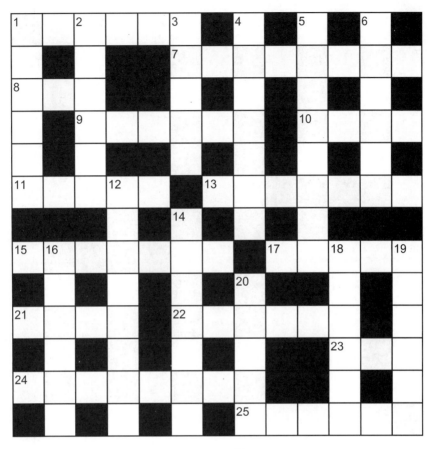

Across

1 Tradition (6)
7 Salve (8)
8 For what reason (3)
9 Inclined at an angle (6)
10 Stub (anag.) (4)
11 Cleans (5)
13 Planned (7)
15 Extinguish a candle (4,3)
17 Early version of a document (5)
21 Smudge (4)
22 Tracks (6)
23 Deep anger (3)
24 Decline (8)
25 Relative social standing (6)

Down

1 One who lacks courage (6)
2 Fashions (6)
3 Large pile of something (5)
4 Contemptuously (7)
5 Copycat (8)
6 Make possible (6)
12 Frustrated (8)
14 Instruction (7)
16 Move with a bounding motion (6)
18 Support; help (6)
19 Absorbent cloths (6)
20 Threads or fibres (5)

PUZZLE 14

CROSSWORD

Across

1 Astound (11)
9 Hit gently (3)
10 Unpleasant facial expression (5)
11 Resided (5)
12 Stares (5)
13 Polite expression of acknowledgement (5,3)
16 Settling for rest (of birds) (8)
18 Destiny (5)
20 Clark ___ : US actor (5)
21 Unit of length (5)
22 Not well (3)
23 Lacking distinguishing characteristics (11)

Down

2 City in Bolivia (2,3)
3 Foundation (5)
4 Sufficient (6)
5 Vexing (7)
6 Looks over in detail (7)
7 Fear in front of an audience (5,6)
8 Formidable (of a person) (11)
14 Mix (7)
15 Have a go at (7)
17 Sugary flower secretion (6)
18 Genuflect (5)
19 Incursions (5)

PUZZLE 15

CROSSWORD

Across

1 Delude (4)
3 Importance; stress (8)
9 Reduced in scope or length (3-4)
10 Intended (5)
11 Startling (4-8)
13 Surpass (6)
15 Relating to stars (6)
17 Resolvable (12)
20 Artifice (5)
21 Vienna's country (7)
22 Navigable channel (8)
23 Stringed instrument (4)

Down

1 12th month of the year (8)
2 Spike used by a climber (5)
4 Be in charge of (6)
5 Vagrancy (12)
6 Data input device (7)
7 Uses a stool (4)
8 Type of bus (6-6)
12 Cause to feel isolated (8)
14 Type of scientist (7)
16 Type of antelope (6)
18 Big and strong (5)
19 Pack carefully and neatly (4)

PUZZLE 16

Across

1 Hardened part of the skin (6)
7 Splitting (8)
8 Tree that bears acorns (3)
9 Blocks of metal (6)
10 Attack at speed (4)
11 Heroic tales (5)
13 Shrine in France (7)
15 Standing erect (7)
17 Waterlogged ground (5)
21 Intertwined segment of rope (4)
22 Place for small boats to dock (6)
23 Male turkey (3)
24 Large retail store (8)
25 Ghost (6)

Down

1 Large groups of people (6)
2 Feeling of fondness (6)
3 Go swiftly (5)
4 Meeting of an official body (7)
5 Create an account deficit (8)
6 Within a space (6)
12 The flying of aircraft (8)
14 Soft suede leather (7)
16 Country in Central America (6)
18 Forum icon (6)
19 Allow (6)
20 Percussion instruments (5)

PUZZLE 17

CROSSWORD

Across

1 Where darts players throw from (4)
3 Progresses (8)
9 Window furnishing (7)
10 Subject of a talk (5)
11 Firework display (12)
14 E.g. pecan (3)
16 Snail (anag.) (5)
17 Bind (3)
18 Changes to a situation (12)
21 Extremely small (prefix) (5)
22 Declaring to be untrue (7)
23 Estimating (8)
24 Reasons; explanations (4)

Down

1 Resident (8)
2 Recruiter (5)
4 University teacher (3)
5 Amazement (12)
6 Closely cropped hairstyle (4,3)
7 Observed (4)
8 Quarrelsome and uncooperative (12)
12 Large city on the Nile (5)
13 Written communications (8)
15 Sticky dark syrup (7)
19 Horse sound (5)
20 Type of air pollution (4)
22 Loud noise (3)

PUZZLE 18

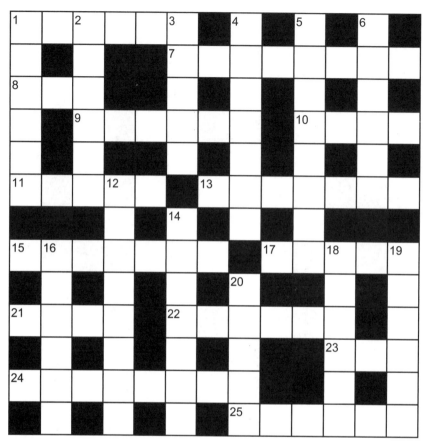

Across

1 Concealed from view (6)
7 Point of contact; masonry support (8)
8 Periodic publication (abbrev.) (3)
9 Reduces to shreds (6)
10 Suffers (4)
11 Edits (anag.) (5)
13 Undo (7)
15 Distributes around (7)
17 Prim and proper (5)
21 Garment of ancient Rome (4)
22 Red salad fruit (6)
23 Bristle-like appendage (3)
24 Hinged surfaces on aeroplane wings (8)
25 Arachnid (6)

Down

1 Small village (6)
2 Persistent in effort (6)
3 Unpleasant (5)
4 Estimates (7)
5 Existing or operating within (8)
6 Male relatives (6)
12 Lifts up (8)
14 Particular version of a text (7)
16 Financial gain (6)
18 On a ship or train (6)
19 Main meal (6)
20 Not quite right (5)

CROSSWORD

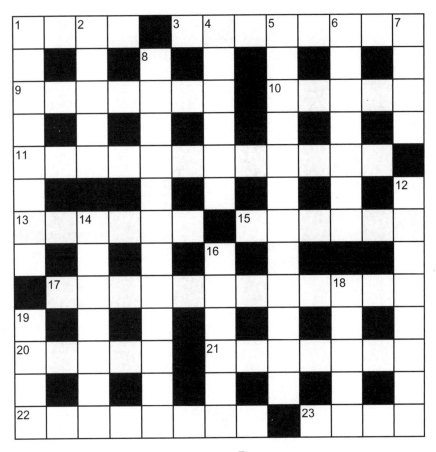

Across

1 Not hard (4)
3 Recent arrival (8)
9 Uncertain (7)
10 Killer whales (5)
11 Metal device for removing tops (6,6)
13 Step down from a job (6)
15 Spiritual head of a diocese (6)
17 Discreditable (12)
20 Lady (5)
21 Anthology (7)
22 Waterside area (8)
23 Goad on (4)

Down

1 Resolute (8)
2 One side of a gem (5)
4 Implant deeply (6)
5 Tight (of clothing) (5-7)
6 Shakespeare play about a Scottish nobleman (7)
7 Deceptive manoeuvre (4)
8 Hostility (12)
12 Peacemaker (8)
14 Of enormous effect (7)
16 Turmoil (6)
18 Jazz genre (5)
19 Was in debt (4)

Across

1 Robbery at sea (6)
4 Hurting (6)
9 Driving out (7)
10 Citadel in Moscow (7)
11 Ooze (5)
12 You usually do this whilst asleep (5)
14 Make less sharp (5)
17 There are 52 of these in a year (5)
19 Men (5)
21 Perennial herb (7)
23 The giving up of rights (7)
24 Female sibling (6)
25 Very cold (6)

Down

1 Positioned a car in a space (6)
2 Intense anger (4)
3 SI unit of electric charge (7)
5 Estimates the price of (5)
6 Begin (8)
7 Silenced (6)
8 Decisions reached by reasoning (11)
13 Surrounds on all sides (8)
15 Small loudspeaker (7)
16 Loose protective garments (6)
18 Kept hold of (6)
20 Steps over a fence (5)
22 Full of excitement (4)

CROSSWORD

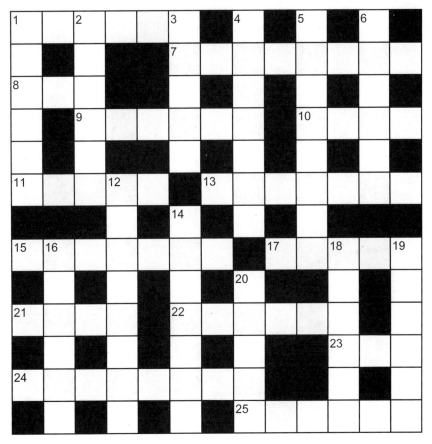

Across

1	Register of duties (6)
7	Indefatigable (8)
8	Shed tears (3)
9	Have as a purpose (6)
10	Travel on water (4)
11	Wise men (5)
13	Recluses (7)
15	Brawl (5-2)
17	Very skilled at something (5)
21	Smack with the hand (4)
22	Unthinkingly eager (4-2)
23	Animal lair (3)
24	Recording device (8)
25	Dried grape (6)

Down

1	Commotion (6)
2	Throwing at a target (6)
3	Reigned (5)
4	Examines in detail (7)
5	Taken for granted (8)
6	Charge with a crime (6)
12	Daydreamer (8)
14	Colloquial speech (7)
16	Remove goods from a van (6)
18	Wears away (6)
19	Substance found in wine (6)
20	Derisive smile (5)

PUZZLE 22

Across

1 Swiftness (8)
5 Opposite of fail (4)
9 Neck warmer (5)
10 Willingly (7)
11 Inspiring action (12)
13 Diacritical mark of two dots (6)
14 Contrapuntal compositions (6)
17 Science of deciphering codes (12)
20 Tall stand used by a preacher (7)
21 Ticks over (5)
22 Roster (4)
23 Mesmerism (8)

Down

1 Corrode (4)
2 Type of pheasant (7)
3 Tricky elements; obstacles (12)
4 Hatred (anag.) (6)
6 Relating to bees (5)
7 Small telescope (8)
8 Surrender (12)
12 Brawny (8)
15 Confirms a decision; supports (7)
16 Service business (6)
18 Sailing vessel (5)
19 Egyptian nature goddess (4)

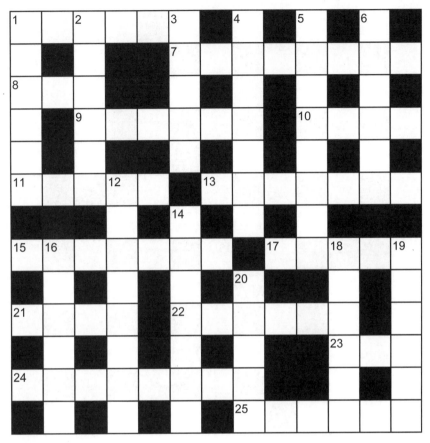

Across

1   E.g. from New Delhi (6)
7   Moment of great revelation (8)
8   Stream of liquid (3)
9   Mixed up or confused (6)
10 Neat in appearance (4)
11 High-pitched cries (5)
13 Inhabitant (7)
15 Extremely shocking things (7)
17 Allowed by official rules (5)
21 Microscopic organism (4)
22 Huge desert in North Africa (6)
23 Horse shade (3)
24 Horticulturist (8)
25 Make angry (6)

Down

1   Wound (6)
2   Nitty-gritty (6)
3   Freshly (5)
4   Take a seat (3,4)
5   Little fib (5,3)
6   Ask a person to come (6)
12 Monumental Egyptian
    structures (8)
14 Deleting (7)
16 Unidirectional (3-3)
18 Assigned scores (6)
19 John ___ : one of the Beatles (6)
20 Appeal (5)

Across

1 The greater part (8)
5 Read quickly (4)
9 Imitative of the past (5)
10 Timidness (7)
11 Ingredient in nail polish remover (7)
12 ___ Mirren: The Queen actress (5)
13 Encourage the development of (6)
14 Dress (6)
17 Receded (5)
19 Diagrams or pictures (7)
20 Guglielmo ___ : inventor associated with the radio (7)
21 Positive type of attitude (3-2)
22 Religious sisters (4)
23 Coerce into doing something (8)

Down

1 American actor (6,7)
2 Extreme nervousness (7)
3 Evergreen shrub (12)
4 Sampled (food) (6)
6 Ring solemnly (5)
7 Misinterpreted (13)
8 Based on legend (12)
15 Capital of Ontario (7)
16 Continent (6)
18 The fifth chemical element (5)

PUZZLE 25

Across

1 Appetiser (6)
4 Fruit drinks (6)
9 Infantile (7)
10 Painkilling drug or medicine (7)
11 Slithering animal (5)
12 Natural talent (5)
14 Combines (5)
15 Move slowly (5)
17 Length of interlaced hair (5)
18 Certificate (7)
20 Return a favour (7)
21 Person with detailed knowledge (6)
22 Deceives; fakes (6)

Down

1 Style and movement in art (6)
2 State of the USA (8)
3 Main (5)
5 Sets free or releases (7)
6 Guinea pig (4)
7 Mouse sound (6)
8 William ___ : English playwright (11)
13 Process of adding air (8)
14 Bridge above another road (7)
15 One who carries golf clubs (6)
16 Throes (anag.) (6)
17 Arouse (interest) (5)
19 Soft or soggy mass (4)

Across

1 Basically (11)
9 Blend together (3)
10 Sink; sag (5)
11 Ceases (5)
12 Small insect (5)
13 Hermits (8)
16 Paint-spraying device (8)
18 Fragile (5)
20 Expels from a position (5)
21 Reject with disdain (5)
22 Round bread roll (3)
23 Integrity; trustworthiness (11)

Down

2 Next after fifth (5)
3 Wrapped up (5)
4 Group of touring entertainers (6)
5 Road or roofing material (7)
6 Lucy ___ : Xena: Warrior Princess actress (7)
7 Diplomatic officials (11)
8 Very successful (of a book) (4-7)
14 Piece of furniture (7)
15 Traversed (7)
17 Residential district (6)
18 Ultimate (5)
19 Head of a monastery (5)

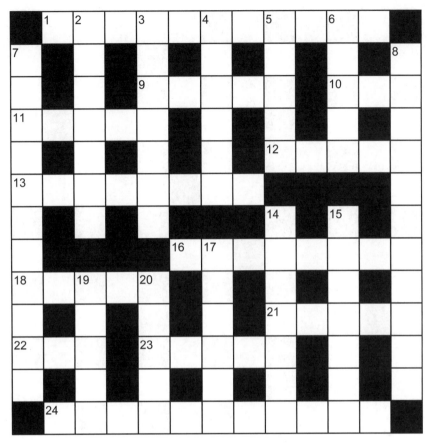

Across

1 Images recorded on film (11)
9 Underground worker (5)
10 Depression (3)
11 Ape (abbrev.) (5)
12 ___ Carell: US actor and comedian (5)
13 Alloy of copper and tin (8)
16 Mentally sharp (8)
18 Folds close together (5)
21 Tennis score (5)
22 Opposite of in (3)
23 Rivulets (5)
24 Action of stealing from a store (11)

Down

2 Cleanliness (7)
3 Enticed (7)
4 Swiss city (6)
5 Land measures (5)
6 Row of bushes (5)
7 Gratitude; acclaim (11)
8 Act of making peace (11)
14 Inclination (7)
15 Tar-like hydrocarbon (7)
17 Cell centres (6)
19 Receive a ball in one's hands (5)
20 Device used to sharpen razors (5)

Across

4 Country in central Africa (6)
7 Single-celled organisms (8)
8 Add together (3)
9 Break suddenly (4)
10 Place where goods are bought and sold (6)
11 Fine or punishment (7)
12 Wide (5)
15 Walked up and down (5)
17 Marsupial (7)
20 Lanes (6)
21 Bowed stringed instrument (4)
22 Cut of pork (3)
23 Familiar description for a person (8)
24 Maxim (6)

Down

1 Ornamental border (6)
2 Obstruction in a passage (8)
3 Horizontal angle of a compass bearing (7)
4 Former name of the Democratic Republic of Congo (5)
5 Small restaurant (6)
6 Nutlike kernel used to make marzipan (6)
13 Germane (8)
14 Item of clerical clothing (7)
15 Shoves (6)
16 Damp and sticky to touch (6)
18 Flowers (6)
19 Existing (5)

CROSSWORD

Across

1 Dawn (8)
5 Metallic element (4)
9 Large fruit with pulpy flesh (5)
10 Skull (7)
11 Non-professional (7)
12 Scoundrel (5)
13 Brushes (6)
14 Portions of a play (6)
17 Not as young (5)
19 Routers (anag.) (7)
20 Country that borders Libya (7)
21 Small woody plant (5)
22 Cheese coated with red wax (4)
23 Dark colour that is virtually black (4,4)

Down

1 Sympathetic and merciful (13)
2 Piece of art made from various materials (7)
3 Characteristic of the present (12)
4 Happens (6)
6 Decorating a cake (5)
7 Measurable by a common standard (13)
8 Unpredictably (12)
15 Nasal opening (7)
16 Canada's capital (6)
18 Unquestioning belief (5)

PUZZLE 30

CROSSWORD

34

Across

1 Device that tests for the presence of something (8)
5 Division of a hospital (4)
9 Donna ___ New York: clothing label (5)
10 Arc of coloured light (7)
11 Not enough (12)
14 Put down (3)
15 Ironic metaphor (5)
16 Edge of a cup (3)
17 Illustration facing the title page of a book (12)
20 Type of newspaper (7)
22 Absolute (5)
23 Tiny specks (4)
24 Speaking many languages (8)

Down

1 Sovereign prince (4)
2 Cruel use of authority (7)
3 Act of discussing something; deliberation (12)
4 Belonging to us (3)
6 Stroll (5)
7 Non-functioning period (8)
8 Science of biological processes (12)
12 Deceives (5)
13 Destined to fail (3-5)
16 Musical performance (7)
18 Fly around a planet (5)
19 Small ink stain (4)
21 Pair of people (3)

CROSSWORD

Across

4 Homes (6)
7 Holding and using (a weapon) (8)
8 Container (3)
9 African antelope (4)
10 Surroundings (6)
11 Reunites (7)
12 Rouse from sleep (5)
15 State of the USA (5)
17 Person who accumulates things (7)
20 Idolise (6)
21 Stop up a hole (4)
22 Facsimile (abbrev.) (3)
23 Control (8)
24 Comes after (6)

Down

1 Sixty seconds (6)
2 Eye disease (8)
3 Dyestuff (7)
4 Spry (5)
5 Expose as being false (6)
6 Church official (6)
13 Suddenly (8)
14 Not native (7)
15 Firm or hard sweet (6)
16 Ancient Persian king (6)
18 Rejoices (6)
19 Prophets (5)

PUZZLE 32

Across

1 Doorway (6)
4 Averts something bad (6)
9 Stopping place for a train (7)
10 Childish display of temper (7)
11 Spacious (5)
12 Open disrespect (5)
14 Waterlogged area of land (5)
15 E.g. newspapers and TV (5)
17 Tennis stroke (5)
18 African country with capital Windhoek (7)
20 Cantered (7)
21 Avow (6)
22 Document fastener (6)

Down

1 Show-offs (6)
2 Argued logically (8)
3 Friendship (5)
5 Sully (7)
6 Change direction suddenly (4)
7 Fish with pink flesh (6)
8 Put questions to (11)
13 Go beyond a limit (8)
14 Little glass balls (7)
15 Capital of the Philippines (6)
16 Hawk (6)
17 Member of the weasel family (5)
19 Without shine; dull (4)

Across

1 Remaining leftovers (8)
5 Succulent (4)
9 Tortoise carapace (5)
10 Kitchen appliance (7)
11 Therapeutic use of plant extracts (12)
14 Make a mistake (3)
15 Well-known (5)
16 Snare or trap; alcoholic spirit (3)
17 Small meteor (8,4)
20 Where you sleep (7)
22 Small curved lake (5)
23 Near (anag.) (4)
24 Additional book matter (8)

Down

1 Monetary unit of Mexico (4)
2 Less obscured (7)
3 Clarification (12)
4 Obtained (3)
6 Extreme (5)
7 Moving at speed (8)
8 Children's toy (12)
12 Largest moon of Saturn (5)
13 Reasonable and judicious (8)
16 Snatched (7)
18 Command (5)
19 Move in water (4)
21 Wet soil (3)

CROSSWORD

Across

1 Unthinking (of a response) (4-4)
5 Having little or no hair (4)
8 Unit of light (5)
9 Temporary camp (7)
10 Large area of land (7)
12 Freezing (3-4)
14 General idea (7)
16 Tomb inscription (7)
18 Meddles with (7)
19 Animal life of a region (5)
20 Fathers (4)
21 Introductory pieces of music (8)

Down

1 Furnace (4)
2 Fur from stoats (6)
3 US actress (4,5)
4 Stole from (6)
6 Female graduate (6)
7 Dilapidated (8)
11 Existing in abundance (9)
12 Introduced fluid into (the body) (8)
13 Recorded on camera (6)
14 Follow-up drink (6)
15 Came next (6)
17 Circuits of a racetrack (4)

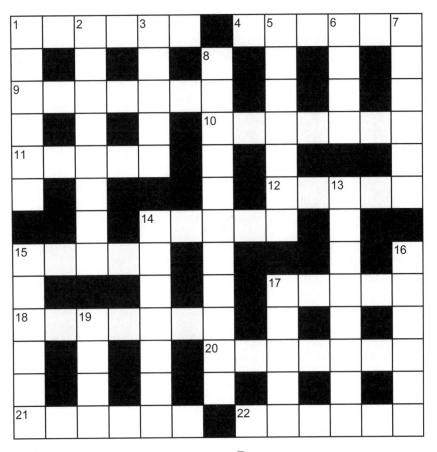

Across

1 Series of eight notes (6)
4 In flower (6)
9 Corneas (anag.) (7)
10 Swell with fluid (7)
11 Misplaces (5)
12 Tease or pester (5)
14 Blood vessels (5)
15 Headdress worn by a bishop (5)
17 Nose of an animal (5)
18 Frenzied (7)
20 Unintelligent (7)
21 Totter or tremble (6)
22 Pleaded with; asked for money (6)

Down

1 Supernatural (6)
2 Cut across (8)
3 Close-fitting garments (5)
5 Spending funds (7)
6 Finished; complete (4)
7 Relatively limited (of an amount) (6)
8 Unambiguous (11)
13 About to take place (8)
14 Trace of something (7)
15 Slightly annoyed (6)
16 Be present at (6)
17 Sharp peak (5)
19 Corrosive substance (4)

PUZZLE 36

Across

1 Creative (8)
5 Skin condition on the face (4)
9 Seize firmly (5)
10 Slackens (7)
11 Art of planning a dance (12)
13 Ronald ___ : former US President (6)
14 A way out (6)
17 Productive insight (12)
20 Hard but fragile (7)
21 Rugby formation (5)
22 Legendary creature (4)
23 Naive or sentimental (4-4)

Down

1 Historical drama film directed by Ben Affleck (4)
2 Windpipe (7)
3 Large grocery stores (12)
4 Ice homes (6)
6 Inexpensive (5)
7 Author (8)
8 Bravely (12)
12 Very likely (8)
15 Ardently; keenly (7)
16 Dairy product (6)
18 George ___ : author of Silas Marner (5)
19 Surrounded by (4)

Across

1 Cheat someone financially (5-6)
9 Getting rid of (5)
10 Pro (3)
11 Parts in a play (5)
12 Sticky sap (5)
13 Unstable (8)
16 Symmetrical open plane curve (8)
18 Book leaves (5)
21 Relish (5)
22 Bashful; reluctant to give details (3)
23 Relating to the kidneys (5)
24 Enthusiastic supporter (11)

Down

2 Unfortunate (7)
3 Cooked meat in the oven (7)
4 Curled or wound (6)
5 Foresee or predict (5)
6 Presents (5)
7 Cautious (11)
8 Gorge in Arizona (5,6)
14 Kneecap (7)
15 Perform magic tricks (7)
17 Lacking a key (of music) (6)
19 Sculptured symbol (5)
20 Shopping binge (5)

Across

1 Fearful of open spaces (11)
9 Deviate off course (3)
10 Viewpoint (5)
11 With ___ breath: anxiously (5)
12 Cornish ___ : food item (5)
13 Branch of mathematics (8)
16 Innocuous (8)
18 Lively Bohemian dance (5)
20 Make fun of in a playful manner (5)
21 Rise to one's feet (3,2)
22 ___ Kilmer: famous actor (3)
23 Without guilt (11)

Down

2 Loose garments (5)
3 Tarnished (of a metal object) (5)
4 Public square in Italy (6)
5 Remote districts of Australia (7)
6 Put in position ready for use (7)
7 Compassionate (11)
8 Not wanted (11)
14 Respire (7)
15 Brisk, in music (7)
17 Ice shoes (6)
18 Student (5)
19 Is enamoured with (5)

CROSSWORD

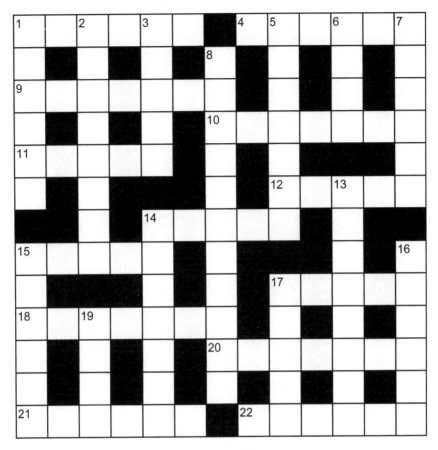

Across

1	Cease to be valid (6)
4	Doze (6)
9	Predatory fish (7)
10	Kind or sort (7)
11	City in West Yorkshire (5)
12	Lumberjack (5)
14	Humid (5)
15	Wash with water (5)
17	Fortunate (5)
18	Garden flower (7)
20	Have inside (7)
21	However (6)
22	Intimidatory remark (6)

Down

1	Gets rid of (6)
2	Type of cheese (8)
3	Leases (5)
5	State of disorder (7)
6	Pleasant (4)
7	Participant in a game (6)
8	A redeeming quality (6,5)
13	Remains of something damaged (8)
14	Significance (7)
15	Feel sorrow for one's deeds (6)
16	Young swan (6)
17	Meal (5)
19	Group of three (4)

PUZZLE 40

Across

4	One who poses for effect (6)
7	Popular fizzy beverage (8)
8	Listening device (3)
9	Chickens lay these (4)
10	Capital of Cuba (6)
11	Reaches (7)
12	Found agreeable (5)
15	Minor road (5)
17	Floor coverings (7)
20	Automata (6)
21	Direct one's gaze at (4)
22	Taxi (3)
23	Cooking in the oven (8)
24	Stable (6)

Down

1	Altitude (6)
2	Greek dish (8)
3	Whipping (7)
4	Annoy (5)
5	Set out on a journey (6)
6	Having a rough surface (of terrain) (6)
13	Rude (8)
14	Officer in the armed forces (7)
15	Blocks of fired clay (6)
16	Sing in a trilling manner (6)
18	Causing distress or trouble (6)
19	Truck (5)

CROSSWORD

Across

1 Well-known sentence (11)
9 Soak up; wipe away (3)
10 Mounds of loose sand (5)
11 Long flat piece of timber (5)
12 Roadside pull-off (3-2)
13 Leonardo ___ : US actor (8)
16 Carve words on something (8)
18 ___ Way: famous Roman road (5)
20 Condescend (5)
21 Musical toy (5)
22 Canine (3)
23 Comprehends (11)

Down

2 Put into service (5)
3 Container for storing items (5)
4 Type of sandwich (6)
5 Prayers (anag.) (7)
6 Indonesian island (7)
7 Petty (5-6)
8 Admit to be true (11)
14 Drug that relieves pain (7)
15 Crease in the skin (7)
17 Fires (6)
18 Plants of a region (5)
19 ___ with: supported (5)

CROSSWORD

Across

1 Paternal (8)
5 Spread clumsily on a surface (4)
8 Bitterly pungent (5)
9 Deform (7)
10 In name only (7)
12 Small hardy range horse (7)
14 Identifying outfit (7)
16 Affairs (7)
18 Not in any place (7)
19 Shoot with great precision (5)
20 Cipher (4)
21 Of many different kinds (8)

Down

1 Accomplishment (4)
2 Pulses (6)
3 Stamina (9)
4 A cargo (6)
6 Makes more attractive (6)
7 Food poisoning (8)
11 Public declaration of policy (9)
12 Assisting the memory (8)
13 Packed carefully and neatly (6)
14 Rushes (anag.) (6)
15 Musician playing a double-reed instrument (6)
17 Long-running dispute (4)

Across

1 Domineering (11)
9 Short sleep (3)
10 Operatic songs (5)
11 Fish and ___ : classic dish (5)
12 Challenges (5)
13 Extremely delicate (8)
16 Puts up with something (8)
18 Striped insects (5)
20 Makes fast with ropes (5)
21 Equine animal (5)
22 Fish appendage (3)
23 Measure of heat (11)

Down

2 Type of snake (5)
3 Highways (5)
4 Evoke (6)
5 Saves from danger (7)
6 Observes (7)
7 Unwise (11)
8 Annoying (11)
14 Decorative framework (7)
15 Fighting vessel (7)
17 Strong feeling of loathing (6)
18 Cereal plant (5)
19 More secure (5)

PUZZLE 44

Across

1 Country in Asia (8)
5 Skin mark from a wound (4)
9 Delicious (5)
10 Circling around (7)
11 Give too much money (7)
12 Respond to (5)
13 Violent uprising (6)
14 Fierce or domineering woman (6)
17 Venomous snake (5)
19 Follows very closely (7)
20 Brushed off the face (of hair) (7)
21 Senseless (5)
22 European volcano (4)
23 Alumni events (8)

Down

1 Film (6,7)
2 Beginning to exist (7)
3 International multi-sport event (7,5)
4 Fillings (6)
6 Porcelain (5)
7 Virtuousness (13)
8 Effective working together of different parts of the body (12)
15 Pear-shaped fruit native to Mexico (7)
16 Insect that transmits sleeping sickness (6)
18 Water container (5)

PUZZLE 45

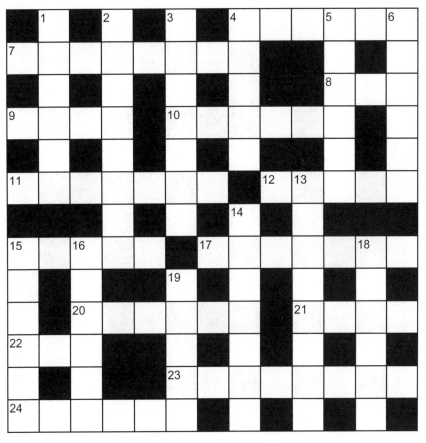

Across

4 Permanent skin marking (6)
7 Grainy (8)
8 Additionally (3)
9 Fever (4)
10 Steering devices (6)
11 Movement conveying an expression (7)
12 Subatomic particle such as a photon (5)
15 These grow on your head (5)
17 Sleepless (7)
20 Yield (6)
21 Counter used in poker (4)
22 Range of knowledge (3)
23 Huge (8)
24 Girded (anag.) (6)

Down

1 Shoe (6)
2 Mammal with a sticky tongue (8)
3 Floral (7)
4 Attempts (5)
5 Raises one's glass to (6)
6 More likely than not (4-2)
13 Defeat (8)
14 Warning (7)
15 Long for (6)
16 Pressed clothes (6)
18 One of a kind (6)
19 Watched secretly (5)

PUZZLE 46

Across

1 Uncovered; displayed (8)
5 Stock of money (4)
9 Recently made (5)
10 Groups of actors (7)
11 Ability to acquire and apply knowledge (12)
14 Unit of resistance (3)
15 A score of two under par on a hole (golf) (5)
16 Domestic animal (3)
17 In accordance with general custom (12)
20 Moved slowly with the current (7)
22 Circumference (5)
23 24-hour periods (4)
24 Person who supports a cause (8)

Down

1 Widespread (4)
2 Country in South East Asia (7)
3 Accomplishments (12)
4 Juvenile newt (3)
6 Unfasten a garment (5)
7 Cuts into bits (8)
8 Version of the blues (6-6)
12 Not heavy (5)
13 Admitted (8)
16 Open area of grassland (7)
18 Very loud (5)
19 Natter (4)
21 Father (3)

PUZZLE 47

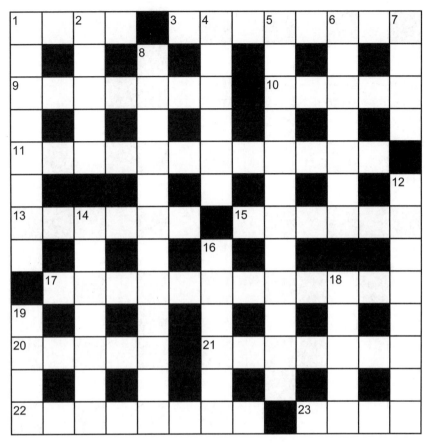

Across

1 Wine container (4)
3 Subsidiary (8)
9 Kitchen implement (7)
10 Make less bright (5)
11 Menacing (12)
13 US state whose capital is
   Carson City (6)
15 Person who fishes (6)
17 Not able to be confirmed (12)
20 Crime of setting something
   on fire (5)
21 Ardent (7)
22 Rigorous investigation (8)
23 Cunning (4)

Down

1 Buffers (8)
2 Barely sufficient (5)
4 Tricksters (6)
5 Strengthen; confirm (12)
6 A number defining position (7)
7 Measure duration (4)
8 Brusque and surly (12)
12 Foliage (8)
14 ___ Hudgens: US actress (7)
16 Swimming costume (6)
18 Small tuned drum (5)
19 Mother (4)

Across

4 Famous London clock (3,3)
7 Struggle helplessly (8)
8 Sap (anag.) (3)
9 Small particles of stone (4)
10 Pencil rubber (6)
11 Bordeaux wines (7)
12 Insectivorous mammal (5)
15 Overly sentimental (5)
17 Raise an ___ : show surprise (7)
20 Deviate suddenly (6)
21 Lean (4)
22 Large vessel (3)
23 Repute; standing (8)
24 Long narrow hilltops (6)

Down

1 Consisting of flowers (6)
2 Flatter (6,2)
3 Commercials (7)
4 Make inoperative (5)
5 One who carries something (6)
6 Son of one's brother or sister (6)
13 Natural homes of animals (8)
14 Prepare for printing (7)
15 Chemical element with symbol 'Ag' (6)
16 Sent in the mail (6)
18 Constrain or compel (6)
19 Items used on stage (5)

Across

1	Emergency service (4,7)
9	Stood up (5)
10	Cheek (slang) (3)
11	Sends out in the post (5)
12	Large residence (5)
13	Took into account (8)
16	Observer (8)
18	Rescued (5)
21	Longest river in Europe (5)
22	E.g. Hedwig in Harry Potter (3)
23	Regular beat (5)
24	Easily made angry (3-8)

Down

2	Encroach (7)
3	These remove pencil marks (7)
4	Novice (6)
5	Twinkle (5)
6	Bob ___ : US singer (5)
7	Sponsor mice (anag.) (11)
8	Fitting (11)
14	Gather (7)
15	Flatter (7)
17	Symbol (6)
19	Roman country house (5)
20	Repository (5)

54

Across

1 Opposite of more (4)
3 E.g. a spider or scorpion (8)
9 Excessive pride; vanity (7)
10 Focal point (5)
11 Act of slowing down (12)
13 Strong ringing sounds (6)
15 Beginning (6)
17 Making no money (12)
20 Large intestine (5)
21 Blanked (7)
22 Showed a TV show (8)
23 Item of footwear (4)

Down

1 Clarity (8)
2 Pertaining to sound (5)
4 Sharp reply (6)
5 Building (12)
6 Harmful (7)
7 Run quickly (4)
8 Hostile aggressiveness (12)
12 Participant in a meeting (8)
14 Ring-shaped (7)
16 Place of work (6)
18 Tree (5)
19 Case (anag.) (4)

Across

1 Pairs of people (4)
3 Lumberjack's tool (8)
9 French city (7)
10 Horse carts (5)
11 In a hostile manner (12)
14 Monstrous humanoid creature (3)
16 Leaf of a fern (5)
17 Helpful hint (3)
18 Gratitude (12)
21 Clear and apparent (5)
22 Marked by prosperity (of a past time) (7)
23 Scorn; disdain (8)
24 Strong beers (4)

Down

1 Organ stop (8)
2 Outstanding (of a debt) (5)
4 Female chicken (3)
5 Separately (12)
6 Faintly illuminated at night (7)
7 Stinging insect (4)
8 Disturbance; act of meddling (12)
12 Unemotional (5)
13 Beginnings (8)
15 Skipper (7)
19 Pastoral poem (5)
20 Heroic poem (4)
22 Leap on one foot (3)

Across

1. Quivered (8)
5. Long deep cut (4)
9. Songbird (5)
10. Walked upon (7)
11. Incessantly (12)
13. Evaluate (6)
14. Decline to do something (6)
17. Branch of astronomy (12)
20. Annoying pain (7)
21. Representative; messenger (5)
22. Mission (4)
23. Makes a high-pitched sound (8)

Down

1. Recording medium (4)
2. Convey a thought in words (7)
3. Type of sweet (12)
4. Distinct being (6)
6. Mountain range in South America (5)
7. Social insect (8)
8. Despair (12)
12. Long-tailed parrot (8)
15. Rude (7)
16. Beat as if with a flail (6)
18. Exhausts (5)
19. Hair colourants (4)

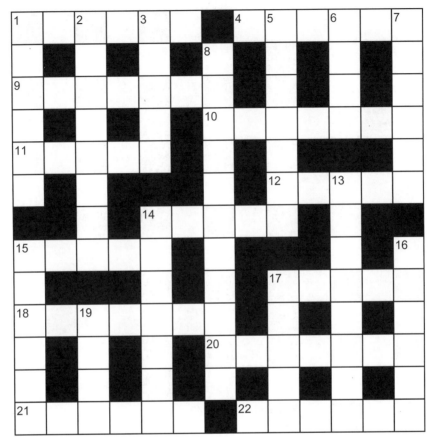

Across

1 Small stone (6)
4 Fly an aircraft (6)
9 Summary of results (7)
10 Strong reaction of anger (7)
11 Pulls along forcefully (5)
12 E.g. oxygen and nitrogen (5)
14 Portion (5)
15 Less (5)
17 Spirit in a bottle (5)
18 A parent's mother (7)
20 Small rounded lumps (7)
21 Long strips of cloth (6)
22 Composite of different species (6)

Down

1 Procession (6)
2 House with one storey (8)
3 Animals that roar (5)
5 Year in which wine was produced (7)
6 Song for a solo voice (4)
7 Goes in (6)
8 Inattentive (11)
13 Fraudster (8)
14 Make from raw materials (7)
15 Engages in combat (6)
16 Came to an end (6)
17 Devout (5)
19 Ends (4)

CROSSWORD

Across

1 Leave a ship (6)
7 Made better (8)
8 Position of employment (3)
9 Sand trap in golf (6)
10 Engrave with acid (4)
11 E.g. incisors and molars (5)
13 Philosophical theory (7)
15 Confound (7)
17 Descend rapidly (5)
21 Italian acknowledgement (4)
22 Instrumental piece of music (6)
23 Close-fitting hat (3)
24 Witty reply (8)
25 Least polite (6)

Down

1 Dishearten (6)
2 Pocket of air in a sphere of liquid (6)
3 Strikes with the foot (5)
4 Stimulated; urged on (7)
5 Cabbage salad (8)
6 Responds to (6)
12 Relating to time (8)
14 Foundation garments (7)
16 Linger aimlessly (6)
18 Seer (6)
19 Marionette (6)
20 Extreme displeasure (5)

CROSSWORD

Across

1 Anxious uncertainty (8)
5 Adjoin (4)
9 Wet thoroughly (5)
10 Bunch of flowers (7)
11 Impossible to achieve (12)
13 Blunt thick needle (6)
14 Free from danger (6)
17 DIY stands for this (2-2-8)
20 Cost (7)
21 Loop with a running knot (5)
22 Playthings (4)
23 Completely preoccupied with (8)

Down

1 Soft drink (US) (4)
2 Rendered senseless (7)
3 Very exciting (12)
4 Tunnel under a road for pedestrians (6)
6 Promotional wording (5)
7 Ragged (8)
8 Most perfect example of a quality (12)
12 Complying with orders (8)
15 Insensitive and cruel (7)
16 Majestic; wonderful (6)
18 Insinuate (5)
19 Large group of cattle (4)

PUZZLE 56

Across

1 Plant of the daisy family (6)
4 Spread out awkwardly (6)
9 Instructions on how to cook dishes (7)
10 Ancient large storage jar (7)
11 Acoustic detection system (5)
12 Damage the reputation of (5)
14 Thick slices (5)
17 Levied (5)
19 Prison compartments (5)
21 Plans to do something (7)
23 Violent wind storm (7)
24 Move or travel hurriedly (6)
25 Bank employee (6)

Down

1 Suspends; prevents (6)
2 Rounded protuberance on a camel (4)
3 Not outside (7)
5 Fills a suitcase (5)
6 Supplemental part of a book (8)
7 Opposite of winners (6)
8 Instance of buying or selling (11)
13 Considers an option (8)
15 Degree of eminence (7)
16 Put an end to (6)
18 Rusted (anag.) (6)
20 Raised floor or platform (5)
22 Invalid; void (4)

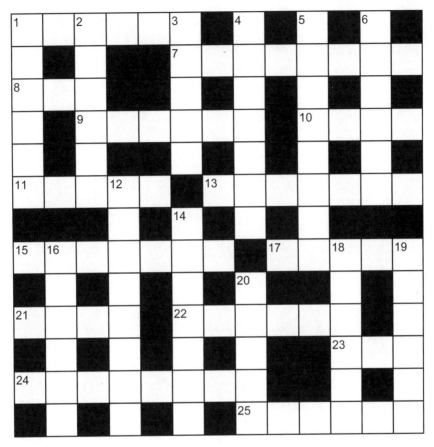

Across

1	Precious stones (6)
7	Section of a train (8)
8	Pen point (3)
9	Simple song (6)
10	Speak angrily (4)
11	Staggers (5)
13	Of the United Kingdom (7)
15	Tapering flag (7)
17	Ascends (5)
21	Ostrichlike bird (4)
22	Selfishness (6)
23	Month (3)
24	Act of removal (8)
25	Male goose (6)

Down

1	Lower in rank (6)
2	Waver (6)
3	Injure with very hot liquid (5)
4	Starred (anag.) (7)
5	Operatic texts (8)
6	Representatives (6)
12	Ancestral lines of descent (8)
14	Meantime (7)
16	Reverberated (6)
18	Added together (6)
19	Woodcutter (6)
20	Opposite of old (5)

PUZZLE 58

Across

4	Woman's garment (6)
7	Grammatical case (8)
8	Embrace (3)
9	Board game (4)
10	Coiffure (6)
11	Sticks to (7)
12	Reddish (5)
15	Relocated (5)
17	Spiders spin these (7)
20	Finish (6)
21	School test (4)
22	At the present time (3)
23	Extreme bitterness (8)
24	Songlike cries (6)

Down

1	Ridiculous (6)
2	Orange pigment found in carrots (8)
3	Less heavy (7)
4	Give a false notion of (5)
5	Maintain a custom (6)
6	Nervously (6)
13	Difficult to move because of its size (8)
14	People who run to keep fit (7)
15	Nastily (6)
16	Watched (6)
18	Talks excessively about one's talents (6)
19	Female opera stars (5)

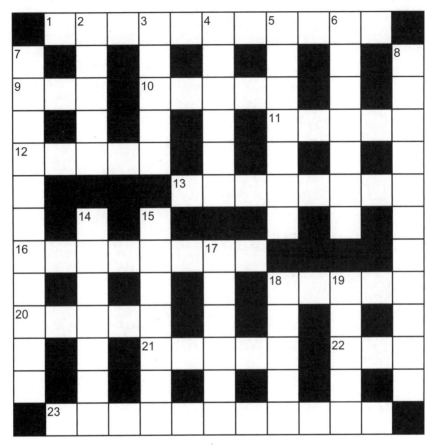

Across

1 Dishonestly (11)
9 Seventh Greek letter (3)
10 The beginning of an era (5)
11 Opposite of before (5)
12 All (5)
13 Classic Spanish soup made from raw vegetables (8)
16 Musical wind instruments (8)
18 Underground railway (5)
20 Get up (5)
21 From the capital of Italy (5)
22 Auction item (3)
23 Inn (6,5)

Down

2 Delete (5)
3 Mournful poem (5)
4 Russian carriage (6)
5 Sad (7)
6 Framework used to support climbing plants (7)
7 Become worse (11)
8 Spoken communication (4,2,5)
14 Reindeer (7)
15 Tallier (anag.) (7)
17 Infinitesimally small (6)
18 Juicy fruit (5)
19 Leans at an angle (5)

CROSSWORD

64

Across

1 Reliable (11)
9 Positive electrode (5)
10 Rubbish holder (3)
11 Set out (5)
12 Woodland spirit (5)
13 Source of annoyance (8)
16 Highly seasoned smoked beef (8)
18 Areas of mown grass (5)
21 Colour of milk chocolate (5)
22 Also (3)
23 Round steering device (5)
24 Substance that arouses desire (11)

Down

2 Competition (7)
3 Written law (7)
4 Stiff and stilted (6)
5 Stinks (5)
6 Established custom (5)
7 Thing that may happen (11)
8 Component parts (11)
14 Buildings for horses (7)
15 Balearic Island (7)
17 Attach (6)
19 Cry of excitement (5)
20 Effluent system (5)

PUZZLE 61

Across

1 Waterproof overshoe (6)
4 Rebukes angrily (6)
9 Republic in South America (7)
10 Sandy shores (7)
11 Sends through the mail (5)
12 Scottish lakes (5)
14 ___ Carlo: area of Monaco (5)
17 Deciduous coniferous tree (5)
19 Moist (of air) (5)
21 Requests the presence of (7)
23 Decorative style of design (3,4)
24 More than is necessary (6)
25 Wild animals (6)

Down

1 Worldwide (6)
2 Brian ___ : West Indian cricketer (4)
3 Clever but false argument (7)
5 Small cluster (5)
6 Guiding light (8)
7 State of mental strain (6)
8 Act of giving up one's job (11)
13 Relating to weather (8)
15 Lift up (7)
16 Saying (6)
18 Makes a sibilant sound (6)
20 Cuts calories (5)
22 Labels (4)

Across

1 Unspecified in number (4)
3 Neat and smart (5-3)
9 Impetuous person (7)
10 Small fruit used for oil (5)
11 State of being in disrepair (12)
14 Limb used for walking (3)
16 Tests (5)
17 Pay (anag.) (3)
18 Unnecessarily careful (12)
21 Feign (3,2)
22 Augmented (7)
23 Intensified (8)
24 Antelopes (4)

Down

1 Timetable (8)
2 E.g. iron or copper (5)
4 Boy (3)
5 Gradual reduction in value (12)
6 Salad plant (7)
7 Level in a hierarchy (4)
8 Re-emergence (12)
12 Stage play (5)
13 Instalments of a TV series (8)
15 French dance (7)
19 Many times (5)
20 Familiar name for a potato (4)
22 Insect which collects pollen (3)

Across

- **1** Read with care (6)
- **4** Moved over ice (6)
- **9** Exceptionally large (7)
- **10** Residence of the Pope (7)
- **11** European country (5)
- **12** Cause to stop sleeping (5)
- **14** Subsequently (5)
- **17** Suspends (5)
- **19** Office records keeper (5)
- **21** Pungent gas (7)
- **23** Last in a series (7)
- **24** Short track for storing trains (6)
- **25** Fish-eating raptor (6)

Down

- **1** Shorebird (6)
- **2** Underground plant part (4)
- **3** School bag (7)
- **5** Toys flown in the wind (5)
- **6** Three-hulled sailing boat (8)
- **7** Changing the colour of hair (6)
- **8** Link together (11)
- **13** Not necessary (8)
- **15** Equilateral parallelogram (7)
- **16** Groups of eight (6)
- **18** Attractive and stylish (6)
- **20** Apprehended with certainty (5)
- **22** Close by (4)

Across

1   Tool; cocktail (11)
9   Your (poetic) (3)
10 Brusque (5)
11 Select; choose (5)
12 Semiaquatic mammal (5)
13 Straddle (8)
16 Exploits to excess (8)
18 Flowering plant (5)
20 Pashmina (5)
21 Accumulate over a period of
    time (5)
22 Sorrowful (3)
23 Type of artist (11)

Down

2   Vault under a church (5)
3   Edward ___ : composer (5)
4   Multiply by two (6)
5   Young children (7)
6   Tallinn's country (7)
7   Awfully (11)
8   Holland (11)
14 In reality; actually (2,5)
15 Live longer than (7)
17 Mistakes in printed matter (6)
18 Go to see (5)
19 Fertile spot in a desert (5)

CROSSWORD

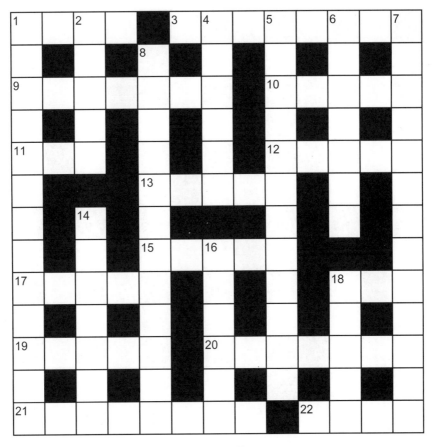

Across

1	Official language of Pakistan (4)
3	Medieval weapon (8)
9	Bring and hand over (7)
10	Humiliate (5)
11	Timid (3)
12	Foot-operated lever (5)
13	Country in North East Africa (5)
15	Crustacean like a shrimp (5)
17	Annelid worm with suckers (5)
18	Type of statistical chart (3)
19	Necessities (5)
20	Not level (7)
21	Salad sauce (8)
22	Singe (4)

Down

1	Lacking in control (13)
2	Act slowly (5)
4	Scarcity (6)
5	Having an acrid wit (5-7)
6	Got on a ship (7)
7	Scheming person (7-6)
8	Excessive stress (12)
14	Go before (7)
16	Reddish-brown hair colour (6)
18	Small flexible bag (5)

PUZZLE 66

Across

- 4 Thief (6)
- 7 Mixture used to flavour food (8)
- 8 Centre of activity (3)
- 9 Vehicle with four-wheel drive (4)
- 10 Ruin; crush (6)
- 11 Employment vacancy (7)
- 12 Locates or places (5)
- 15 Grade (anag.) (5)
- 17 Starting up (of software) (7)
- 20 Journey by sea (6)
- 21 Feeble (of an excuse) (4)
- 22 Farewell remark (3)
- 23 Radioactive element (8)
- 24 Drive away (6)

Down

- 1 Fictional (4,2)
- 2 Distribute (8)
- 3 Injuring (7)
- 4 Jockey's straps (5)
- 5 Bidding (6)
- 6 Precious red gems (6)
- 13 Habitually lazy (8)
- 14 Veracity (7)
- 15 Mocked (6)
- 16 Donors (6)
- 18 Large dark cloud (6)
- 19 Hackneyed (5)

Across

1 Quarrels (8)
5 Thought or suggestion (4)
9 Rope with a running noose (5)
10 Process of wearing away (7)
11 Repository for misplaced items (4,8)
14 Group of whales (3)
15 Venomous African snake (5)
16 Net (anag.) (3)
17 Large Brazilian city (3,2,7)
20 Biggest (7)
22 Garbage or drivel (5)
23 Hasty or reckless (4)
24 Ability to float (8)

Down

1 Droop; lose energy (4)
2 Take flight (7)
3 Easy-going (4-8)
4 Watch closely (3)
6 Less moist (5)
7 Irritating (8)
8 In a self-satisfied manner (12)
12 Cuban dance (5)
13 Handheld firework (8)
16 Twisting force (7)
18 Mythical monsters (5)
19 Challenge; openly resist (4)
21 19th Greek letter (3)

PUZZLE 68

Across

1 Of considerable size (11)
9 Religious table (5)
10 Amp (anag.) (3)
11 Raucous (5)
12 Country in North East Africa (5)
13 Madly (8)
16 Famous (8)
18 Loose scrums (rugby) (5)
21 Long wooden seat (5)
22 In favour of (3)
23 Coral reef (5)
24 Ending (11)

Down

2 Disentangle (7)
3 Remaining (7)
4 Clever or skilful (6)
5 Small lakes (5)
6 Directed at (5)
7 Instrument for recording heart activity (11)
8 Straightforward (4-3-4)
14 Short close-fitting jacket (7)
15 Unfamiliar (7)
17 Issue instructions (6)
19 Laborious task (5)
20 Group of bees (5)

Across

1 Gloomy (6)
7 Orchestral piece at the beginning of an opera (8)
8 Evergreen coniferous tree (3)
9 Senior tribal figures (6)
10 Symbol (4)
11 Delicious (5)
13 More sugary (7)
15 Looked quickly (7)
17 Stagnant (5)
21 Performs on stage (4)
22 Strong-smelling bulb (6)
23 Sewn edge (3)
24 Spacecraft (8)
25 ___ and Gretel: fairy tale (6)

Down

1 Dexterously (6)
2 Continuous flow (6)
3 Intimate companion (5)
4 Moves up and down repeatedly (7)
5 Harsh; grating (8)
6 Furrow (6)
12 The priesthood (8)
14 Very long (7)
16 Track down (6)
18 Self-supporting structures (6)
19 Hard tooth coating (6)
20 Type of diagram (5)

PUZZLE 70

Across

1 Military post (8)
5 Constructed (4)
9 Self-supporting wooden frame (5)
10 Ballroom dance (7)
11 Electronic security device (7,5)
14 Removed from sight (3)
15 Makes less dense (5)
16 Division of a tennis match (3)
17 Not allowable (12)
20 The small details of something (7)
22 Bring great joy to (5)
23 Immediately following (4)
24 Listen to again (4,4)

Down

1 Dull colour (4)
2 Ring or echo (7)
3 Unlawful (12)
4 Clumsy person (3)
6 Main artery (5)
7 Approximate (8)
8 Thoroughly (12)
12 Goodbye (Spanish) (5)
13 Male presiding officer (8)
16 Seedless raisin (7)
18 Building add-on (5)
19 Not strong (4)
21 Be unwell (3)

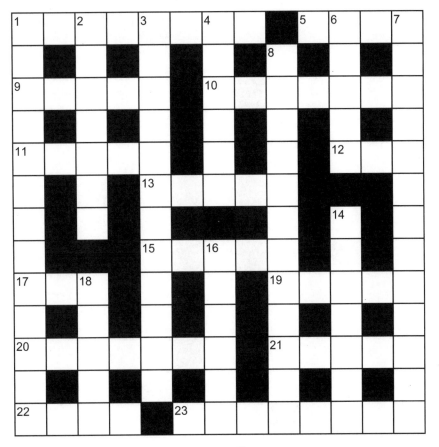

Across

1 Third in order (8)
5 Domesticated ox (4)
9 Assisted (5)
10 Erupt suddenly (5-2)
11 Be sparing with (5)
12 Golf peg (3)
13 Made a mistake (5)
15 Mark of repetition (5)
17 Male child (3)
19 Explore or examine (5)
20 Brought about (7)
21 Paint (anag.) (5)
22 Robert De ___ : actor (4)
23 Front of an advancing army (8)

Down

1 Violation of a law (13)
2 Performing a task again (7)
3 Freedom from control (12)
4 Roof beam (6)
6 Apply pressure (5)
7 Unparalleled (13)
8 Practice of mentioning famous people one knows (4-8)
14 Small-scale model (7)
16 Treeless Arctic region (6)
18 Lowest point (5)

PUZZLE 72

Across

1. Tied up (8)
5. Flightless bird (4)
9. Metric unit of capacity (5)
10. Dinner party; feast (7)
11. Deserved (7)
12. Doglike mammal (5)
13. Wirelesses (6)
14. Academy Awards (6)
17. Piece of writing (5)
19. Raising (7)
20. E.g. a resident of Rome (7)
21. Instruct; teach (5)
22. Look at with an open mouth (4)
23. Substantial (8)

Down

1. Advertising by telephone (13)
2. Coached (7)
3. Decomposition by a current (12)
4. Symbolise (6)
6. Accustom to something (5)
7. Inflexibility (13)
8. Very eager; keen (12)
15. Disturb (7)
16. Mustang; wild horse (6)
18. Skin on top of the head (5)

PUZZLE 73

CROSSWORD

Across

1 Chef (4)
3 Worldwide outbreak (8)
9 Collection of sheets of paper (7)
10 Swagger (5)
11 Stage performer (5)
12 Offensively discourteous (7)
13 Enrol in the armed services (6)
15 Large wine bottle (6)
17 Sum of money paid to someone regularly (7)
18 Ring-shaped object (5)
20 Suffuse with colour (5)
21 Sheer dress fabric (7)
22 Recently married person (5-3)
23 Not new (4)

Down

1 Series of linked things (13)
2 Group of eight (5)
4 Advance evidence for (6)
5 Drawback (12)
6 Inhabitant of Mars (7)
7 Reach the required standard (3,3,7)
8 Brutally; harshly (12)
14 Archer's weapon (7)
16 Belonging to an earlier time (6)
19 Turns (anag.) (5)

Across

1 Large wine bottle (8)
5 ___ Fisher: Australian actress (4)
9 Capital of Vietnam (5)
10 Let in to a place again (7)
11 Germicide (12)
13 Enter into combat with (6)
14 Overjoyed (6)
17 Type of cloud (12)
20 Fragrant gum or spice (7)
21 Mature insect (5)
22 Men (4)
23 Piece of artwork (8)

Down

1 Fourth Gospel (4)
2 Sounding a bell (7)
3 Temperature at which water turns to vapour (7,5)
4 Afloat (6)
6 Brazilian ballroom dance (5)
7 Manner; mental state (8)
8 Annulment (12)
12 Retrieving (8)
15 Huge wave (7)
16 Greek goddess (6)
18 Unsteady (5)
19 Musical composition (4)

CROSSWORD

Across

1 Small pet rodent (6)
4 Urges to act (6)
9 Newsworthy (7)
10 London district (4,3)
11 Relating to the sun (5)
12 Inapt (anag.) (5)
14 TV presenters (5)
17 Fixes (5)
19 Youngsters aged 13 - 19 (5)
21 Delivered from memory (7)
23 Curved inwards (of a surface) (7)
24 Most peculiar (6)
25 Request earnestly (6)

Down

1 Throw in the towel (4,2)
2 Male sheep (pl.) (4)
3 Thoroughly (2,5)
5 Apportions a punishment (5)
6 Give courage (8)
7 Asparagus shoots (6)
8 Gives extra weight to (11)
13 Confined as a prisoner (8)
15 Hit hard (7)
16 Plaster for coating walls (6)
18 Attract powerfully (6)
20 Closes securely (5)
22 Product made from soya beans (4)

Across

1 Daring; bold (11)
9 Queen ___ : fairy in Romeo and Juliet (3)
10 Balance (5)
11 Amplify a signal (5)
12 Relating to country life (5)
13 Clearly defined area (8)
16 Set out on a voyage (8)
18 Decaf (anag.) (5)
20 Long poems derived from ancient tradition (5)
21 Ringo ___ : drummer for the Beatles (5)
22 Came first in a race (3)
23 E.g. Huw Edwards and Krishnan Guru-Murthy (11)

Down

2 Suspend; prevent (5)
3 Kick out (5)
4 Garment maker (6)
5 European deer (7)
6 Not valid or true (7)
7 A change for the better (11)
8 Amazingly good (11)
14 Slanting (7)
15 Pushes (7)
17 Breathe out (6)
18 Discharged a weapon (5)
19 Crouch down in fear (5)

Across

1 Paul ___ : former England footballer (4)
3 Scatter in drops (8)
9 Robbers (7)
10 Flour dough used in cooking (5)
11 Neighbour of Chad and Algeria (5)
12 Meriting (7)
13 Halogen (6)
15 Combination of two things into one (6)
17 Planet in our solar system (7)
18 Entice to do something (5)
20 Not telling the truth (5)
21 Poked (7)
22 Submissive (8)
23 Extremely (4)

Down

1 Deliberately (13)
2 Hold on to tightly (5)
4 Overtakes (6)
5 Flaw (12)
6 Locking lips (7)
7 In an inflated manner (13)
8 Ate excessively (12)
14 Prevent from having (7)
16 Increase; extend (6)
19 Gnat (5)

PUZZLE 78

Across

1 Sustenance (11)
9 Rise to one's feet (5)
10 Attempt to do (3)
11 Recess (5)
12 Perhaps (5)
13 Motionless (8)
16 Brilliant performers (8)
18 Wading birds (5)
21 Steered a car (5)
22 Burdensome charge (3)
23 Edge of a knife (5)
24 Pretentious display (11)

Down

2 End result (7)
3 Keep for future use (7)
4 E.g. spring or winter (6)
5 Polite address for a woman (5)
6 Crazy (5)
7 Peculiarity (11)
8 Devices popular before computers existed (11)
14 Learner (7)
15 Country in northwestern Africa (7)
17 Effect; force (6)
19 Mends (5)
20 Cavalry sword (5)

Across

1	Disadvantage (8)
5	Axe-like tool (4)
9	Trunk of the body (5)
10	Sewing aid (7)
11	Bewitchingly (12)
14	Beer (3)
15	Train tracks (5)
16	___ Thurman: Pulp Fiction actress (3)
17	Break up (12)
20	Perfect happiness (7)
22	Intense (5)
23	Resistance unit (pl.) (4)
24	Margaret ___ : former Prime Minister (8)

Down

1	Go out with (4)
2	Place in order (7)
3	Male relation by marriage (7-2-3)
4	Feline animal (3)
6	Remove errors from software (5)
7	Quotidian (8)
8	Public official (5,7)
12	Foolishly credulous (5)
13	Spanish dance (8)
16	Lie (7)
18	Run away (5)
19	Prophet (4)
21	Residue from a fire (3)

PUZZLE 80

Across

1 Trophies (4)
3 Official document (8)
9 English county (7)
10 Dramatic musical work (5)
11 Domain (5)
12 Countries (7)
13 Scarcely (6)
15 Festival (6)
17 Food samplers (7)
18 Waterslide (5)
20 Weirdly (5)
21 Why one might visit a hair salon (7)
22 Emaciated (8)
23 Depend on (4)

Down

1 Things that are given (13)
2 Weatherproof coat (5)
4 Requesting (6)
5 Malfunction or fail (of an electrical device) (5-7)
6 Burdensome (7)
7 Party lanterns (anag.) (13)
8 Pungent gas used as a preservative (12)
14 Remains (7)
16 Respiratory condition (6)
19 Male relation (5)

CROSSWORD

Across

1 Refuge (8)
5 Became older (4)
9 Roles (anag.) (5)
10 Type of humour (7)
11 School for young children (12)
13 Employing (6)
14 Japanese robe (6)
17 Ineptness (12)
20 Expressive (of music) (7)
21 Give out; discharge (5)
22 Light beams (4)
23 Stiff cat hairs (8)

Down

1 Assist (4)
2 Written record (7)
3 Study of the properties of moving air (12)
4 Guarantee (6)
6 Work hard (5)
7 Control (8)
8 Inventiveness (12)
12 Film with an exciting plot (8)
15 Block (7)
16 Affluence (6)
18 Not straight (of hair) (5)
19 Tennis court dividers (4)

PUZZLE 82

Across

1 Ancestors (11)
9 SI unit of frequency (5)
10 Flower that is not yet open (3)
11 Mediterranean island country (5)
12 Cloth woven from flax (5)
13 Ominous (8)
16 Area of the zodiac (4,4)
18 Gave away (5)
21 Cry out loudly (5)
22 First on the list (3)
23 Middle of the body (5)
24 Type of fat (11)

Down

2 Not connected to the internet (7)
3 Make weary (7)
4 Reach a destination (6)
5 Shrub; eye colour (5)
6 Red-chested bird (5)
7 Tame (11)
8 Forever (2,9)
14 One who holds property for another (7)
15 Hot wind blowing from North Africa (7)
17 Teaches (6)
19 Extent (5)
20 Lowed (anag.) (5)

Across

1 Incorporates (8)
5 Cab (4)
9 E.g. an Oscar or Grammy (5)
10 Unfurls (7)
11 Enhancements (12)
14 Four-wheeled road vehicle (3)
15 Weary (5)
16 Affirmative vote (3)
17 State of dissatisfaction (12)
20 Iron attractors (7)
22 Secret rendezvous (5)
23 Reduces in length (4)
24 Conclusive examination (4,4)

Down

1 ___ Lendl: former tennis star (4)
2 Charismatic person (7)
3 Inadequately manned (12)
4 Water, in France (3)
6 Lion who rules over Narnia (5)
7 Took a firm stand (8)
8 Planned in advance (12)
12 Stanza of a poem (5)
13 Relating to education and scholarship (8)
16 Assistant; follower (7)
18 Sense of seeing (5)
19 Test (anag.) (4)
21 Pouch (3)

Across

1 Lure (6)
4 Engineless aircraft (6)
9 David ___ : former Prime Minister (7)
10 Look into (7)
11 Young females (5)
12 More liquid than is expected (5)
14 Doctrine (5)
15 Precious stone (5)
17 First Pope (5)
18 Martial art (2-5)
20 Irregularity (7)
21 End of the period when something is valid (6)
22 Inferior (6)

Down

1 Coop up (6)
2 The day after today (8)
3 Feels affection for; is interested in (5)
5 Large spotted cat (7)
6 Extinct bird (4)
7 Make less dense (6)
8 Not achieving the desired result (11)
13 Impartial parties (8)
14 Rattling noise (7)
15 Puerile; superficial (6)
16 Request made to God (6)
17 Establish as the truth (5)
19 Leap (4)

PUZZLE 85

CROSSWORD

Across

1 Tree parts (8)
5 Heroic tale (4)
9 Mature human (5)
10 Able to read minds (7)
11 Terms of office (7)
12 Possessed (5)
13 Remains preserved in rock (6)
14 Easy victory (4-2)
17 Up to the time when (5)
19 Sauce made from tomatoes (7)
20 Schematic (7)
21 Stringed instrument (5)
22 Prying (4)
23 Extremely compatible partner (8)

Down

1 Animal used for heavy work (5,2,6)
2 Former student (7)
3 Butterfly larvae (12)
4 Reveal (6)
6 Very pale (5)
7 Liable to get injured (8-5)
8 Conjectural (12)
15 Character in Hamlet (7)
16 With hands on the hips (6)
18 Shallow carrying containers (5)

PUZZLE 86

CROSSWORD

Across

1 Public houses (4)
3 Tells a story (8)
9 Persuasive relevance (7)
10 Tortilla topped with cheese (5)
11 Usage measuring device (5)
12 Candid (7)
13 Gas with formula 'C2H6' (6)
15 Selected (6)
17 Vacates (7)
18 Very masculine (5)
20 Name of a book (5)
21 E.g. Iceland and Borneo (7)
22 Boating (8)
23 Watery part of milk (4)

Down

1 Ineptly (13)
2 This follows day (5)
4 Shelter (6)
5 Not special (3-2-3-4)
6 Wealthy businesspeople (7)
7 Impulsively (13)
8 Inflexible (12)
14 Pertaining to the liver (7)
16 Mete out (6)
19 A sure thing; easy task (5)

PUZZLE 87

CROSSWORD

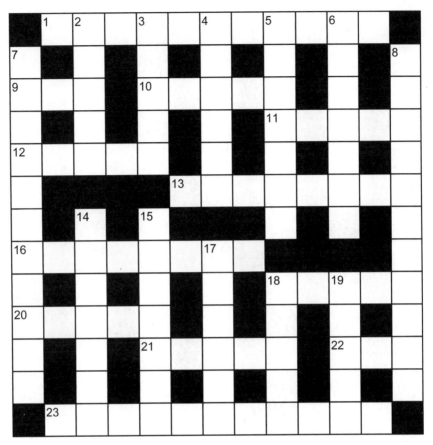

Across

1 Word used by magicians (11)
9 Steal (3)
10 Happening (5)
11 Brown earth pigment (5)
12 Dismiss from office (5)
13 In the open air (8)
16 Careful (8)
18 Move as fast as possible (5)
20 Suit (5)
21 Oneness (5)
22 Cry of a cat or gull (3)
23 Betray (6-5)

Down

2 Religious book (5)
3 Separated (5)
4 Open declaration of affirmation (6)
5 Insurance calculator (7)
6 Litter (7)
7 Final (11)
8 Former Labour Prime Minister (6,5)
14 Bison (7)
15 Move something; agitate (7)
17 Bearlike (6)
18 City leader (5)
19 Domesticates (5)

Across

1	Expression of praise (8)
5	Fill to capacity (4)
8	Exploiting unfairly (5)
9	Emotional shocks (7)
10	Mark written under a letter (7)
12	Knife attached to a rifle (7)
14	Uncovers; reveals (7)
16	Modifies (7)
18	More fortunate (7)
19	Entertain (5)
20	Chat (4)
21	Small loudspeakers (8)

Down

1	Chemical salt (4)
2	Unpleasantly cold (6)
3	This is seen before one hears thunder (9)
4	Discover (6)
6	Wander without a route (6)
7	Errors (8)
11	Belittle (9)
12	Wristband (8)
13	Call off (6)
14	Cowers (anag.) (6)
15	Safe (6)
17	State of confusion (4)

CROSSWORD

Across

1 Contributes information (6)
4 Agreement (6)
9 Distance travelled (7)
10 Absence of sound (7)
11 Colours lightly (5)
12 Curbs; muffles (5)
14 Bring about (5)
15 Person who goes on long walks (5)
17 Moved slowly (5)
18 Snack food (7)
20 Earthenware container (7)
21 Protects (6)
22 Mixes up or confuses (6)

Down

1 Prisoner (6)
2 Type of sweater (4,4)
3 Froglike amphibians (5)
5 Crash together (7)
6 Cooking appliance (4)
7 Multiples of twelve (6)
8 Eating establishments (11)
13 Cloth or fabric (8)
14 Not straight (7)
15 Wishing for (6)
16 Soaks in liquid (6)
17 Raced (anag.) (5)
19 Insect stage (4)

PUZZLE 90

Across

1 Government by a king or queen (8)
5 Primates (4)
9 Stomach exercise (3-2)
10 Thief (7)
11 Popular district in London (6,6)
13 Bangle worn at the top of the foot (6)
14 Cooked slowly in liquid (6)
17 Lawfully (12)
20 Better for the environment (7)
21 Quartz-like gems (5)
22 ___ of the d'Urbervilles: novel by Thomas Hardy (4)
23 Secondary personality (5,3)

Down

1 Perfume ingredient (4)
2 System of interconnected things (7)
3 Symbolising (12)
4 Customs; settled tendencies (6)
6 Plied (anag.) (5)
7 Song from a suitor (8)
8 Swimming technique (12)
12 Small window (8)
15 Health and fortunes of a group (7)
16 Unethical (6)
18 Estimate (5)
19 Norway's capital (4)

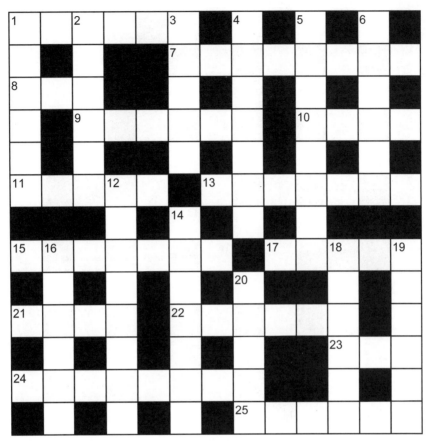

Across

1 Glowing remains of a fire (6)
7 Impudent (8)
8 Domestic bovine animal (3)
9 Not sinking (6)
10 Large wading bird (4)
11 Puny (5)
13 Princess Diana's surname at birth (7)
15 Shore birds (7)
17 Felts (anag.) (5)
21 E.g. petrol (4)
22 Writhe (6)
23 Knot with a double loop (3)
24 Light sandal (4-4)
25 Protect from danger (6)

Down

1 Abstain from (6)
2 Look out (6)
3 Grain storage chambers (5)
4 Form of an element (7)
5 Association created for mutual benefit (8)
6 Injudicious (6)
12 Grows more mature (8)
14 Stiff coarse hair (7)
16 Noisily (6)
18 Handle clumsily (6)
19 Displayed (6)
20 Devices for inflating tyres (5)

PUZZLE 92

Across

1 Exceptional (8)
5 Plant used for flavouring (4)
9 Play a guitar (5)
10 E.g. anger or love (7)
11 Imitator (12)
13 Small parrot (informal) (6)
14 Package (6)
17 Air ___ : this is useful in warm climates (12)
20 Government income (7)
21 Form of humour (5)
22 Shallow food container (4)
23 Mike ___ : former England opening batsman (8)

Down

1 West's opposite (4)
2 A pharoah's tomb is often found under this structure (7)
3 Contests (12)
4 Strongly opposed (6)
6 Announcement (5)
7 Finance something (8)
8 Hillside (12)
12 Partially hidden (8)
15 Twist out of shape (7)
16 Turn aside (6)
18 Ben ___ : Scottish mountain (5)
19 Religious song (4)

Across

1 Safe place (6)
4 Burning (6)
9 Grain (7)
10 Rank in the forces (7)
11 Arduous journeys (5)
12 Walks through water (5)
14 Covers with gold (5)
15 Go about stealthily (5)
17 Francis ___ : English statesman (5)
18 Request (7)
20 Oval (7)
21 Obtain by coercion (6)
22 Alludes to (6)

Down

1 Legal entitlements (6)
2 Ballroom dance (8)
3 Insect larvae (5)
5 Pursues (7)
6 So be it (4)
7 Large birds of prey (6)
8 Remembered (11)
13 Follower (8)
14 Slowly moving mass of ice (7)
15 Mortar's partner (6)
16 Smiles contemptuously (6)
17 Nonsense (5)
19 Preparation for Easter (4)

PUZZLE 94

CROSSWORD

Across

1 Striking noisily (8)
5 Musical composition (4)
9 Iron alloy (5)
10 Due to the fact that (7)
11 Person who listens into conversations (12)
13 Pointed projectiles (6)
14 Cause bafflement (6)
17 Limitless (12)
20 Have a positive impact on (7)
21 ___ Milan: Italian football team (5)
22 Optimistic (4)
23 Cautions (8)

Down

1 Lock lips (4)
2 Alfresco (4-3)
3 Orcas (6,6)
4 Nonentity (6)
6 Chubby (5)
7 Fortified wines (8)
8 Sensory system used by dolphins (12)
12 Appeaser (8)
15 An edible jelly (7)
16 World's largest country (6)
18 Sulks (5)
19 Vases (4)

CROSSWORD

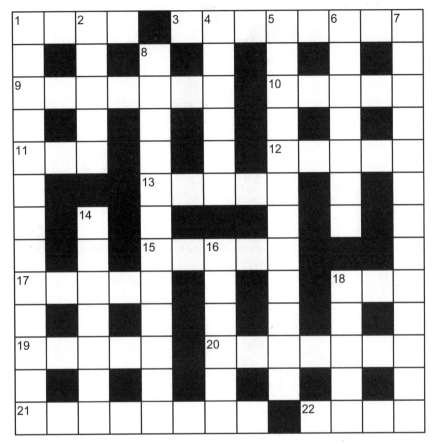

Across

1 Head of a university faculty (4)
3 Aromatic plant used in cooking (8)
9 E.g. swords and guns (7)
10 Sing like a bird (5)
11 Charged particle (3)
12 Daisy-like flower (5)
13 Connection; link (3-2)
15 Red cosmetic powder (5)
17 Musical pace (5)
18 Wetland (3)
19 Sprites (5)
20 Talking incessantly (of a person) (7)
21 Delaying (8)
22 Went away (4)

Down

1 Where the Prime Minister lives (7,6)
2 Once more (5)
4 Settle snugly (6)
5 Capable of being traded (12)
6 Inane (7)
7 Act of distribution (13)
8 In a carefree manner (12)
14 Russian tea urn (7)
16 Bumpy (6)
18 Dietary roughage (5)

PUZZLE 96

Across

1 Suffers the consequences (4)
3 The scholastic world (8)
9 Throw into disorder (7)
10 Cancel (5)
11 Bump (12)
13 Brain-related (6)
15 Complete failure (6)
17 Sound of quick light steps (6-6)
20 Earlier (5)
21 Capital of the US state of Georgia (7)
22 Remaining (8)
23 Network of lines (4)

Down

1 Fattening (8)
2 Loutish person (5)
4 Intelligent (6)
5 Strikingly (12)
6 Threatens (7)
7 Shaft on which a wheel rotates (4)
8 Made (12)
12 Heath (8)
14 Joins together (7)
16 Large group of warships (6)
18 Radio receiver (5)
19 Strong pole on a ship (4)

CROSSWORD

Across

- **1** Scrape (anag.) (6)
- **4** Tool used to hit things (6)
- **9** Simian (7)
- **10** Wash and iron (7)
- **11** Growing thickly (5)
- **12** Crunch; wear down (5)
- **14** Turned to ice (5)
- **15** Discourage (5)
- **17** Contest for knights (5)
- **18** Quarrel or haggle (7)
- **20** Beverage made from grapes (3,4)
- **21** Uttered coarsely (6)
- **22** Jams tight (6)

Down

- **1** Peevish and annoyed (6)
- **2** Large game bird (8)
- **3** Wet (of weather) (5)
- **5** Declare to be the case (7)
- **6** Not spicy (4)
- **7** Brought up (6)
- **8** Aircraft (pl.) (11)
- **13** Attributing to (8)
- **14** Easily broken (7)
- **15** Water diviner (6)
- **16** Semiaquatic fish-eating mammals (6)
- **17** Arbiter (5)
- **19** Seabirds (4)

PUZZLE 98

Across

1 Speaks (6)
7 Relating to an empire (8)
8 Cooking appliance (3)
9 Prowler (6)
10 Areas of ground for growing plants (4)
11 Type of water lily (5)
13 Streets (7)
15 Involving active participation (5-2)
17 Type of airship (5)
21 Decant (4)
22 Lump or blob (6)
23 Climbing shrub (3)
24 Circle of constant longitude (8)
25 Ran quickly (6)

Down

1 Difficult (6)
2 Plaque (6)
3 Basins (5)
4 Sanction (7)
5 Court of justice (8)
6 Seat on the back of a horse (6)
12 Form the base for (8)
14 Pipe (7)
16 Loved deeply (6)
18 Mischievous (6)
19 Entreated; beseeched (6)
20 Impossible to see round (of a bend) (5)

Across

1   Rural scenery (11)
9   Uptight (5)
10 Place where one sees animals (3)
11 Happening (5)
12 Carrying chair (5)
13 Conceptual thinker (8)
16 Sears (8)
18 Too bright in colour (5)
21 Concur (5)
22 Tree of the genus Ulmus (3)
23 Dish of raw vegetables (5)
24 Amazing (11)

Down

2   Commanded (7)
3   Chats (7)
4   Rejuvenates (6)
5   Ladder rungs (5)
6   Slumbered (5)
7   Dejected (11)
8   Expert critic (11)
14 Width (7)
15 Heighten (7)
17 Hot pepper (6)
19 Slopes (5)
20 Dance hall (5)

Across

1 Renounce (8)
5 Come down to earth (4)
9 Direct competitor (5)
10 Efficiency (7)
11 Detective (12)
14 Belonging to him (3)
15 Work at a loom (5)
16 Commander; chief (3)
17 Baked product containing seasoned meat (7,5)
20 Large jug (7)
22 Turn of phrase (5)
23 Assistant (4)
24 Glove (8)

Down

1 Configuration; shape (4)
2 Deep gorges (7)
3 Boxing class division (12)
4 Epoch (3)
6 In the air (5)
7 Dawn (8)
8 Gathering of people (12)
12 Instruct (5)
13 Yellowish edible seed (8)
16 Mound made by insects (7)
18 Judged; ranked (5)
19 Give out (4)
21 Mens ____ : criminal intention (3)

Across

1 Bulbous plant (8)
5 Applaud (4)
9 Wood used to make models (5)
10 Ordains (anag.) (7)
11 Action of breaking a law (12)
13 Take for granted (6)
14 Pilot (6)
17 The proprietor of an eating establishment (12)
20 Conjuring up feelings (7)
21 Broom made of twigs (5)
22 Eyelid infection (4)
23 Opposites (8)

Down

1 Weeps (4)
2 Elongated rectangles (7)
3 Graphical (12)
4 East (6)
6 Let (5)
7 Suggesting (8)
8 Overwhelmingly compelling (12)
12 People who shape horseshoes (8)
15 Chilled desserts (7)
16 Starting point (6)
18 Work of fiction (5)
19 Flightless birds (4)

Across

1	Shop selling medicinal drugs (8)
5	Bivalve marine mollusc (4)
9	Titles (5)
10	Not carrying weapons (7)
11	A long time ago (4,3)
12	Vital organ (5)
13	Truly (6)
14	Parcel (anag.) (6)
17	Military trainee (5)
19	Country in West Africa (7)
20	Turns upside down (7)
21	Small boat (5)
22	Precious metal (4)
23	Church of England member (8)

Down

1	Miserly (5-8)
2	Swimming aid (7)
3	Mishap (12)
4	Enumerates (6)
6	Subsidiary proposition (5)
7	Large sea (13)
8	Caused by disease (12)
15	Long-lasting and recurrent (7)
16	Concord (6)
18	Evil spirit (5)

CROSSWORD

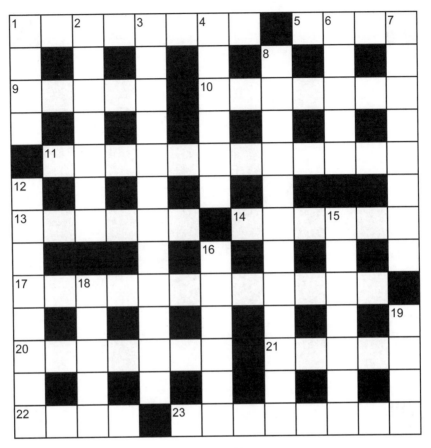

Across

1 Food of the gods (8)
5 Lyric poems (4)
9 Precipice (5)
10 More amusing (7)
11 First language (6,6)
13 Go to bed (6)
14 Abdominal organ (6)
17 Prediction or expectation (12)
20 Raging fire (7)
21 Constructed (5)
22 Simplicity (4)
23 Pennant (8)

Down

1 Curved shape (4)
2 Withdraw from a commitment (4,3)
3 Unofficially (3,3,6)
4 Impart knowledge (6)
6 Performing (5)
7 Estrange (anag.) (8)
8 Unfriendly (12)
12 Imaginative (8)
15 Selfishness (7)
16 Destroy (6)
18 Bunches (5)
19 Agitate a liquid (4)

PUZZLE 104

Across

1 Angry dispute (11)
9 Bun (anag.) (3)
10 Distinguishing character (5)
11 Comedy performances (5)
12 Glorify (5)
13 Easy chair (8)
16 Undeserving (8)
18 Hides (5)
20 Unit of heat (5)
21 Worked steadily at (5)
22 Forbid (3)
23 Initiators (11)

Down

2 Sign of the zodiac (5)
3 Turn inside out (5)
4 Hold fast (6)
5 Adornments of hanging threads (7)
6 Choices (7)
7 Caused to stop (11)
8 Upsetting (11)
14 Cause to taste more sugary (7)
15 Brass wind instrument (7)
17 ___ pigeon: trained bird (6)
18 In the middle of (5)
19 Moderate and well-balanced (5)

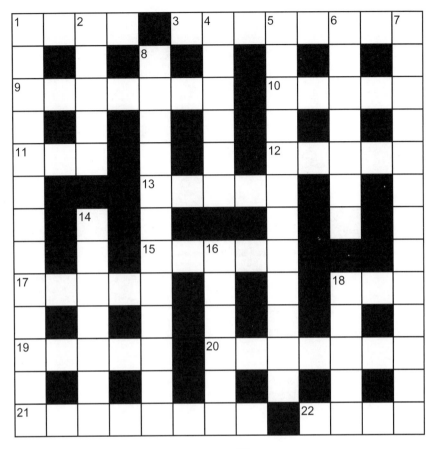

Across

1 Unattractive (4)
3 Roomy (8)
9 Parcel (7)
10 Royal (5)
11 Large salt water body (3)
12 Speak one's mind (5)
13 Old French currency (5)
15 Gorge (5)
17 Settle for sleep (of birds) (5)
18 Expected at a certain time (3)
19 Absolute (5)
20 Noisiest (7)
21 Disloyal person (8)
22 Participate in a game (4)

Down

1 Not heat-treated (of milk) (13)
2 City in Tuscany (5)
4 Spanish rice dish (6)
5 Type of cloud (12)
6 Continuing (7)
7 Obviously (4-9)
8 Maker (12)
14 Small storage rooms or cupboards (7)
16 ___ Mauresmo: French former tennis star (6)
18 Reside (5)

PUZZLE 106

110

Across

1 Actor (8)
5 Outdoor swimming pool (4)
8 Opposite of best (5)
9 Pariah (7)
10 Analyse (7)
12 Stuck on the bottom (of a ship) (7)
14 Active part of a fire (7)
16 Elusive (7)
18 Duty-bound (7)
19 Wild dog of Australia (5)
20 Young female (4)
21 Mileage tracker (8)

Down

1 Pulls a vehicle (4)
2 Creepier (6)
3 Medley of dried petals (9)
4 Declared (6)
6 Sloping (of a typeface) (6)
7 Precisely (2,3,3)
11 Dutch capital (9)
12 Chamber leading to a larger space (8)
13 Pieces of furniture (6)
14 Rounded up animals (6)
15 Untape (anag.) (6)
17 Number after three (4)

CROSSWORD

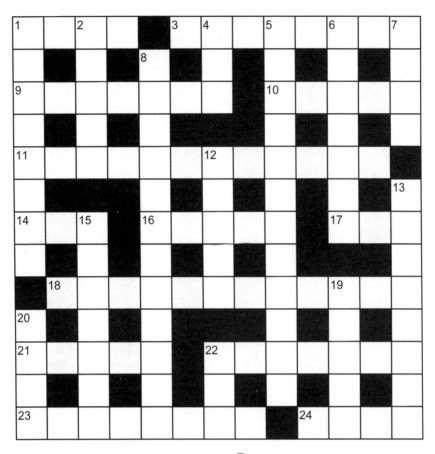

Across

1 Concave roof (4)
3 Pinching sharply (8)
9 Place out of sight (7)
10 Covered the inside of a bin (5)
11 Extreme irritation (12)
14 Lay seed in the ground (3)
16 Wanderer (5)
17 Dip food in liquid (3)
18 Clarity (12)
21 Billie ___ : English actress and former singer (5)
22 State of the USA (7)
23 Tedious (8)
24 Fish-eating eagle (4)

Down

1 Spread out (8)
2 Type of coffee drink (5)
4 Great sorrow (3)
5 Repetition of the same sound (12)
6 Having solidified from lava (of rock) (7)
7 Deities (4)
8 Peruse matter (anag.) (12)
12 Large crow (5)
13 Religious deserter (8)
15 Speak very softly (7)
19 ___ Allan Poe: US writer (5)
20 Petty quarrel (4)
22 Jewel (3)

PUZZLE 108

Across

1 Intense beams of light (6)
4 Declines sharply (6)
9 Lively festivities (7)
10 Wheeled supermarket vehicle (7)
11 Respected person in a field (5)
12 Trivial (5)
14 Shrill sound (5)
17 Use to one's advantage (5)
19 Steals (5)
21 Found (7)
23 Plaited lock of hair (7)
24 Wrongdoer (6)
25 Bivalve mollusc (6)

Down

1 Portable computer (6)
2 Performance by one actor (4)
3 Shows again (7)
5 Adored (5)
6 SE Asian country (8)
7 Observing furtively (6)
8 Obscurely (11)
13 Sledge (8)
15 Theft of property (7)
16 Slants (6)
18 Climbing tool (6)
20 State of disgrace (5)
22 Sharp or acid in taste (4)

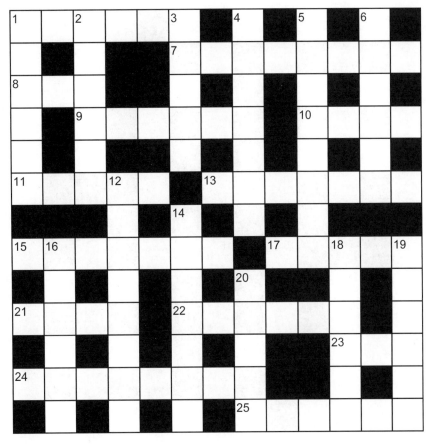

Across

1 Whole (6)
7 Distinctive feature (8)
8 Not many (3)
9 Far from the intended target (6)
10 European mountain range (4)
11 Insects related to butterflies (5)
13 Pig's foot (7)
15 Clothing (7)
17 Microscopic organisms (5)
21 ___ Fey: US actress and comedian (4)
22 Strikes firmly (6)
23 Snip (3)
24 Took the trouble to do something (8)
25 Shouted out (6)

Down

1 Weak through age or illness (6)
2 Oppose a plan successfully (6)
3 Bronze medal position (5)
4 Game participants (7)
5 Fortify against attack (8)
6 Multiply by three (6)
12 Worrying problem (8)
14 Hot water spouts (7)
16 Jail (6)
18 Scoundrel (6)
19 Scolded strongly (6)
20 Dizzy (5)

Across

1 Bite (8)
5 Crazy (informal) (4)
9 Abatement (5)
10 Procedure; standard (7)
11 Funny person (5)
12 Title of a married woman (3)
13 Greeting (5)
15 Nosed (anag.) (5)
17 Use (anag.) (3)
19 Slatted wooden box (5)
20 Act of avoiding capture (7)
21 Earthy pigment (5)
22 Locate or place (4)
23 Vision (8)

Down

1 Spite (13)
2 Wild (of an animal) (7)
3 Valetudinarianism (12)
4 Unfurl (6)
6 General hatred (5)
7 Exaggeration (13)
8 Part of the mind (12)
14 Strong embrace (4,3)
16 Of delicate beauty (6)
18 Show triumphant joy (5)

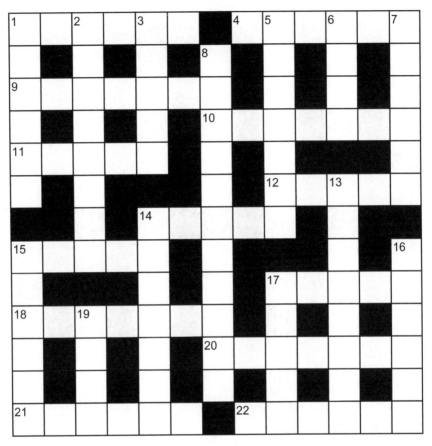

Across

1 Be preoccupied with a topic (6)
4 Navigational instrument (6)
9 Less clean (7)
10 Increases a deadline (7)
11 Domestic cat (5)
12 Raised to the third power (5)
14 E.g. performs karaoke (5)
15 Perspire (5)
17 Flow with a whirling motion (5)
18 Branch of maths (7)
20 Dwelling (7)
21 Moved at an easy pace (6)
22 Despot (6)

Down

1 Eccentricity (6)
2 Scrawl (8)
3 Piquant (5)
5 Reviewers (7)
6 Related by blood (4)
7 Made fun of (6)
8 Centralised (anag.) (11)
13 Roman building (8)
14 Light beard (7)
15 Basic metrical unit in a poem (6)
16 Pledge solemnly (6)
17 Regrettably (5)
19 Insect larva (4)

PUZZLE 112

Across

1 Last (8)
5 Film about a shark (4)
8 Slender piece of wood (5)
9 Serviettes (7)
10 Impose one's will (7)
12 Storage tank (7)
14 Protectors (7)
16 Apprentice (7)
18 Firmly fix in a person (7)
19 Spherical body (5)
20 Memo (4)
21 Squashes (8)

Down

1 Garden watering device (4)
2 Equine sounds (6)
3 Be coherent (4,5)
4 Deeply recessed (of someone's eyes) (6)
6 Bird enclosure (6)
7 Stops temporarily (8)
11 Prescience (9)
12 Crusade (8)
13 Purchased (6)
14 Inner part of a seed (6)
15 Encrypt (6)
17 Streams of liquid or gas (4)

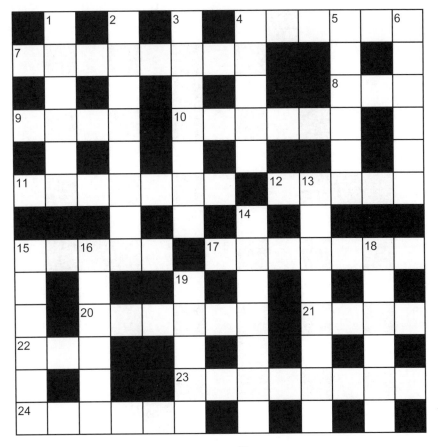

Across

4	Feels uncertain about (6)
7	Having pH greater than 7 (8)
8	Broad inlet of the sea (3)
9	Male deer (4)
10	Mix socially (6)
11	Retails (anag.) (7)
12	Spirited horse (5)
15	Harsh and grating in sound (5)
17	Paired (7)
20	The science of light (6)
21	Knowledge (abbrev.) (4)
22	Cut grass (3)
23	Sufficiency (8)
24	Red dog (anag.) (6)

Down

1	Entice or attract (6)
2	Reverse somersault (8)
3	Wealthiest (7)
4	Famous Epsom horse race (5)
5	Talk foolishly (6)
6	Fashioned (6)
13	Ringing in the ears (8)
14	Gnarled (7)
15	Very crowded (of a place) (6)
16	Decreased one's speed (6)
18	Special ___ : film illusion (6)
19	Clergyman (5)

Across

1	Money given to the poor (4)
3	Spread throughout (8)
9	Passion (7)
10	Detection technology (5)
11	Growing stronger (12)
13	Checked; examined (6)
15	Books (6)
17	Very sad (12)
20	Third Greek letter (5)
21	Periods of 60 seconds (7)
22	Group of musicians (8)
23	Part of the eye (4)

Down

1	Causes pain or suffering (8)
2	Worthiness (5)
4	Nocturnal insect (6)
5	Amusement park ride (5-2-5)
6	Moderately slow tempo (music) (7)
7	British nobleman (4)
8	Comical tuner (anag.) (12)
12	Judges; evaluates (8)
14	Symbols of disgrace (7)
16	Beast (6)
18	Awake and out of bed (5)
19	Look at amorously (4)

CROSSWORD

Across

1 Platform (4)
3 Legendary island (8)
9 Spanish drink containing wine and fruit (7)
10 Fishing net (5)
11 Repeat something once more (5)
12 Japanese flower arranging (7)
13 Housing (6)
15 ___ Artois: type of beer (6)
17 Floating mass of frozen water (7)
18 Selected (5)
20 Musical with lyrics by Tim Rice (5)
21 Exceptional; not usual (7)
22 Christmas season (8)
23 Sues (anag.) (4)

Down

1 Devastatingly (13)
2 Type of chemical bond (5)
4 Calamitous (6)
5 Establish as genuine (12)
6 Burdensome work (7)
7 Conscious knowledge of oneself (4-9)
8 Surpassing in influence (12)
14 Exceptionally good (7)
16 Concurred (6)
19 Baking appliances (5)

PUZZLE 116

Across

1 Absence of passion (6)
4 Moves forward at speed (6)
9 Let up (7)
10 Welcomed (7)
11 Gives as a reference (5)
12 Artificial waterway (5)
14 Inadequately (5)
15 Person who eats in a restaurant (5)
17 Roofed entrance to a house (5)
18 Eyelash cosmetic (7)
20 Pierces with something sharp (7)
21 Send for sale overseas (6)
22 ___ up: botches or bungles (6)

Down

1 Region of France (6)
2 Aspiration (8)
3 Shire (anag.) (5)
5 Measure of how pressing something is (7)
6 Essence (4)
7 Open type of footwear (6)
8 Deception (11)
13 Low-cost travel package (2-6)
14 Heavy sea wave (7)
15 Reserved and coy (6)
16 Long essay or dissertation (6)
17 Immature insects (5)
19 Buy things (4)

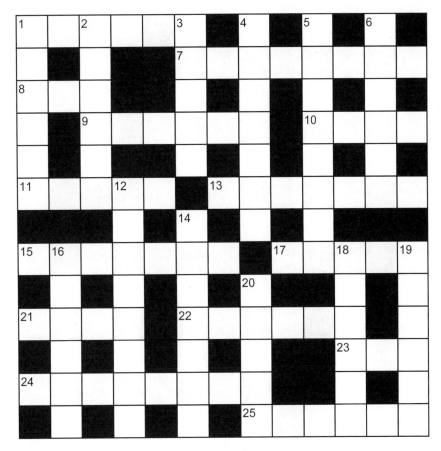

Across

1 Forever (6)
7 Flight carriers (8)
8 Animal fodder (3)
9 Touched down (6)
10 Gap; empty space (4)
11 Manner of writing (5)
13 Catching (7)
15 Farm vehicle (7)
17 Public meeting for open discussion (5)
21 Large family (4)
22 Strike hard (6)
23 Tavern (3)
24 African country (8)
25 Mourn the loss of (6)

Down

1 Capital of Greece (6)
2 Accost; hold up (6)
3 ___ Lyle: Scottish golfer (5)
4 Three-pronged weapon (7)
5 Until now (8)
6 Magician in Arthurian legend (6)
12 Permits to do something (8)
14 Evergreen tree (7)
16 Refill (6)
18 Small wave (6)
19 Mutter (6)
20 Hurled (5)

Across

1 Grammatical mistake (8)
5 Business (4)
9 Angry dispute (3-2)
10 Ice cream flavour (7)
11 Unhappy (12)
13 Lethargic (6)
14 Guardian (6)
17 Person's physical state (12)
20 Things done (7)
21 Open and close the eyes quickly (5)
22 Variety of chalcedony (4)
23 Space rock (8)

Down

1 One of the Channel Islands (4)
2 Taller and thinner (7)
3 Compulsory military service (12)
4 Rescuing (6)
6 Small piece of land (5)
7 Wanders at random (8)
8 Not discernible (12)
12 Cats coat (anag.) (8)
15 Stipulation (7)
16 Stagnation or inactivity (6)
18 Stylish (5)
19 Slide; lose grip (4)

CROSSWORD

Across

1	Joke-telling entertainer (8)
5	Dominion (4)
9	Golf shots (5)
10	Patella (7)
11	Indifferent to (12)
14	Fish eggs eaten as food (3)
15	Two cubed (5)
16	Floor covering (3)
17	Compensate for (12)
20	Concoctions (7)
22	Frostily (5)
23	Moved quickly (4)
24	Example (8)

Down

1	Imitate (4)
2	Afternoon performance (7)
3	Destruction of bacteria (12)
4	Diving bird (3)
6	Unabridged (5)
7	Speed up (8)
8	Person who receives office visitors (12)
12	Keen (5)
13	Writs or warrants (8)
16	Specify by name (7)
18	Undo (5)
19	Sort (4)
21	What our planet orbits (3)

PUZZLE 120

Across

1 Causing a blockage (11)
9 Removes the skin from (5)
10 How (anag.) (3)
11 Underside of a projecting roof (5)
12 Egg centres (5)
13 Mexican pancake (8)
16 Deliberately damage (8)
18 Ancient measure of length (5)
21 Punctuation mark (5)
22 Exclamation of contempt (3)
23 Worship (5)
24 Not having a written constitution (11)

Down

2 Courage (7)
3 Surface layer of earth (7)
4 Of practical benefit (6)
5 Peevish (5)
6 Speech sound (5)
7 Form of energy (11)
8 Thoughtful (11)
14 Admit (7)
15 Crimson colour (7)
17 Protective covering (6)
19 Relay device (5)
20 Household garbage (5)

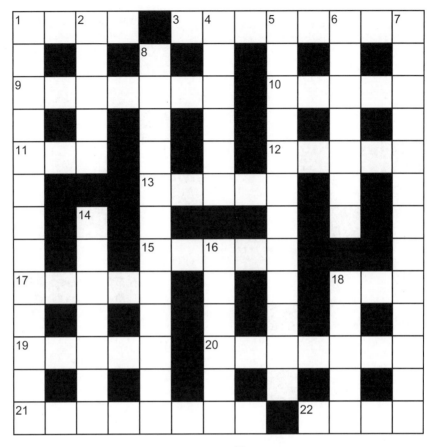

Across

- **1** Obtains (4)
- **3** Lacking humility (8)
- **9** Animal fat (7)
- **10** Portion of a play (5)
- **11** Extremity (3)
- **12** Speak (5)
- **13** Tool for boring holes (5)
- **15** Living in a city (5)
- **17** Plant flower (5)
- **18** Involuntary spasm (3)
- **19** Edible seaweed (5)
- **20** Coming from the south (7)
- **21** Improves in flavour (8)
- **22** Move from side to side (4)

Down

- **1** 50th anniversary of a major event (6,7)
- **2** Shaped up (5)
- **4** Digging for minerals (6)
- **5** Obfuscation (12)
- **6** Voter (7)
- **7** Conceptually (13)
- **8** Using letters and numbers (12)
- **14** However (anag.) (7)
- **16** Act properly (6)
- **18** Worth (anag.) (5)

PUZZLE 122

Across

1 Wily (8)
5 Small quantity (4)
8 Polish monetary unit (5)
9 Exclusion from the workplace (7)
10 Witticism (7)
12 Not spiritual or sacred (7)
14 Takes a firm stand (7)
16 Combined metals (7)
18 Tumult (7)
19 Musical note (5)
20 Yellow part of an egg (4)
21 Highly regarded (8)

Down

1 Stare (4)
2 Easily identifiable (6)
3 The origin of a word (9)
4 Less attractive (6)
6 Smells (6)
7 Tries (8)
11 Irritable (9)
12 Furtive (8)
13 Not singular (6)
14 Grown-ups (6)
15 Restore honour (6)
17 Document of ownership (4)

Across

1 Part of a sleeve (4)
3 In these times (8)
9 Object used in the kitchen (7)
10 Mournful song (5)
11 English royal house (5)
12 Observed (7)
13 Ranking (6)
15 Part of the eye (6)
17 Moderates; mitigates (7)
18 Representative (5)
20 Wide open (of the mouth) (5)
21 Fall back (7)
22 Trinkets (anag.) (8)
23 Exercise venues (4)

Down

1 Respond aggressively to military action (7-6)
2 Released from jail (5)
4 Elongated rectangle (6)
5 Also (12)
6 E.g. from Ethiopia (7)
7 Loyalty in the face of trouble (13)
8 Separation; alienation (12)
14 Kettledrums (7)
16 Loan shark (6)
19 Not containing anything (5)

PUZZLE 124

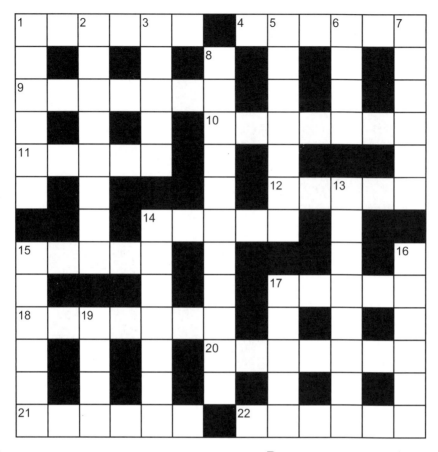

Across

1 Arrange laws systematically (6)
4 Attack with severe criticism (6)
9 Ill-fated (7)
10 Excessive bureaucracy (3,4)
11 Counterfeit (5)
12 Long-necked birds (5)
14 Collection of ships (5)
15 Asian pepper plant (5)
17 Oppress grievously (5)
18 Central bolt (7)
20 Asked to come along (7)
21 Avaricious (6)
22 Dwarfish creatures (6)

Down

1 Round and plump (6)
2 Industrious (8)
3 Concentrate on (5)
5 Least warm (7)
6 Fish (4)
7 Teaser (anag.) (6)
8 Relating to fireworks (11)
13 Make physically used to something (8)
14 Turned over; became very angry (7)
15 Cooking in the oven (6)
16 Protects from direct sunlight (6)
17 Assembly of witches (5)
19 Not any of (4)

Across

1 Observant (8)
5 Short tail (4)
8 Isolated (5)
9 20th letter of the Greek alphabet (7)
10 Strong verbal attack (7)
12 Demilitarises (7)
14 Sourness (7)
16 Moved away from the right course (7)
18 Desiring what someone else has (7)
19 Deep sky-blue colour (5)
20 Disposed of for money (4)
21 Fugitives (8)

Down

1 Raised area of skin (4)
2 Mythical monsters (6)
3 Pecking order (9)
4 Takes the place of (6)
6 Vertical pillar (6)
7 Determination; doggedness (8)
11 State of the USA (9)
12 Kitchen sideboards (8)
13 Worthless information (6)
14 Maxims (6)
15 Damage (6)
17 Optical device (4)

PUZZLE 126

Across

1 Process of getting ready for use (11)
9 Dry and mocking (3)
10 Sound (5)
11 Jumps in the air (5)
12 Agree or correspond (5)
13 Clenching (one's teeth) (8)
16 Game of chance (8)
18 Fortune-telling card (5)
20 Put a question to (5)
21 Very untypical (5)
22 ___ Rida: American rapper (3)
23 Quality of being timeless (11)

Down

2 Regal (5)
3 Variety of viola (5)
4 Plunderer (6)
5 ___ Night: Shakespeare play (7)
6 Derived from living matter (7)
7 European country (11)
8 Official title (11)
14 E.g. using a straw (7)
15 Attentive (7)
17 Stopwatches (6)
18 Symbol (5)
19 Floating timber platforms (5)

CROSSWORD

Across

1 Reactive metal (6)
4 Far away from home (6)
9 Prodding with the elbow (7)
10 Exchanges of several strokes in tennis (7)
11 Male bee (5)
12 Snag; minor problem (5)
14 Melts (5)
17 Pinch; squeeze (5)
19 Badgers' homes (5)
21 Rod used in weightlifting (7)
23 Small amount (7)
24 Alcove (6)
25 Think rationally (6)

Down

1 Seek out (6)
2 Child's toy figurine (4)
3 Tense (7)
5 Grew fainter (5)
6 Concluding section (8)
7 Sharp bend in a road (3-3)
8 Indescribable (11)
13 Relating to construction (8)
15 Germ-free (7)
16 Book of the Bible (6)
18 SI unit of thermodynamic temperature (6)
20 Goes through in detail (5)
22 Female sheep (pl.) (4)

CROSSWORD 132

Across

1 Irritably (8)
5 Cry with sorrow or grief (4)
9 Large hunting knife (5)
10 Pope (7)
11 Not staying the same throughout (12)
14 Long-leaved lettuce (3)
15 ___ firma: dry land (5)
16 Make less bright (3)
17 Study of human societies (12)
20 Seize and take custody of (7)
22 Tasteless (5)
23 Plant stem part from which a leaf emerges (4)
24 Inactivity (8)

Down

1 Desert in northern China (4)
2 Relaxes (7)
3 Absurd (12)
4 One circuit of a track (3)
6 Similar (5)
7 Period during which you live (8)
8 Impregnable (12)
12 Sticky sweet liquid (5)
13 Particular event (8)
16 Break down chemically (7)
18 Used a computer keyboard (5)
19 Sums together (4)
21 Achieved (3)

PUZZLE 129

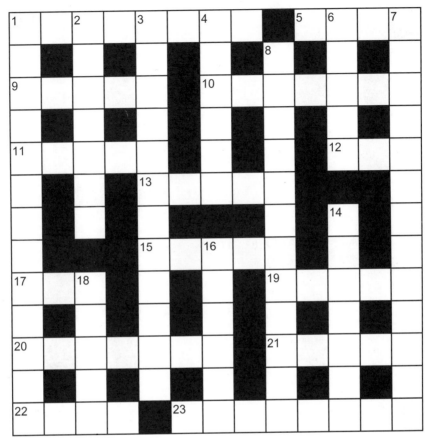

Across

1 Crucial (8)
5 Move fast in a straight line (4)
9 Steer (anag.) (5)
10 Henry David ___ : US essayist (7)
11 Country in the Himalayas (5)
12 Friend (3)
13 In a slow tempo (of music) (5)
15 Zest (5)
17 Acquire; obtain (3)
19 Money (5)
20 European primula (7)
21 Deliberate; cogitate (5)
22 Speech impediment (4)
23 Fully aware (4-4)

Down

1 Arranged in temporal order (13)
2 Vapid (7)
3 Comprehensible (12)
4 Deer horn (6)
6 Young bird's cry (5)
7 Verified again (6-7)
8 Worldly (12)
14 Fortunately (7)
16 Sumptuous and large (of a meal) (4-2)
18 Municipalities (5)

Across

1 Science of building aircraft (11)
9 Armistice (5)
10 Male sheep (3)
11 Actor's words (5)
12 Sheet (anag.) (5)
13 Withdraws (8)
16 Formerly Ceylon (3,5)
18 Weighty (5)
21 T-shirt size (5)
22 Bottle top (3)
23 Item of cutlery (5)
24 Embodies (11)

Down

2 Issue forth (7)
3 Last longer than (a rival) (7)
4 Charm (6)
5 Special reward (5)
6 Cut a joint of meat (5)
7 Green pigment in plants (11)
8 Instantly (11)
14 Blank page in a book (7)
15 Trespass (7)
17 Share out food sparingly (6)
19 Type of sweet (5)
20 Bonds of union (5)

CROSSWORD

Across

1 Huge groups of insects (6)
4 Does penance (6)
9 Cornmeal (7)
10 Small crown (7)
11 Slips (anag.) (5)
12 Concise and full of meaning (5)
14 Hazy (5)
15 Spree (5)
17 Directly opposite in character (5)
18 Armed helicopter (7)
20 Provoked; encouraged (7)
21 Fatty matter (6)
22 Immature insects (6)

Down

1 Provide (6)
2 Indirect reference (8)
3 Lists of restaurants dishes (5)
5 Type of treatment for a disorder (7)
6 Word that identifies a thing (4)
7 Having pimples (6)
8 Visible to the naked eye (11)
13 Work surface (8)
14 Ways of doing things (7)
15 Important person (6)
16 Women who are about to marry (6)
17 Finicky (5)
19 Give a particular title to (4)

PUZZLE 132

Across

1 Living thing (8)
5 ___ Raducanu: British tennis player (4)
9 Loud resonant noise (5)
10 Adult (5-2)
11 Unemotional and practical (6-2-4)
14 Distant and unfriendly (3)
15 Pertaining to the moon (5)
16 Head covering (3)
17 Uncertain (12)
20 In the place of (7)
22 Conclude; deduce (5)
23 Critical examination (4)
24 Lessened (8)

Down

1 Killer whale (4)
2 Storehouse for grain (7)
3 Garments worn in bed (12)
4 Droop (3)
6 Obsession (5)
7 Desire for food (8)
8 Shape of something (12)
12 Musical form with a recurrent theme (5)
13 Anxiety (8)
16 Useful (7)
18 Gets less difficult (5)
19 Walked or stepped (4)
21 Ground condensation (3)

Across

1 State of preoccupation (11)
9 Interdict (3)
10 Fissures (5)
11 Fast (5)
12 Hear a court case anew (5)
13 Wall of large wooden posts (8)
16 Makes remote; cuts off (8)
18 Small replica version (5)
20 Diacritical mark (5)
21 Not as common (5)
22 Compete for (3)
23 Extend by inference (11)

Down

2 Destroyed by fire (5)
3 Delay or linger (5)
4 Have an impact on (6)
5 Tuft of grass (7)
6 Passing around a town (of a road) (7)
7 Shortened (11)
8 Insects with brightly coloured wings (11)
14 Chest for implements (7)
15 Someone who provides food (7)
17 Catch or snare (6)
18 ___ Streep: Mamma Mia! actress (5)
19 Clod of turf (5)

PUZZLE 134

Across

1. E.g. a trumpeter or pianist (8)
5. Having inherent ability (4)
9. Cotton twill fabric (5)
10. Increase in size (7)
11. Loving (12)
14. Convent dweller (3)
15. Should (5)
16. Hip (anag.) (3)
17. Body of voters in a specified region (12)
20. This starts on 1st January (3,4)
22. Media (anag.) (5)
23. ___ Hathaway: actress (4)
24. Extravagant fuss (8)

Down

1. Speed relative to sound (4)
2. Become rigid (7)
3. Reticent; secretive (12)
4. Wonder (3)
6. Former name of Myanmar (5)
7. Critical explanation (8)
8. Unseen observer (3,2,3,4)
12. Taut (5)
13. Constricting snake (8)
16. Somewhat hungry (7)
18. Certain to fail (2-3)
19. Emperor of Rome 54-68 AD (4)
21. Drowned river valley (3)

Across

1 Loot (4)
3 State of the USA (8)
9 Type of computer (7)
10 Round cap (5)
11 Dark reddish-brown pigment (5)
12 Regain strength (7)
13 Subatomic particle such as an electron (6)
15 Where crops are grown (6)
17 Walk aimlessly (7)
18 Musical speeds (5)
20 Visual representation (5)
21 Increase the duration of (7)
22 Assembled (8)
23 Get a glimpse of (4)

Down

1 Very funny (4-9)
2 Greek fabulist (5)
4 Deposit knowledge (6)
5 Advance payment (12)
6 Disentangle (7)
7 Fascinatingly (13)
8 Atmospheric layer (12)
14 Anapest (anag.) (7)
16 Place of worship (6)
19 Natural satellites (5)

PUZZLE 136

Across

1 Talented (6)
7 Formidable (8)
8 Plaything (3)
9 Wore away gradually (6)
10 Benicio del ___ : actor (4)
11 Thin fogs (5)
13 Part of a chair (7)
15 Film or play texts (7)
17 Fruit of the oak (5)
21 Game played on horseback (4)
22 Shining with light (6)
23 Consumed food (3)
24 Mathematically aware (8)
25 Sagely; prudently (6)

Down

1 ___ City: where Batman lives (6)
2 Small handbills (6)
3 Semiconductor (5)
4 Arachnids (7)
5 Abstruse (8)
6 Entraps (6)
12 Customised (of clothes) (8)
14 Pertaining to the stars (7)
16 Part of a song (6)
18 Colourless flammable hydrocarbon (6)
19 That is to say (6)
20 Sharp-pointed metal pin (5)

CROSSWORD

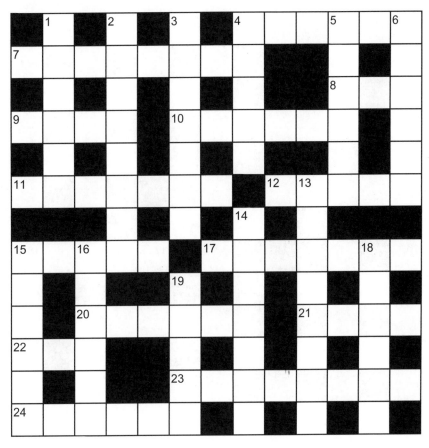

Across

4 Disallow; prevent (6)
7 Of a court of law (8)
8 Remove branches (3)
9 Greek spirit (4)
10 Generic term for a martial art (4,2)
11 Line of rulers (7)
12 Ornamental stone (5)
15 Dissenting religious groups (5)
17 Skilled worker (7)
20 Set on fire (6)
21 Fertile type of soil (4)
22 Rodent (3)
23 Choosing from various sources (8)
24 Plants with sword-shaped leaves (6)

Down

1 State of great comfort (6)
2 Unit of power (8)
3 Small doors or gates (7)
4 Throw forcefully (5)
5 Source of caviar (6)
6 Mottled marking (6)
13 Severe traffic congestion (8)
14 Trials (7)
15 County in SE England (6)
16 Reviewer (6)
18 Leguminous tree (6)
19 Shuffles together (5)

PUZZLE 138

Across

1 Column (6)
4 Customary practices (6)
9 Type of bill (7)
10 Spreads out (7)
11 Freshwater fish (5)
12 Pellucid (5)
14 Sudden sharp pains (5)
17 Leg joints (5)
19 Plummeted (5)
21 Brutal; cruel (7)
23 Religious ceremonies (7)
24 Capital of New South Wales (6)
25 Shears (anag.) (6)

Down

1 Astronomical distance (6)
2 Fibber (4)
3 Most populous city in Belgium (7)
5 Divide by cutting (5)
6 Direction; general help (8)
7 Fume (6)
8 Recognise as different (11)
13 Raised (8)
15 Very great (3-4)
16 Loves greatly (6)
18 Pieces of tough fibrous tissue (6)
20 Male duck (5)
22 Bleak upland (4)

Across

1 Sample of cloth (6)
4 Complied with orders (6)
9 Draw back (7)
10 Cricket overs in which no runs are scored (7)
11 Crave; desire (5)
12 Hard to please (5)
14 Stares with the mouth wide open (5)
15 Very large (5)
17 Grape (anag.) (5)
18 Vehicle towed by another (7)
20 Foolishly (7)
21 Bog (6)
22 Wrestling hold (6)

Down

1 Coniferous tree (6)
2 Policy of direct action (8)
3 Thorax (5)
5 Firm opinions (7)
6 Another word for Christmas (4)
7 Showy (6)
8 Creating an evocative mood (11)
13 Cosiness (8)
14 Atheistic (7)
15 Debris at sea (6)
16 Stick of coloured wax (6)
17 Stage (5)
19 ___ Khan: British boxer (4)

Across

1   Daring (11)
9   Dried kernel of the coconut (5)
10 Lively dance (3)
11 Trail (5)
12 Ethical (5)
13 Alleviated (8)
16 Having no worries (8)
18 Revel (anag.) (5)
21 A Fish Called ___ : film (5)
22 Boolean operator (3)
23 Not clearly stated (5)
24 Region including Cornwall and Devon (4,7)

Down

2   Not varying (7)
3   Touches the skin of another lightly (7)
4   Fame (6)
5   Sudden constriction (5)
6   Important and significant (5)
7   Large fruits with red pulp (11)
8   Form into a cluster (11)
14 Among (7)
15 Computer peripheral (7)
17 In slow time (of music) (6)
19 Vigour and spirit (5)
20 Bolt for fastening metal plates (5)

CROSSWORD

Across

1 Wharf (4)
3 Very small unit of length (8)
9 Friendly (7)
10 Bound (5)
11 Herb; regret (3)
12 Ousel (anag.) (5)
13 Small house (5)
15 Things to be done (5)
17 Commerce (5)
18 Flightless bird (3)
19 Recycle (5)
20 Play havoc with (7)
21 On the shore of a sea (8)
22 Wet with condensation (4)

Down

1 Four-sided figure (13)
2 Not dead (5)
4 Required (6)
5 Altruism (12)
6 Whispers (7)
7 Where you were born (6,7)
8 Lowest possible temperature (8,4)
14 Bridgelike structure (7)
16 Sporting arenas (6)
18 Escape from (5)

Across

1 Policemen or women (8)
5 Always (4)
9 Protective garment (5)
10 Father of a parent (7)
11 Intended to attract notice (12)
14 Lowest cardinal number (3)
15 Belonging to them (5)
16 Level golf score (3)
17 Commensurate (12)
20 Part exchange for something new (5-2)
22 Plainly apparent (5)
23 Sound of a lion (4)
24 Recreational area for children (8)

Down

1 Egg-shaped (4)
2 Envisage (7)
3 Someone who makes sweets (12)
4 Floor cover (3)
6 Record on tape (5)
7 Assimilate again (8)
8 Study of microorganisms (12)
12 Act of stealing (5)
13 Machine used to surf the internet (8)
16 Inactive pill (7)
18 Barack ___ : 44th US President (5)
19 Basic unit of matter (4)
21 Nothing (3)

CROSSWORD

Across

1 Eager; keen (4)
3 E.g. resident of Cairo (8)
9 Baffling puzzle (7)
10 Become ready to eat (of fruit) (5)
11 Baseball teams (5)
12 Heroic deed (7)
13 Sweltering (6)
15 Robinson ___ : novel (6)
17 Ways of doing things (7)
18 Lukewarm (5)
20 Mortise insert (5)
21 Idealistic (7)
22 Sorriest (anag.) (8)
23 Land surrounded by water (4)

Down

1 Person performing official duties (13)
2 Henrik ___ : Norwegian playwright (5)
4 Hot spring (6)
5 Sweat (12)
6 Irreligious (7)
7 Failure to be present at (13)
8 Calculations of dimensions (12)
14 Mythical stories (7)
16 Old Portuguese currency (6)
19 Buckets (5)

PUZZLE 144

Across

1 Mocking (8)
5 Arthur ___ : a Wimbledon winner (4)
9 Type of stopwatch (5)
10 Acquire from a relative (7)
11 Daydream (7)
12 Remnant of a dying fire (5)
13 Demand forcefully to have something (6)
14 Spain and Portugal (6)
17 Extra component (3-2)
19 Vehicle equipped for living in (7)
20 Separated; remote (7)
21 Snow leopard (5)
22 Facial feature (4)
23 Shape of the waxing moon (8)

Down

1 Firmness of purpose (13)
2 Takes away (7)
3 Shockingly (12)
4 States an opinion (6)
6 Cleanse by rubbing (5)
7 Amusement (13)
8 Small garden carts (12)
15 Form of retaliation (7)
16 Cricket statistician (6)
18 Amounts of medication (5)

CROSSWORD

Across

1 Practice of drawing maps (11)
9 Composition for a solo instrument (5)
10 Pointed tool (3)
11 Beer (5)
12 Risky (5)
13 Annual (8)
16 Affluent (4-2-2)
18 Extinct birds (5)
21 Harsh and serious in manner (5)
22 ___ Truss: former Prime Minister (3)
23 Astonish (5)
24 Absorbing; intriguing (11)

Down

2 Rearranged letters of a word (7)
3 Thus; as a result (7)
4 South American cowboy (6)
5 Alter (5)
6 Detected a sound (5)
7 Pamper (11)
8 Recreational areas for children (11)
14 Nearest (7)
15 Precede (7)
17 Get away from (6)
19 Twelve (5)
20 Move on ice (5)

Across

1 Travels on foot (6)
4 Kitchen strainers (6)
9 Solidify (7)
10 Ungrateful person (7)
11 Lingers furtively (5)
12 Brings up (5)
14 ___ Davro: comedian (5)
15 Intimidate (5)
17 Sing softly (5)
18 Dark pigment in skin (7)
20 Decaying organic matter (7)
21 Layers (anag.) (6)
22 Rode a bike (6)

Down

1 Equipment for fishing (6)
2 Unusual (8)
3 Platforms leading out to sea (5)
5 Figurative language (7)
6 Entry document (4)
7 Small, mole-like mammals (6)
8 Symbol of reconciliation (5,6)
13 Structure giving lift in flight (8)
14 Eventually (2,3,2)
15 Exceptionally successful (6)
16 Joined together (6)
17 Snug and nice to wear (5)
19 Hang loosely; droop (4)

CROSSWORD

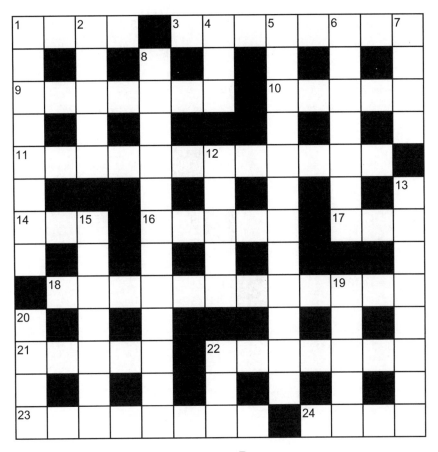

Across

1 Wipes up (4)
3 No longer in fashion (8)
9 Marine mammal (7)
10 Excellent (5)
11 Minimum purchase cost at auction (7,5)
14 Bat (anag.) (3)
16 Spy (5)
17 False statement (3)
18 Insubordination (12)
21 Expect to happen (5)
22 Where you watch films (7)
23 Financially ruined (8)
24 Landlocked country in Africa (4)

Down

1 Not extreme (8)
2 Heaps (5)
4 Type of vase (3)
5 Detailed reports (12)
6 Representative (7)
7 Challenge (4)
8 Marksman (12)
12 Bring to the conscious mind (5)
13 Set free (8)
15 Great ___ : island (7)
19 Insect larva (5)
20 Young sheep (4)
22 Container for a drink (3)

Across

1 Repudiate (8)
5 Pal (4)
9 Supple (5)
10 Posting (7)
11 Overshadow (7)
12 Biter (anag.) (5)
13 Close tightly (6)
14 Third sign of the zodiac (6)
17 Mix up (5)
19 Make less taut (7)
20 Nominal (7)
21 Person who always puts in a lot of effort (5)
22 Raised edges (4)
23 Physical power (8)

Down

1 Amusement park ride (6,7)
2 ___ Portman: actress (7)
3 By chance (12)
4 Force to do something (6)
6 Port-au-Prince's location (5)
7 Direction to which a compass points (8,5)
8 Chatter (6-6)
15 Vague understanding; hint (7)
16 Liveliness (6)
18 Single piece of information (5)

Across

1 Entry pass (6)
7 Reserved (8)
8 Gang (3)
9 Obstruct (6)
10 Tidy (4)
11 Outdated (5)
13 Took the place of (7)
15 Someone who dithers (7)
17 Spoke softly (5)
21 Give notice (4)
22 Moved very quickly (6)
23 Metric unit of measurement (historical) (3)
24 Added salt and pepper (8)
25 Gained deservedly (6)

Down

1 Drum (3-3)
2 Private rooms on ships (6)
3 Large woody plants (5)
4 Non-believer in God (7)
5 Plot outline (8)
6 Inborn (6)
12 Orderliness (8)
14 Awaiting decision (7)
16 Lets up (6)
18 Make a priest (6)
19 Rely on (6)
20 Woman getting married (5)

Across

1 Light from our star (8)
5 Plant stalk (4)
9 Supply with; furnish (5)
10 Type of optician (7)
11 Ahead of time (5)
12 Bustle (3)
13 Diving bird (5)
15 People not ordained (5)
17 Liveliness (3)
19 Rocky; harsh (5)
20 Laugh (7)
21 Legendary Himalayan creatures (5)
22 Falsehoods (4)
23 Fragrant toiletries (8)

Down

1 Lacking originality (13)
2 Impartial (7)
3 Carefree (5-2-5)
4 Pasta strip (6)
6 Part of the leg (5)
7 Process of transformation (of an insect) (13)
8 Short tale told to children (7,5)
14 Living in water (7)
16 Reasons (6)
18 Long cloud of smoke (5)

CROSSWORD

Across

1 Tumultuous (6)
4 Violent gust of wind (6)
9 High spirits (7)
10 Smallest amount (7)
11 Lift with effort (5)
12 Used up (5)
14 Pastime (5)
17 Portable source of light (5)
19 Stiff (5)
21 Tapers (7)
23 Pertaining to plants (7)
24 Metrical foot (6)
25 Foist (upon) (6)

Down

1 Waterlogged areas of ground (6)
2 Portent (4)
3 Large extinct elephant (7)
5 Subdue (5)
6 One who stirs up trouble (8)
7 Connected (6)
8 A recollection (11)
13 Relating to critical explanation (8)
15 Chemical element (7)
16 Investigated in detail (6)
18 Jostle or push roughly (6)
20 Fop (5)
22 US state (4)

Across

1 Innate behaviour (8)
5 ___ bear: ursine cartoon character (4)
9 Jeopardy (5)
10 Rise into the air (of an aircraft) (4,3)
11 Shield of Zeus (5)
12 Sprint (3)
13 Come to a point (5)
15 Terrible (5)
17 Young bear (3)
19 Seven (anag.) (5)
20 Round discs sewn on garments (7)
21 Water vapour (5)
22 Sound reflection (4)
23 Hairstyle (8)

Down

1 Unfeasible (13)
2 Scrawny (7)
3 Picture (12)
4 Summon to serve in the armed forces (4-2)
6 Perfume smell (5)
7 Extremely small (13)
8 Easily (12)
14 ___ May: former Prime Minister (7)
16 Wall painting; mural (6)
18 Group (5)

PUZZLE 153

CROSSWORD

Across

1 Founded (11)
9 Check carefully (3)
10 Way in (5)
11 Exposes secret information (5)
12 Tarns (anag.) (5)
13 Material used as a colourant (8)
16 Heated surface used for cooking food (8)
18 Relating to a city (5)
20 Upright (5)
21 Hermann ___ : author of Steppenwolf (5)
22 Solid form of water (3)
23 Spookiness (11)

Down

2 Silk fabric (5)
3 Assists in a crime (5)
4 Recently (6)
5 Chic (7)
6 Error in printing or writing (7)
7 Do better than expected (11)
8 Discontented (11)
14 Extend an arm or leg (7)
15 Apparel (7)
17 Flowering plant with a prickly stem (6)
18 Free from dirt (5)
19 Concealing garments (5)

PUZZLE 154

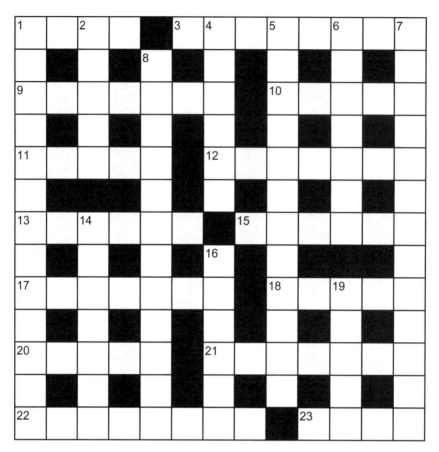

Across

1 Complain (4)
3 Fighter in close combat (8)
9 Enlarged; puffy (7)
10 Musical note (5)
11 Feeling of deep anxiety (5)
12 Illness (7)
13 Not disposed to cheat (6)
15 Alanis Morissette hit song (6)
17 Highest singing voice (7)
18 Bird claw (5)
20 Strong thread (5)
21 Idealist; visionary (7)
22 Living alone (8)
23 Ring a bell (4)

Down

1 State of the USA (13)
2 With a forward motion (5)
4 Where aeroplanes take off and land (6)
5 Areas of commonality (12)
6 Portable lamp (7)
7 Device for changing TV channel (6,7)
8 First part of the Bible (3,9)
14 Pertaining to marriage (7)
16 Awe (6)
19 West Indian dance (5)

Across

1 Chair at the rear of a vehicle (4,4)
5 Wetlands (4)
8 Device that clears a car windscreen (5)
9 Game played on a lawn (7)
10 Johannes ___ : Dutch painter (7)
12 Cause to absorb water (7)
14 Greet (7)
16 A percussion instrument (7)
18 Start (4,3)
19 Pointed projectile (5)
20 Uncommon (4)
21 Variants (8)

Down

1 Send down a ball in cricket (4)
2 Emulated (6)
3 Scheme (9)
4 Recess (6)
6 Dodged (6)
7 Drench (8)
11 Compels by coercion (9)
12 Forceful blow (8)
13 Food merchant (6)
14 Talk nonsense (6)
15 Exaggerate (6)
17 Pairs (4)

Across

1 Burden (4)
3 Created in the house (8)
9 Show (7)
10 Money container (5)
11 Major type of food nutrient (12)
14 Insane (3)
16 Deprive of weapons (5)
17 Hair colourant (3)
18 Impudence (12)
21 Door part (5)
22 Nuclear ___ : device that generates energy (7)
23 Rump (8)
24 Fraud (4)

Down

1 Defeated (8)
2 Wedding official (5)
4 Top (anag.) (3)
5 Based on untested ideas (12)
6 Introduced air to (7)
7 Level and regular (4)
8 Completeness (12)
12 Dough raiser (5)
13 Part of the brain (8)
15 Extremely cruel (7)
19 Incision; indent (5)
20 Freshwater game fish (4)
22 Relieve or free from (3)

CROSSWORD

Across

1 A surprisingly easy task (8)
5 Norse god (4)
9 Of the nose (5)
10 Box of useful equipment (7)
11 Cab ride (anag.) (7)
12 Thigh bone (5)
13 Expression of praise (6)
14 Instrument panel of a car (6)
17 Implied (5)
19 River of East Africa (7)
20 Relating to sight (7)
21 Nobleman (5)
22 Indian dress (4)
23 Fatherly (8)

Down

1 Characterised by great care (13)
2 Small falcon (7)
3 Supporting cane (7,5)
4 Alphabetical character (6)
6 Loose fibre from old rope (5)
7 Between countries (13)
8 Not catching fire easily (12)
15 V-shaped mark (7)
16 Deciduous flowering shrub (6)
18 Supply with food (5)

Across

1 German car manufacturer (4)
3 Put in order (8)
9 Art of clipping shrubs decoratively (7)
10 Indian rice dish (5)
11 Beads (anag.) (5)
12 Look something over (7)
13 Glass container (6)
15 Frenzied (6)
17 Feeling jealous (7)
18 Group of shots (5)
20 Snow home (5)
21 Evident (7)
22 Intelligentsia (8)
23 Couple (4)

Down

1 Destroying microorganisms (13)
2 Deceives or misleads (5)
4 Had corresponding sounds (6)
5 Uneasy (12)
6 Chivalrous (7)
7 Betrayer (6-7)
8 Bride's primary attendant (4,2,6)
14 Brook (7)
16 Arrange into groups (6)
19 ___ Lewis: British singer (5)

Across

- **1** Consecrate (8)
- **5** Delighted (4)
- **9** Animal that eats bamboo (5)
- **10** Aquatic invertebrates (7)
- **11** Print anew (7)
- **12** More pleasant (5)
- **13** Attack someone (6)
- **14** Wanted to happen (6)
- **17** Effigies (5)
- **19** Sweet effervescent powder (7)
- **20** Shut in (7)
- **21** Beat (5)
- **22** City in North Yorkshire (4)
- **23** Worker (8)

Down

- **1** Magnificently (13)
- **2** Children's carers (7)
- **3** Act of sending a message (12)
- **4** Bustled about nervously (6)
- **6** Good sense (5)
- **7** Disreputable (13)
- **8** Occurring at the same time (12)
- **15** Freedom (7)
- **16** Respect and admire (6)
- **18** Arise (5)

Across

1 An unspecified person (8)
5 Tranquil (4)
9 Hot fluid rock (5)
10 Gusty winds (7)
11 Not capable of reply (12)
13 Theatrical works (6)
14 Showed around (6)
17 Emergency touchdown (5-7)
20 Colossal (7)
21 Synthetic fabric (5)
22 Froth of soap and water (4)
23 Unequal; biased (3-5)

Down

1 Wrestling sport (4)
2 Purplish red colour (7)
3 Forcible indoctrination (12)
4 Repudiate (6)
6 Spontaneous remark (2-5)
7 Wrongdoings (8)
8 Environment (12)
12 Teaches (8)
15 Held out enticingly (7)
16 Bird of prey (6)
18 Performed on stage (5)
19 ___ Blyton: English children's writer (4)

CROSSWORD

Across

1	Tuna (anag.) (4)
3	Card game (8)
9	Surround completely (7)
10	Double-reed instruments (5)
11	Food shop (12)
14	Arrest (3)
16	Path or road (5)
17	Snow runner (3)
18	Thick-skinned herbivorous animal (12)
21	Many-headed snake (5)
22	Cork for sealing a bottle (7)
23	Snakes (8)
24	Makes damp (4)

Down

1	Changing (8)
2	What an author writes (5)
4	Unit of current (3)
5	Sample of a larger group (5,7)
6	Violent troublemakers (7)
7	Elephant tooth (4)
8	Coat with a metal (12)
12	Outdo (5)
13	Cracks (8)
15	Constructor (7)
19	Acer tree (5)
20	Therefore (4)
22	Took an exam (3)

Across

1 Needleworker (11)
9 Smack (3)
10 Long-necked Indian lute (5)
11 Smooth transition (5)
12 Proposal of marriage; bid (5)
13 Rare (8)
16 Having a striking beauty (8)
18 Legend (5)
20 Fruit (5)
21 Bandage that supports an arm (5)
22 Long-haired ox (3)
23 Money spent (11)

Down

2 Dominant theme (5)
3 Vertical part of a step (5)
4 Confine or impound (6)
5 Hearing range (7)
6 Final stage of a chess match (7)
7 Accurate timer (11)
8 Pleasant to think about but unrealistic (3,2,3,3)
14 Complicated (7)
15 Skill (7)
17 Undone (6)
18 Take part in combat (5)
19 Purchaser (5)

Across

1 Song for several voices (8)
5 Incandescent lamp (4)
9 Simple (5)
10 Done in full awareness (7)
11 Importance (12)
14 Nay (anag.) (3)
15 Laud (5)
16 Ease into a chair (3)
17 Immediately (12)
20 Make a substantial profit (5,2)
22 Alphabetical list in a book (5)
23 Thin fog (4)
24 Creased (8)

Down

1 Gangs (4)
2 Fate (7)
3 Awkward (12)
4 Put a question to (3)
6 Marriage (5)
7 French bread stick (8)
8 Placation (12)
12 Retrieve (5)
13 Pepper plant (8)
16 Thing causing outrage (7)
18 Submerged ridges of rock (5)
19 Chopped; cancelled (4)
21 For each (3)

PUZZLE 164

Across

4	Diving waterbirds (6)
7	Majesty (8)
8	A man's dinner jacket (abbrev.) (3)
9	Country whose capital is Havana (4)
10	Treat indulgently (6)
11	Selects (7)
12	Gush out in a jet (5)
15	Have faith in (5)
17	Melodious (7)
20	Alcoholic drink (6)
21	Recedes (4)
22	Soft animal hair (3)
23	Taking away (8)
24	Level plain without trees (6)

Down

1	Natural depression (6)
2	Well known for some bad deed (8)
3	Instructor (7)
4	Networks of lines (5)
5	Flat-bottomed rowing boat (6)
6	Group of six (6)
13	Jam or marmalade (8)
14	Repositories of antiques (7)
15	Robberies (6)
16	False (6)
18	Straightened (6)
19	Part of a church tower (5)

PUZZLE 165

Across

1 Go before in time (8)
5 Roman poet (4)
9 Solid geometric figure (5)
10 Canvas shelters (7)
11 River in South America (7)
12 Supplied with weapons (5)
13 Relations by marriage (2-4)
14 Gaseous envelope of the sun (6)
17 Capital of Ghana (5)
19 Palest (7)
20 Clumsily (7)
21 Strong ringing sound (5)
22 E.g. pecan and cashew (4)
23 Learnt (8)

Down

1 Estimation (13)
2 Unimportant (7)
3 A grouping of states (12)
4 Ordained minister (6)
6 Snake toxin (5)
7 Deprived (13)
8 Unfriendly (12)
15 Perform in an exaggerated manner (7)
16 Moved back and forth (6)
18 Break the rules (5)

Across

1 Actually (6)
7 Justified in terms of profitability (8)
8 24-hour period (3)
9 Sailing barge (6)
10 Look or bearing (4)
11 Faithful (5)
13 Fish-eating birds of prey (7)
15 People who copy out documents (7)
17 Legendary stories (5)
21 Distinctive atmosphere created by a person (4)
22 Embarrassing mistake (3-3)
23 Tear (3)
24 Outmoded (8)
25 Extinguished (6)

Down

1 Arranged like rays (6)
2 Regardless (6)
3 Resay (anag.) (5)
4 Imitator (7)
5 Previously (8)
6 Thinly (6)
12 Cartoon artist (8)
14 Small stones (7)
16 Tiny bits of bread (6)
18 Plant spikes (6)
19 Unintelligent (6)
20 Prodded (5)

CROSSWORD

Across

4 Howl (6)
7 Musical compositions (8)
8 Gave a meal to (3)
9 Father (4)
10 Bird; crazy (6)
11 Searching carefully (7)
12 ___ Midler: US singer-songwriter (5)
15 Travels by bicycle (5)
17 Grapple with (7)
20 One who addresses an audience (6)
21 Sage (4)
22 Fasten with stitches (3)
23 Words representing numbers (8)
24 E.g. using a towel (6)

Down

1 Trinidad and ___ : country (6)
2 Clamber (8)
3 Finding by investigation (7)
4 From that time (5)
5 Exertion (6)
6 Title used for a French woman (6)
13 Opposite of westward (8)
14 Ancient warship (7)
15 Awakened (6)
16 Lethargic; sleepy (6)
18 Finally (6)
19 Wounded by a wasp (5)

PUZZLE 168

Across

1 Slight cut (4)
3 Playhouses (8)
9 Harden (7)
10 Brilliant and clear (5)
11 Effects or results (12)
13 Tensed (anag.) (6)
15 Honolulu's state (6)
17 Deceitfully (12)
20 Held on to something tightly (5)
21 Critical (7)
22 Abandoned (8)
23 Large bodies of water (4)

Down

1 Observing (8)
2 Machine for making butter (5)
4 Respect; great esteem (6)
5 Beneficial (12)
6 Mediterranean coastal region (7)
7 Team (4)
8 Fast food item (12)
12 Two-wheeled vehicles (8)
14 Disguises or covers (7)
16 Brawn; strength (6)
18 In a ___ : very quickly (5)
19 Decorated a cake (4)

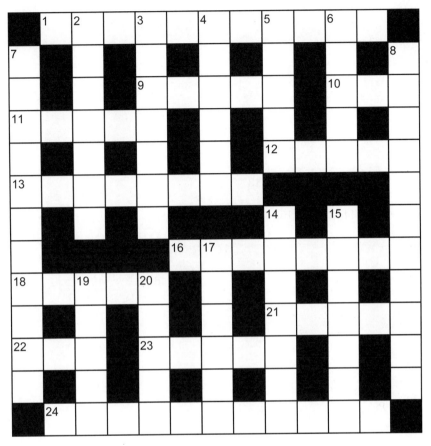

Across

1 Causing difficulties (11)
9 Hurled away (5)
10 Court (3)
11 Indian monetary unit (5)
12 Kind of wheat (5)
13 Grow in number (8)
16 Far on in development (8)
18 Fastens shut with a key (5)
21 Two times (5)
22 Athletic facility (3)
23 Saying (5)
24 Designed for usefulness (11)

Down

2 Admire deeply (7)
3 Spoke (7)
4 Song words (6)
5 Stitched (5)
6 Garden tool for cutting grass (5)
7 Phraseology (11)
8 Divine rule (11)
14 Snobbishness (7)
15 Spiny anteater (7)
17 Pour from one container to another (6)
19 Celestial body (5)
20 Stable compartment (5)

Across

1 Serving to enlighten; instructive (11)
9 Animal foot (3)
10 Positions in a hierarchy (5)
11 Mark of insertion (5)
12 Shyly (5)
13 Beginning (8)
16 Muddled (8)
18 Glazed earthenware (5)
20 Reluctant (5)
21 Aromatic vegetable (5)
22 Ash (anag.) (3)
23 Quantification (11)

Down

2 Fluffy and soft (5)
3 Spiced dish (5)
4 Occupant (6)
5 Vague and uncertain (7)
6 Human-like robot (7)
7 Extremely impressive (11)
8 Defect in the eye (11)
14 All together (2,5)
15 Writers (7)
17 Simpler (6)
18 Fabric used to make jeans (5)
19 Lindsay ___ : Mean Girls actress (5)

Across

1 Yearly (6)
4 Sea in northern Europe (6)
9 Boorish (7)
10 Unity (7)
11 Functions correctly (5)
12 Three-note chord (5)
14 Groups together (5)
15 Penned (5)
17 Consecrate (5)
18 Copy (7)
20 Spouse (7)
21 Subject to a penalty (6)
22 Cools down (6)

Down

1 Lets happen (6)
2 Neutral particle with negligible mass (8)
3 Sour substances (5)
5 Characteristics; features (7)
6 Melody (4)
7 Opposite of open (6)
8 Compose a dance routine (11)
13 Situated on the inside (8)
14 Portions of time (7)
15 Stretch prior to exercise (4-2)
16 Egyptian god (6)
17 Mooring for a ship (5)
19 Unpleasant sensation (4)

PUZZLE 172

Across

1 Scheme (4)
3 Yielded (8)
9 Irreverence (7)
10 Leashes (5)
11 Female relatives (5)
12 Illuminate (5,2)
13 Number of Apostles (6)
15 Heavy food (6)
17 Gives an account of (7)
18 Higher in place (5)
20 Tree with an edible nut (5)
21 Make more entertaining (7)
22 Tanks for storing water (8)
23 Lied (anag.) (4)

Down

1 Benevolent and generous (13)
2 Trembling poplar (5)
4 Casino ___ : James Bond film (6)
5 Charmingly (12)
6 End chat (anag.) (7)
7 Act of vanishing (13)
8 Persistence (12)
14 Anticipates (7)
16 Towards the rear of a ship (6)
19 E.g. covered with bricks (5)

CROSSWORD

Across

1 Front of a building (6)
4 State publicly (6)
9 Uncovered (7)
10 Person in overall charge (7)
11 A written document (5)
12 Dines (anag.) (5)
14 Moneys owed (5)
17 Timepiece (5)
19 Thread-weaving machines (5)
21 Followed behind (7)
23 Companion (7)
24 Water ice (6)
25 Silly tricks (6)

Down

1 Narrow-necked bottles (6)
2 Complain unreasonably; fish (4)
3 Not crying (3-4)
5 Frustrated and annoyed (3,2)
6 Unskilled; amateur (8)
7 Sadness (6)
8 Film that is a great success (11)
13 Mole (8)
15 Knitted garment (7)
16 Pieces of bread (6)
18 Fences made of bushes (6)
20 Long flower-stalk (5)
22 Give temporarily (4)

PUZZLE 174

Across

1 Desert illusion (6)
4 Divided into two parts (6)
9 ___ Monroe: famous actress (7)
10 Hit hard (7)
11 Ice cream is often served in these (5)
12 Uneven (of a road) (5)
14 Low value US coins (5)
15 Pulpy (5)
17 Sweeping implement (5)
18 Sleeveless garment (7)
20 Set aside for a purpose (7)
21 From Denmark (6)
22 Predatory marine fish (pl.) (6)

Down

1 Copies (6)
2 Scarceness (8)
3 Bodies of water (5)
5 Takes in (7)
6 Action word (4)
7 Very much (6)
8 Not joined together (11)
13 Monster in Greek myth (8)
14 One-eyed giant (7)
15 Disguised (6)
16 Cooks in wood chippings (6)
17 Time when life begins (5)
19 Noble gas (4)

CROSSWORD

Across

1 Pester (6)
7 Female pilot (8)
8 Frying pan (3)
9 Wading birds (6)
10 Silent (4)
11 Takes a breather (5)
13 Ripple on water (7)
15 Getting bigger (7)
17 Sandy wasteland (5)
21 Large washing bowl (4)
22 Avoids (6)
23 Marry (3)
24 Designers of trendy clothes (8)
25 Background actors (6)

Down

1 Type of cricketer (6)
2 Streak (anag.) (6)
3 Maurice ___ : French composer (5)
4 Male blood relation (7)
5 Mad rush (8)
6 Moral excellence (6)
12 Building used by local government (4,4)
14 Opposite (7)
16 Cooks in the oven (6)
18 Reply (6)
19 Throngs (6)
20 Temporary stop (5)

PUZZLE 176

Across

1 Meaner (anag.) (6)
4 Season before Christmas (6)
9 Put in someone's care (7)
10 Last longer than (7)
11 Break (5)
12 Perfume (5)
14 Chute (5)
17 Components (5)
19 Turns over and over (5)
21 Type of tooth (7)
23 Fear of heights (7)
24 Walk casually (6)
25 Rental agreements (6)

Down

1 Barber's tools (6)
2 Small amphibian (4)
3 Points in time (7)
5 Loves uncritically (5)
6 Copier (8)
7 Irritable (6)
8 Negligence (11)
13 Adventurer (8)
15 Gourmet (7)
16 Shows beyond doubt (6)
18 Narrow drinking tubes (6)
20 Ability; talent (5)
22 Droops (4)

Across

1 Youth (11)
9 Touch gently (3)
10 Operate a motor vehicle (5)
11 Section of a long poem (5)
12 Noble gas (5)
13 Beaten (8)
16 Not appropriate (8)
18 Manages (5)
20 Make right (5)
21 Singing voices (5)
22 Sue (anag.) (3)
23 Pain in a person's belly (7,4)

Down

2 Showered with love (5)
3 Burdened (5)
4 Evening party (6)
5 Driven out (7)
6 Imply as a condition (7)
7 Not exact (11)
8 Company that transmits TV shows (11)
14 Assign a role to (7)
15 Prepare beforehand (7)
17 Excitingly strange (6)
18 ___ del Sol: region of Spain (5)
19 Lavish (5)

Across

1 Expense (4)
3 Yellow flower (8)
9 Found out about (7)
10 Shrewdness; understanding (5)
11 Easy to converse with (12)
14 Dry (of wine) (3)
16 Long-___ owl: bird (5)
17 Joke (3)
18 Perform below expectation (12)
21 Type of cravat (5)
22 Religious sacrament (7)
23 Our galaxy (5,3)
24 Remain (4)

Down

1 Cave in (8)
2 Impress a pattern on (5)
4 Increase in amount (3)
5 Popular takeaway food (4,3,5)
6 Bring to maturity (7)
7 Puts down (4)
8 Incomprehensibly (12)
12 Papal court (5)
13 Not proper (of behaviour) (8)
15 Sceptical (7)
19 Turf out (5)
20 Injure (4)
22 Bleat of a sheep (3)

Across

1 Heavy rain (8)
5 Piece of metal used as money (4)
8 Cylinder of smoking tobacco (5)
9 Agitate (7)
10 Concealed (7)
12 Bird of prey (7)
14 Clergymen (7)
16 Clothes for washing (7)
18 Administrative division (7)
19 Large tree (5)
20 Greek god of love (4)
21 Person not expected to win (8)

Down

1 Passage (4)
2 Gambles (6)
3 Talked into doing something (9)
4 Remove from a container (6)
6 Body of work (6)
7 People of no note (8)
11 Genuine; real (9)
12 Easily deceived (8)
13 A size of book page (6)
14 Snake (6)
15 Astute (6)
17 Dull car sound (4)

CROSSWORD

Across

1	Creative (11)
9	Pertaining to the ear (5)
10	SI unit of illuminance (3)
11	Infectious agent (5)
12	Type of military operation (5)
13	Portable device to keep the rain off (8)
16	Type of pasta (8)
18	Precious gem (5)
21	Smart; ache (5)
22	Asp (anag.) (3)
23	Greenish-bronze fish (5)
24	Freedom from dirt (11)

Down

2	Bacterium (7)
3	Understood; held (7)
4	Regular (6)
5	Speaks (5)
6	Regard highly (5)
7	Biased treatment (11)
8	Extremely (11)
14	Male rower (7)
15	Cosmetic liquids (7)
17	Descend down a rock face (6)
19	Proceeding from the pope (5)
20	Striped animal (5)

CROSSWORD

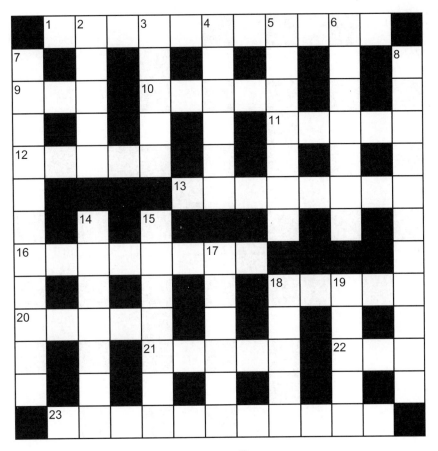

Across

1 Happenings (11)
9 Of a low standard (3)
10 Uncalled for (5)
11 Evade (5)
12 Uptight and edgy (5)
13 Unproven (8)
16 Usually (8)
18 Large mast (5)
20 Come in (5)
21 Asserts (5)
22 Female kangaroo (3)
23 Explained the meaning of (11)

Down

2 Type of tree (5)
3 High lending practice (5)
4 Blush (6)
5 Provoked or teased (7)
6 Learnt (7)
7 Withdrawal of support (11)
8 Person who earns the household income (11)
14 Formal speech (7)
15 Give a spoken account of (7)
17 Batting order (4-2)
18 Adhesive substance (5)
19 Type of shelf (5)

PUZZLE 182

CROSSWORD

Across

4 Helix (6)
7 Outer (8)
8 Large (3)
9 ___ Amos: US singer-songwriter (4)
10 Boards (anag.) (6)
11 Showed a person to their seat (7)
12 Lacking enthusiasm; weary (5)
15 Value (5)
17 Childish (7)
20 Almost (6)
21 Small shelters (4)
22 Relations (3)
23 Awesome (8)
24 Become angry (6)

Down

1 Self-evident truths (6)
2 Send to a different place (8)
3 Entered in a hostile manner (7)
4 Make a long narrow gash (5)
5 Massaged (6)
6 Molecule that binds to another (6)
13 Breed of dairy cattle (8)
14 Hiding underground (7)
15 Laboured (6)
16 Jogger (6)
18 Dye used as a test of acidity (6)
19 Headdress of a monarch (5)

PUZZLE 183

Across

1 Recitals (anag.) (8)
5 Silence (4)
8 Tall plants of the grass family (5)
9 Lottery (7)
10 Meaninglessness (7)
12 Strongly influencing later developments (7)
14 Side by side (7)
16 Pays no attention to (7)
18 Brushed the coat of (an animal) (7)
19 Mingle with something else (5)
20 A person's individuality (4)
21 Austere people (8)

Down

1 Well-ventilated (4)
2 Belief in a god or gods (6)
3 Joint advocate (9)
4 Have as a consequence (6)
6 System of social perfection (6)
7 Stocky (8)
11 Sum total (9)
12 Tubes for ejecting liquids (8)
13 Unwind (6)
14 Incidental remarks (6)
15 Graduates of a college (6)
17 Hatchets (4)

PUZZLE 184

Across

1 Arrange by category (8)
5 Link a town with another (4)
9 Cook meat in the oven (5)
10 Mournful (7)
11 Strong desires (5)
12 17th Greek letter (3)
13 Muscular tissue (5)
15 Amusing people (5)
17 Quarrel (3)
19 Wading bird (5)
20 Kenya's capital (7)
21 Extent or limit (5)
22 Pitcher (4)
23 Flowering plant (5,3)

Down

1 Line that bounds a circle (13)
2 Mercury alloy (7)
3 Contentment (12)
4 Violin (6)
6 Thin crisp biscuit (5)
7 Former President of South Africa (6,7)
8 Framework for washed garments (7,5)
14 Root vegetable (7)
16 Examine again (6)
18 Pen (5)

PUZZLE 185

Across

1	Most secure (6)
4	Renounce an oath (6)
9	Itemising (7)
10	Total amount of wages paid to employees (7)
11	Opposite of tall (5)
12	Uncertain; risky (5)
14	Conveyed by gestures (5)
17	Exposes to danger (5)
19	Parts of the cerebrum (5)
21	Prompts (7)
23	Igneous rock (7)
24	A score (6)
25	Not working (6)

Down

1	Inclined (6)
2	Wear away (4)
3	Word having a similar meaning (7)
5	Public transport vehicles (5)
6	Creatures with one horn (8)
7	Next after seventh (6)
8	Irritable (3-8)
13	Card game (8)
15	Percussion musician (7)
16	Get off (6)
18	Small finch (6)
20	Move from one place to another (5)
22	Cranny (4)

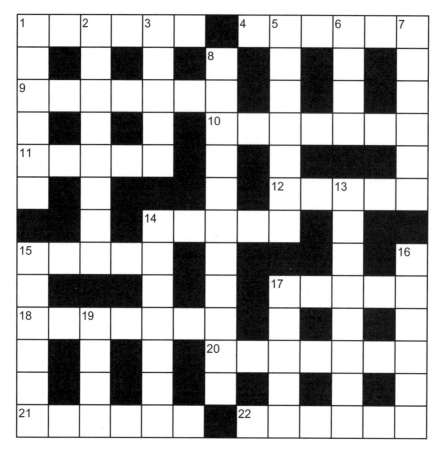

Across

1 Suggestion (6)
4 Pushes filling inside (6)
9 Heart-shaped (7)
10 Artificial (3-4)
11 Closes (5)
12 Roost (5)
14 Scores an exam paper (5)
15 Higher than (5)
17 Completely; really (5)
18 Tiredness (7)
20 Indigenous people (7)
21 Table linen; woven fabric (6)
22 Arm joints (6)

Down

1 Right to enter (6)
2 Person highly skilled in music (8)
3 Fellows (5)
5 Root vegetables (7)
6 Greek cheese (4)
7 Spoken address (6)
8 Character; nature (11)
13 Assuages (8)
14 Acts of union (7)
15 Have sufficient money to pay for (6)
16 Makes fun of someone (6)
17 Country in Western Asia (5)
19 ___ Yorke: Radiohead lead singer (4)

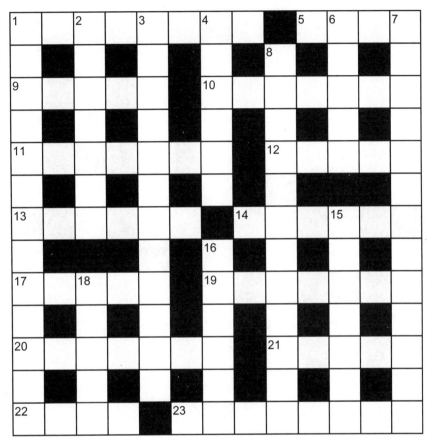

Across

1 Search for minerals (8)
5 Gets older (4)
9 Select group of people (5)
10 Mythical being (7)
11 A curse; wicked look (4,3)
12 ___ Nash: US poet (5)
13 Fine cloth (6)
14 Unmoving (6)
17 Stares at amorously (5)
19 Dry red table wine of Italy (7)
20 Evidence of disease (7)
21 Taken ___ : surprised (5)
22 Pull abruptly (4)
23 Final teenage year (8)

Down

1 Affectedly (13)
2 Beginnings (7)
3 Precondition (12)
4 Rides a bike (6)
6 Secreting organ (5)
7 Young person (6,7)
8 Teach to accept a belief uncritically (12)
15 Tax imposed on ships (7)
16 Large prawns (6)
18 Citrus fruit (5)

PUZZLE 188

Across

1	Change (6)
4	Departs (6)
9	Very young infant (7)
10	Sceptic (7)
11	Contest (5)
12	Loses colour (5)
14	Reads quickly (5)
15	Tall and slim (5)
17	Aromatic resin (5)
18	Water container (7)
20	Merciful (7)
21	First born (6)
22	Entirely (6)

Down

1	Capital of Bahrain (6)
2	Decline in activity (8)
3	Foam (5)
5	Envelops (7)
6	Sleeveless garment (4)
7	Gazes at (6)
8	Incapable of being split (11)
13	Push button outside a house (8)
14	Complex wholes (7)
15	Refund (6)
16	Talkative (6)
17	Eat steadily (5)
19	Narrated (4)

CROSSWORD

Across

1 Considerable (11)
9 Small sprite (3)
10 Express gratitude (5)
11 Caused persistent dull pain (5)
12 Vertical spars for sails (5)
13 Signal that danger is over (3-5)
16 Inquired into a subject (8)
18 Relinquish (5)
20 Mark ___ : US writer (5)
21 Major African river (5)
22 Finish first (3)
23 Introductory (11)

Down

2 Swells (5)
3 Formal ceremonies (5)
4 Place of worship (6)
5 With an attitude of suspicion (7)
6 Make less heavy (7)
7 Opposite of temporarily (11)
8 Below the planet's surface (11)
14 Person talking (7)
15 A governing body in a county (7)
17 US rapper (6)
18 Scowl (5)
19 Oarsman (5)

PUZZLE 190

Across

1 Leave the nest (6)
4 Measuring system (6)
9 Earthquake scale (7)
10 Hammers (7)
11 Oily; greasy (5)
12 Blowing in puffs (of wind) (5)
14 Silly (5)
15 Hold responsible (5)
17 Cluster (5)
18 Extreme enthusiast (7)
20 Small holes in cloth or leather (7)
21 Kicks out (6)
22 Adjusts (6)

Down

1 A long way away (3,3)
2 And so on (2,6)
3 Full of nerve (5)
5 Branch of biology (7)
6 Actor's part in a film (4)
7 Firm and dry (of food) (6)
8 The military (5,6)
13 Superficial (4-4)
14 Stinted (anag.) (7)
15 Opposite of after (6)
16 Pursues (6)
17 Let air escape from a valve (5)
19 Three squared (4)

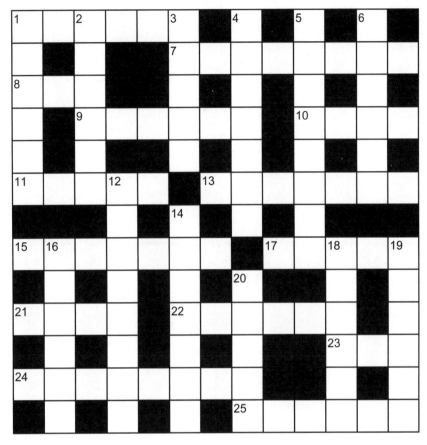

Across

1 Wildcat (6)
7 Assigns a job to (8)
8 Pull at (3)
9 Unfastened (6)
10 Leave (4)
11 Towering (5)
13 Cooked over boiling water (7)
15 Mischief (7)
17 Sailing boat (5)
21 Sorrow or compassion (4)
22 Woodland (6)
23 Cook in hot oil (3)
24 Small dagger (8)
25 Liquefied (6)

Down

1 Popular soup flavour (6)
2 Surround (6)
3 Mexican tortilla wraps (5)
4 Galore (7)
5 Computer security system (8)
6 Conflict (6)
12 Vehicle with three wheels (8)
14 Financial gains (7)
16 Removes from one's property (6)
18 Set of clothes (6)
19 Made a victim of (6)
20 Marrying man (5)

PUZZLE 192

Across

4	Moves smoothly (6)
7	Athletics event (4,4)
8	Mouthpiece attached to a bridle (3)
9	Incline (4)
10	Figure of speech (6)
11	Manned (7)
12	Female sovereign (5)
15	Daft (5)
17	Intonation (7)
20	Where one finds Oslo (6)
21	Days before (4)
22	Negligent (3)
23	___ Cruz: Spanish actress (8)
24	Church services (6)

Down

1	Soundless (6)
2	Grateful (8)
3	Greedy drinker (7)
4	Part of a teapot (5)
5	Discussion (6)
6	Sixth planet from the sun (6)
13	In an unequal manner (8)
14	Fluctuating (7)
15	Type of ski race (6)
16	Wildcats (6)
18	Weird (6)
19	Exchanges (5)

Across

1 Hits hard (6)
4 Spiny-finned fish (6)
9 Selling (7)
10 Abundantly supplied (7)
11 Radiancy; gloss (5)
12 Brief smell (5)
14 Individual piece of snow (5)
17 Levies (5)
19 Young sheep (5)
21 Item used by asthma sufferers (7)
23 Soften the effect of (7)
24 Creative act (6)
25 Concurs (6)

Down

1 Dig a hole (6)
2 Cease (4)
3 Become less severe (4,3)
5 Steps on a ladder (5)
6 Malicious (8)
7 Border (6)
8 Eternal (11)
13 Makes a list (8)
15 Engraving (7)
16 Cut up (6)
18 Removes all coverings from (6)
20 Move back and forth (5)
22 Deep affection (4)

PUZZLE 194

Across

1 Opportune (6)
7 Exclamations of protest (8)
8 Be nosy (3)
9 Timothy ___ : James Bond actor (6)
10 Not warm (4)
11 Entrance hallway (5)
13 The beginning of the universe (3,4)
15 Instruct (7)
17 Outdoor fundraising events (5)
21 Lids (anag.) (4)
22 For a short time (6)
23 Light brown colour (3)
24 Set a boat in motion (8)
25 Longs (for) (6)

Down

1 Inside information (3-3)
2 Distress signal (6)
3 Period between childhood and adulthood (5)
4 Template (7)
5 Vessel for molten metal (8)
6 Capital of Germany (6)
12 Encrypting (8)
14 Person on the staff of an ambassador (7)
16 US monetary unit (6)
18 Move unsteadily (6)
19 Catapults (6)
20 Disreputable (5)

CROSSWORD

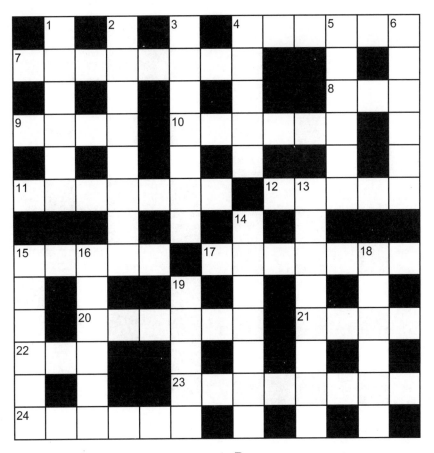

Across

4 Glimpsed (6)
7 Friendliness (8)
8 Sphere or globe (3)
9 Apparatus for weaving (4)
10 Spacecraft (6)
11 Male chicken (7)
12 Flinch away in pain (5)
15 Covers in paper (5)
17 The gathering of crops (7)
20 Be imminent (6)
21 Cut of meat (4)
22 Swish (of an animal's tail) (3)
23 Increases (8)
24 Prayer book (6)

Down

1 Pygmy chimpanzee (6)
2 Sign of approval (6-2)
3 Neaten (7)
4 Freedom from war (5)
5 Quantum of electromagnetic radiation (6)
6 Take a casual interest in (6)
13 Implicated in (8)
14 Wound covering (7)
15 Conical tent (6)
16 Signal (anag.) (6)
18 Evasive; devious (6)
19 Gold ___ : award for coming first (5)

PUZZLE 196

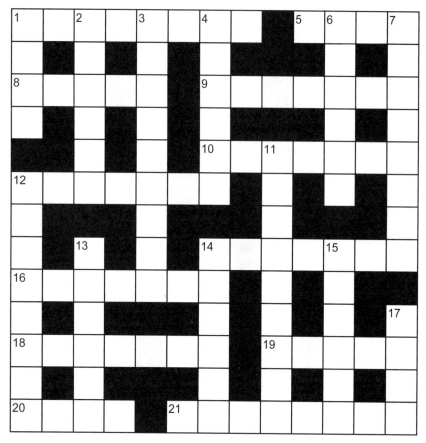

Across

1	The West (8)
5	Floor covers (4)
8	Pile of stones as a landmark (5)
9	Kind of whisky (7)
10	Secret affair (7)
12	Very odd (7)
14	Item used to cut metal (7)
16	Fulfil a desire (7)
18	Leftovers (7)
19	Smooth cream of vegetables (5)
20	Golf pegs (4)
21	Spattered with liquid (8)

Down

1	A single time (4)
2	Printed cotton fabric (6)
3	Perilous (9)
4	Take small bites out of (6)
6	Superior of a nunnery (6)
7	Husband of one's daughter (3-2-3)
11	Non-canonical religious texts (9)
12	A large spar (8)
13	Hinder the progress of (6)
14	Bushy plant of the mint family (6)
15	Complex carbohydrate (6)
17	Geek (4)

Across

1 Cloth worn around the waist (4)
3 Base of a statue (8)
9 See (7)
10 Make indistinct (5)
11 One who steals (5)
12 Without flaws (7)
13 Entangle (6)
15 Sightseeing trip in Africa (6)
17 Colonnade (7)
18 Informal language (5)
20 Rule (5)
21 Name (7)
22 Bleak; stark (8)
23 Transmit (4)

Down

1 Easily angered (5-8)
2 Japanese dish (5)
4 Free from a liability (6)
5 Awkward (12)
6 Crisp plain fabric (7)
7 Prone to steal (5-8)
8 Opposite of amateur (12)
14 Joins in matrimony (7)
16 Way something is set out (6)
19 Foot joint (5)

Across

1 Graze (6)
4 Possessors (6)
9 Is relevant (7)
10 Live together (7)
11 Connected series of rooms (5)
12 Growl with bare teeth (5)
14 Ditches (5)
17 Handle a tool effectively (5)
19 Ice hockey buildings (5)
21 Act of entering (7)
23 Kind of breakfast cereal (7)
24 Gossip or idle talk (6)
25 Brusque and irritable (6)

Down

1 Aromatic flavourings (6)
2 Move with urgent haste (4)
3 Variegated (7)
5 Totally erases (5)
6 Qualified for entry (8)
7 Method (6)
8 Pertaining to marriage (11)
13 Abounding (8)
15 Strut about (7)
16 Radiating light; clever (6)
18 Disappointment (6)
20 Reel for winding yarn (5)
22 Sell (anag.) (4)

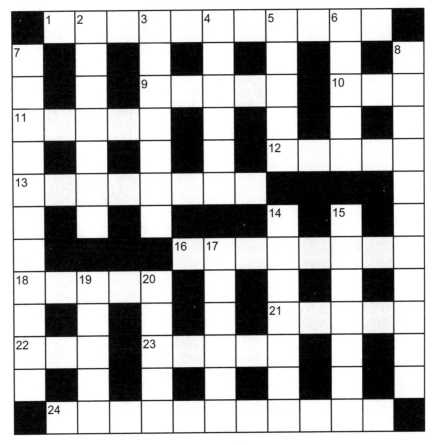

Across

1 Maths students use these devices (11)
9 Pulls a sulky face (5)
10 Bath vessel (3)
11 Exchange of tennis strokes (5)
12 Soar; rush (5)
13 Uses a piece of machinery (8)
16 Unauthorised writing on walls (8)
18 Bores (anag.) (5)
21 Spear (5)
22 Large beer cask (3)
23 Bird droppings used as fertiliser (5)
24 Plant of the cabbage family (11)

Down

2 Artist's workplace (7)
3 Imitator (7)
4 French museum (6)
5 Exams (5)
6 A moving part of a generator (5)
7 Confirm (11)
8 Compulsively (11)
14 Get rid of something (7)
15 Organs (7)
17 Fix (6)
19 Stringed instrument (5)
20 Emits a breath of relief (5)

Across

1 In a very poor condition (8)
5 Part of a door fastening (4)
9 Invigorating medicine (5)
10 High-pitched flute (7)
11 Pass a rope through (5)
12 Sticky substance (3)
13 Walk heavily and firmly (5)
15 Drinking tube (5)
17 Curved shape (3)
19 Wireless (5)
20 Irritating; hankering (7)
21 Leg bone (5)
22 Christmas (4)
23 Respite (8)

Down

1 Process of worsening (13)
2 Competitors in a sprint (7)
3 As quickly as possible (7-5)
4 Domed roof (6)
6 In the midst of (5)
7 Corresponding (13)
8 Author of screenplays (12)
14 Within earshot (7)
16 Style of popular music (6)
18 Secret store (5)

Across

1 Ability to produce a desired result (8)
5 Image of a god (4)
9 Broadcast again (5)
10 Restrain (7)
11 Irresistible (12)
13 Round caps (6)
14 Confused or disconcerted (6)
17 Hard to fathom (12)
20 Disciple (7)
21 Cloak (5)
22 University in Connecticut (4)
23 Paper printout of data (4,4)

Down

1 Auditory receptors (4)
2 At all times (7)
3 Pay tribute to another (12)
4 Trite remark (6)
6 Most populous city in the UAE (5)
7 Person engaged in a lawsuit (8)
8 Showing complete commitment (12)
12 Resoluteness (8)
15 ___ Bloom: actor in The Lord of The Rings (7)
16 Taxonomic groupings (6)
18 Become very hot (5)
19 Having pains (4)

Across

1 Insatiable desire (4)
3 Range of colours (8)
9 Teller (7)
10 A central point (5)
11 Negative vote (3)
12 Antelope (5)
13 Opposite one of two (5)
15 Country whose capital is Tripoli (5)
17 Dark wood (5)
18 23rd Greek letter (3)
19 Put to shame (5)
20 Mental collapse (7)
21 Tempting (8)
22 Sixty minutes (4)

Down

1 Thoughtless (13)
2 Easy (of a job) (5)
4 Small Church district (6)
5 Room attached to a house (12)
6 Exposes; shows (7)
7 Manage badly (13)
8 Written in pictorial symbols (12)
14 Substance used to remove heat (7)
16 Type of sweet (6)
18 Camera image (5)

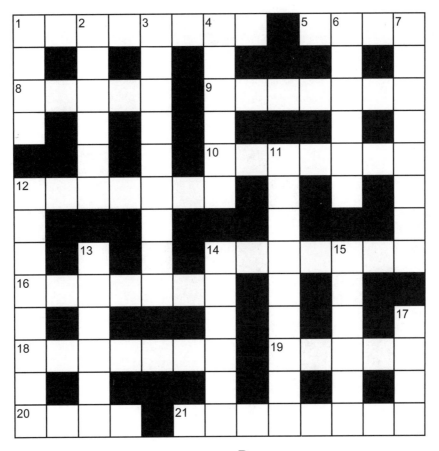

Across

1 Split into subdivisions (8)
5 Unpleasantly moist (4)
8 Dairy product (5)
9 Imaginary (7)
10 Makes a mess (7)
12 Put in the ground (7)
14 E.g. Usain Bolt (7)
16 Mental process or idea (7)
18 Birthplace of Napoleon (7)
19 Allotted quantity (5)
20 Shelf at the foot of a window opening (4)
21 Disturb (8)

Down

1 Opposite of front (4)
2 Plan of action (6)
3 Fixing in place (9)
4 Envelop (6)
6 Tolerates (6)
7 Memento (8)
11 Way of doing something (9)
12 Shields from (8)
13 Plant used in salads (6)
14 Reach a specified level (6)
15 Urge (6)
17 Spice made from nutmeg (4)

Across

1 Money received (6)
4 Comes up (6)
9 Dry biscuit (7)
10 Friendly (7)
11 Coin-toss call (5)
12 Very long periods of time (5)
14 Tokyo's country (5)
15 Burst of light (5)
17 Item won in a competition (5)
18 Reduce the worth of (7)
20 Biting sharply (7)
21 Oily (6)
22 Small hole (6)

Down

1 Provoke (6)
2 Personal magnetism (8)
3 Creates (5)
5 Violent and lawless person (7)
6 Protective crust (4)
7 Travels too quickly (6)
8 Diaphanous (11)
13 Public and formal (8)
14 Envious (7)
15 Growing dimmer (6)
16 Measure of heaviness (6)
17 Flower of remembrance (5)
19 Dell (4)

CROSSWORD

Across

1 Dishes of leafy greens (6)
4 Bribe (6)
9 Draws forth (7)
10 Far-reaching; thorough (7)
11 Aromatic flavouring (5)
12 Holding or grasping device (5)
14 Block of wood (5)
17 Angered; irritated (5)
19 Head over ___ : totally (in love) (5)
21 Quell (7)
23 Cigarette constituent (7)
24 Suffer destruction (6)
25 Irritates (6)

Down

1 Kept private; unknown by others (6)
2 Edible fat (4)
3 Debate (7)
5 Assumed name (5)
6 Inventive; creative (8)
7 Seeks information indirectly (6)
8 Restraint (4-7)
13 11th month of the year (8)
15 Inert gaseous element (7)
16 Stop talking (4,2)
18 Dancing clubs (6)
20 These keep your feet warm (5)
22 Large trade show (4)

Across

1 Bright red mineral (8)
5 Settee (4)
9 Ape (5)
10 Good luck charms (7)
11 Most prominent position (5,2,5)
13 Lubricating (6)
14 The spirit or soul (6)
17 Displeased (12)
20 Makes possible (7)
21 Immature stage of an insect (5)
22 Perceives (4)
23 Infancy (8)

Down

1 Arrived (4)
2 Digit (7)
3 Not on purpose; inadvertently (12)
4 River in South America (6)
6 24th Greek letter (5)
7 Responded to (8)
8 Resolutely (12)
12 Military people (8)
15 Friendly farewell (7)
16 Afternoon sleep (6)
18 Hand shovel (5)
19 Beach constituent (4)

Across

1 Hidden storage places (6)
4 Metamorphic rock (6)
9 Erase or remove (7)
10 Easily moulded (7)
11 Extreme fear (5)
12 Resides (5)
14 Musical sounds (5)
17 Residence (5)
19 Making a knot in (5)
21 Readable (7)
23 Country in West Africa (7)
24 Spirited horses (6)
25 Ancient or well-established (3-3)

Down

1 Part of a flower (6)
2 Sparkling wine (4)
3 Selfish person (7)
5 Cloaked (5)
6 An indirect implication (8)
7 Patterns (6)
8 Having four right angles (of a shape) (11)
13 Changeable (8)
15 Drooping (7)
16 Main plant stems (6)
18 Flattened out (6)
20 Pierced by a bull's horn (5)
22 Lead singer of U2 (4)

Across

1 Hind part (4)
3 Not obligatory (8)
9 Make less intense (7)
10 ___ Andronicus: Shakespeare play (5)
11 Flowering plant (5,7)
13 Thick wet mud (6)
15 Where one watches films (6)
17 Feeling let down (12)
20 Measure heaviness (5)
21 Unsurpassed (3-4)
22 Female head of a town (8)
23 Dejected (4)

Down

1 Re-evaluate (8)
2 Passage between rows of seats (5)
4 Event which precedes another (6)
5 Understandably (12)
6 Nattier (anag.) (7)
7 Get beaten (4)
8 Mapmaker (12)
12 Reverie (8)
14 Service; state of being useful (7)
16 Talks (6)
18 Fabric with parallel ribs (5)
19 Moved through water (4)

Across

1 Glass-like volcanic rock (8)
5 Con; swindle (4)
8 Low dull sounds (5)
9 Affluent (7)
10 Omission of a sound when speaking (7)
12 Expressed disapproval facially (7)
14 Long seats (7)
16 Form of public worship (7)
18 Herb related to parsley (7)
19 Strong thick rope (5)
20 Plant containers (4)
21 Course of study (8)

Down

1 Oust (anag.) (4)
2 Workroom of a painter (6)
3 State of shame (9)
4 Made reparation for (6)
6 Recognition (6)
7 Afternoon performances (8)
11 Alike in every way (9)
12 Paper size (8)
13 Thoroughfare (6)
14 Incidental activity (6)
15 Confused noise (6)
17 Short pins used to attach clothes to a washing line (4)

Across

1	Cavalry swords (6)
4	Exist in great numbers (6)
9	Makes ineffective (7)
10	Rip hats (anag.) (7)
11	Linear measures of three feet (5)
12	Parasitic arachnids (5)
14	Military vehicles (5)
17	Gate fastener (5)
19	Where one finds Cardiff (5)
21	Type of heron (7)
23	Not physically existing (7)
24	Measurement of extent (6)
25	Shady garden alcove (6)

Down

1	Item worn on the head on a hot day (3,3)
2	Endure; large animal (4)
3	Creepiest (7)
5	Baby carriage (5)
6	Force lifting something up (8)
7	Cease (6)
8	Unimaginable (11)
13	Progeny (8)
15	Move like a snake (7)
16	Pivot (6)
18	Aircraft housing (6)
20	Trick or feat of daring (5)
22	Therefore (Latin) (4)

CROSSWORD

Across

1 Part of a candle (4)
3 Apartment cohabitant (8)
9 Caring for (7)
10 Spiny yellow-flowered shrub (5)
11 Dictatorial (12)
14 Fizzy drink (3)
16 Female relation (5)
17 Give a nickname to (3)
18 Not guided by good sense (12)
21 Timber beam (5)
22 Quantities of medicine (7)
23 Lack of flexibility (8)
24 Noes (anag.) (4)

Down

1 Trachea (8)
2 Bend (5)
4 Carry a heavy object (3)
5 Fellowship (12)
6 Reached a destination (7)
7 Fencing sword (4)
8 Unplugged (12)
12 Individual things (5)
13 Thinks about something continually (8)
15 Photography technique (7)
19 Commence (5)
20 Partly open (4)
22 Speck (3)

PUZZLE 212

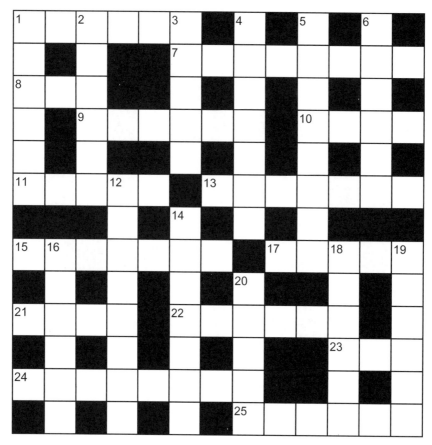

Across

1 Surprise attack (6)
7 Physically strong and active (8)
8 Sharp blow (3)
9 Split into two (6)
10 Solely (4)
11 In pitch (5)
13 Settle a dispute (7)
15 Worry (7)
17 Moves on foot (5)
21 Aromatic herb (4)
22 Gambling house (6)
23 Lipid (3)
24 Woollen clothing (8)
25 Tiny bag (6)

Down

1 Showing utter resignation (6)
2 Cylinder holding thread (6)
3 Place of refuge (5)
4 Personal possession (7)
5 Hard grains left after the milling of flour (8)
6 Plant with deep purple flowers (6)
12 Increase (8)
14 Type of handicraft (7)
16 Pungent edible bulbs (6)
18 Bathtub sponge (6)
19 Group of seven (6)
20 Stars (anag.) (5)

CROSSWORD

Across

1 Where one finds Kabul (11)
9 Purchase (3)
10 Circular in shape (5)
11 Shadow (5)
12 Recorded (5)
13 Amicable (8)
16 Opposite of floors (8)
18 One who avoids animal products (5)
20 Standpoint (5)
21 Having three dimensions (5)
22 Enemy (3)
23 Narrator (11)

Down

2 Traditional English breakfast (3-2)
3 Gave a job to (5)
4 Gender of nouns in some languages (6)
5 Attracts powerfully (7)
6 A person in general (7)
7 Style of painting (8,3)
8 Unnecessarily forceful (5-6)
14 Lock of curly hair (7)
15 Motorcycle attachment (7)
17 Ploy (6)
18 Pertaining to the voice (5)
19 Blunder (5)

Across

1 Business run jointly by its members (11)
9 Happen again (5)
10 Sheltered side (3)
11 Chessmen (5)
12 Projecting horizontal ledge (5)
13 Repugnance (8)
16 Places where fruit trees are grown (8)
18 Shoe ties (5)
21 Not at all (5)
22 Chatter (3)
23 Advocated strongly (5)
24 E.g. Shakespeare and Bernard Shaw (11)

Down

2 Argued against (7)
3 Continue with (7)
4 Excessively ornate (of music) (6)
5 Slabs of peat for fuel (5)
6 One-way flow structure (5)
7 Branch of medicine dealing with skin disorders (11)
8 Confident (4-7)
14 Party (7)
15 Stop from occurring (7)
17 Erring (anag.) (6)
19 Inner circle (5)
20 Analyse; examine (5)

Across

1 Next to (6)
4 Bandage (6)
9 Set apart (7)
10 Firmly; closely (7)
11 Units of heredity (5)
12 Follow the position of (5)
14 Songs of praise (5)
15 Alleviate (5)
17 Hit hard (5)
18 Polish dance (7)
20 Loud sound following lightning (7)
21 Welcomes (6)
22 Of inferior quality (6)

Down

1 Takes along (6)
2 Cooking measure (8)
3 Reads (anag.) (5)
5 What a bodybuilder lifts (7)
6 Temporary outside shelter (4)
7 Biochemical catalyst (6)
8 Having definite limits (11)
13 Agreed (8)
14 Pipe from which water can be drawn (7)
15 Equipping with weapons (6)
16 Robust (6)
17 Well-mannered (5)
19 Sector (4)

Across

1 Raise to the third power (4)
3 Awful (8)
9 Harms (7)
10 Feeling of fear (5)
11 Female fellow national (12)
13 Wake-up calls (6)
15 Imperial capacity measure (6)
17 Directions (12)
20 Shade of purple (5)
21 Chuckle (7)
22 Interfering (8)
23 E.g. haematite and magnetite (4)

Down

1 Gossip (4-4)
2 Small and elegant (5)
4 Opinion pieces (6)
5 Duplication (12)
6 Below (7)
7 Every (4)
8 Relating to numeric calculations (12)
12 Groups of similar things (8)
14 Segmented worm (7)
16 Roman god of fire (6)
18 External (5)
19 Slender (4)

Across

1 Making less clear (8)
5 The wise men (4)
9 Follows orders (5)
10 Road that has no exit (4,3)
11 Compress (7)
12 Personnel at work (5)
13 Anxious (6)
14 Configure in advance (6)
17 Principle or belief (5)
19 Stuffing (7)
20 Pasta pockets (7)
21 Tiny piece of food (5)
22 Bell-shaped flower (4)
23 Appear as the star of the show (8)

Down

1 Dealing with different societies (5-8)
2 Exploit to excess (7)
3 Exemption from a rule (12)
4 Indicated assent (6)
6 Stadium (5)
7 Untiring (13)
8 Made in bulk (4-8)
15 Nerve impulses (7)
16 John ___ : US novelist (6)
18 Maritime (5)

Across

1 Type of book cover (8)
5 Spoken test (4)
9 Foreign language (informal) (5)
10 Sour in taste (7)
11 Gardening tool (5)
12 Mauna ___ : active volcano (3)
13 Summed together (5)
15 Plantain lily (5)
17 Recede (3)
19 Repasts (5)
20 Musical composition (7)
21 Subject matter (5)
22 Regretted (4)
23 Relating to deep feelings (8)

Down

1 Fairground ride (6-7)
2 Goes back on a promise (7)
3 Pertaining to a person's life (12)
4 Pursued (6)
6 Insurgent or revolutionary (5)
7 Lazy (13)
8 Histrionic (12)
14 More in focus (7)
16 Italian sausage (6)
18 Game similar to bowls (5)

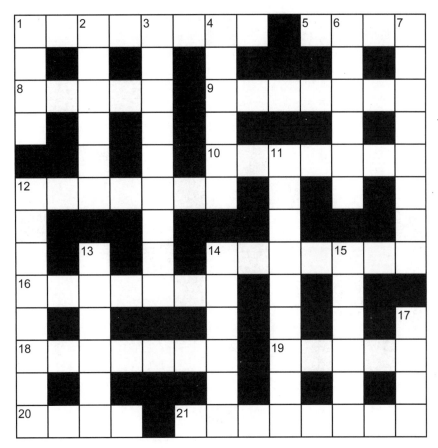

Across

1 Suitable; appropriate (8)
5 Johann Sebastian ___ : composer (4)
8 Five lines on which music is written (5)
9 Furry nocturnal omnivorous mammal (7)
10 Short trips on another's behalf (7)
12 Went to see (7)
14 Provide money for (7)
16 Branch of linguistics (7)
18 Ceasing trading (7)
19 Put up with (5)
20 Tardy (4)
21 Most precipitous (8)

Down

1 Break or burst (4)
2 Asserts to be the case (6)
3 Powerful whirlpool (9)
4 Gave medical care (6)
6 Quantity (6)
7 Good-looking (8)
11 Restore to use (9)
12 Vindictive (8)
13 Hammerlike tool (6)
14 Sudden fear (6)
15 Indigenous (6)
17 Touched (4)

Across

1 Moves very slowly (6)
4 Regime (anag.) (6)
9 Protective location (7)
10 Rags (7)
11 Chuckle (5)
12 Strong cords (5)
14 Rhythm and ___ : music genre (5)
15 Lively; cheerful (5)
17 Increase in size (5)
18 Back up (7)
20 Stimulates; provokes (7)
21 Deactivate (6)
22 Upward slope (6)

Down

1 Fortified medieval building (6)
2 Person implementing a will (8)
3 Business proposal; playing field (5)
5 The ___ : major golf tournament (7)
6 Departed (4)
7 Has objective reality (6)
8 Hinged; segmented (11)
13 Holder of invention rights (8)
14 Past events (7)
15 Elapsed (of time) (6)
16 Enclosed recess (6)
17 Large bags (5)
19 Light blast of wind (4)

Across

1 Set in from the margin (8)
5 First man (4)
9 ___ DeGeneres: US comedienne (5)
10 Preparing food (7)
11 Jewel from an oyster shell (5)
12 Positive answer (3)
13 Board game (5)
15 ___ Klum: supermodel (5)
17 Unit of energy (3)
19 Island in the Bay of Naples (5)
20 Spicy Spanish sausage (7)
21 Mythical monster (5)
22 Land site for waste (4)
23 Hard work (8)

Down

1 Wet behind the ears (13)
2 Foolish person (7)
3 Not intoxicating (of a drink) (12)
4 Reason for not doing something (6)
6 Store that sells milk products (5)
7 Dictatorially (13)
8 Tamed (12)
14 Assume (7)
16 Not outside (6)
18 Murkiness (5)

Across

1 Young deer (4)
3 Vegetables (8)
9 Kind of music (7)
10 Egg-shaped (5)
11 Boxing class (12)
14 Thing that fails to work properly (3)
16 Ethos (anag.) (5)
17 Snooker stick (3)
18 Medicine taken when blocked-up (12)
21 Urns (5)
22 Strips of wood (7)
23 A period of 366 days (4,4)
24 Surprise greatly (4)

Down

1 Portend (8)
2 Four-wheeled vehicle (5)
4 Excellent serve (3)
5 Variety of wildlife in an area (12)
6 Vivid (7)
7 Grain that grows into a new plant (4)
8 Ruinously (12)
12 Mistaken (5)
13 Discard; abandon (8)
15 Part of the ocean (4,3)
19 Prevent (5)
20 Wicked (4)
22 Tropical constrictor (3)

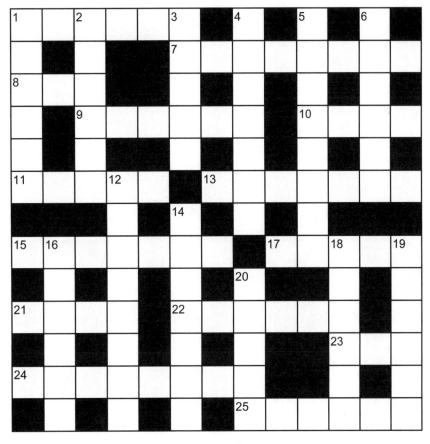

Across

1 Tropical bird (6)
7 Blushed (8)
8 Cry (3)
9 Female monster (6)
10 Snare (4)
11 Short simple song (5)
13 Wordy (7)
15 Run with light steps (7)
17 Written agreements (5)
21 Brown meat quickly (4)
22 Mariner (6)
23 Excavated soil (3)
24 Victim of an accident (8)
25 Hidden (6)

Down

1 Shoved (6)
2 Restart a computer (6)
3 Attempted (5)
4 Adventurous journey (7)
5 Segment of the spinal column (8)
6 Decomposes (6)
12 Easily frightened (8)
14 Flesher (anag.) (7)
16 Title used by Roman emperors (6)
18 Coagulate (6)
19 Small in degree (6)
20 Type of plastic; record (5)

PUZZLE 224

Across

4	Mexican cloak (6)
7	Australian state (8)
8	Flexible container (3)
9	Official records (4)
10	Edible plant tuber (6)
11	Determined (7)
12	Fits of violent anger (5)
15	Large ovens (5)
17	Secretion of an endocrine gland (7)
20	Banner or flag (6)
21	Bird of prey (4)
22	Opposite of high (3)
23	Sweet on a stick (8)
24	Poems; sounds alike (6)

Down

1	Coax into doing something (6)
2	Act of leaving out (8)
3	Fragment (7)
4	Little pie (5)
5	Being with organic and cybernetic parts (6)
6	Church instruments (6)
13	Comfy seat (8)
14	Together (7)
15	Johannes ___ : German astronomer (6)
16	Wiggle room (6)
18	Isaac ___ : physicist (6)
19	Charges (a sum of money) (5)

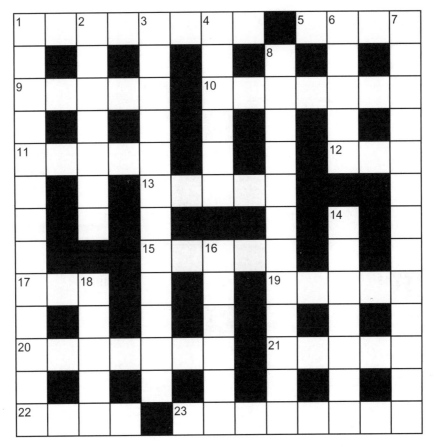

Across

1	Business organisations (8)
5	Earnest appeal (4)
9	Sharp end (5)
10	Non-specific (7)
11	Mental impressions (5)
12	Life force (3)
13	Culinary herb (5)
15	Ellipses (5)
17	Annoy (3)
19	River cove; bay (5)
20	List one by one (7)
21	Bring on oneself (5)
22	Jedi Master in Star Wars films (4)
23	Depending on the time of year (8)

Down

1	Relevance (13)
2	Urgent (7)
3	Extremely harmful (12)
4	Fourscore (6)
6	A line from a piece of music (5)
7	Pertaining to building design (13)
8	Educational institutions (12)
14	Large web-footed bird (7)
16	Assert (6)
18	Manipulate dough (5)

PUZZLE 226

Across

1 River in England (4)
3 Elastic (8)
9 Larval frog (7)
10 Monotonous hum (5)
11 State of the USA (12)
14 Blade for rowing a boat (3)
16 Public square (5)
17 ___ Tyler: US actress (3)
18 Formal praise (12)
21 Place providing accommodation (5)
22 Spouts (7)
23 Topsides (anag.) (8)
24 Extravagant publicity (4)

Down

1 Sentence sung before a psalm (8)
2 Antiquated (5)
4 Foot extremity (3)
5 Lavish event (12)
6 Warm and friendly (7)
7 Sweet potatoes (4)
8 Skin response to cold weather (5,7)
12 Acquire knowledge of (5)
13 Disappear gradually (8)
15 Highest vantage point of a building (7)
19 Embed; type of filling (5)
20 Garden outbuilding (4)
22 Word expressing negation (3)

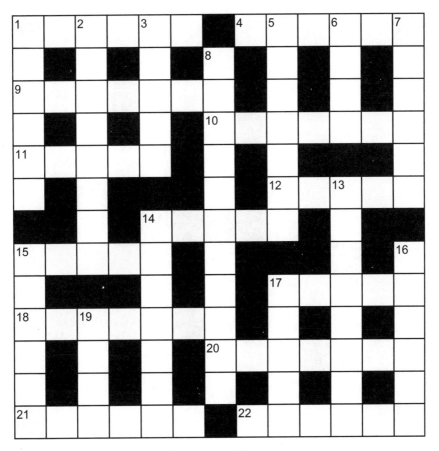

Across

1 Tennis official (6)
4 Garments worn by cricketers (6)
9 Unite together (7)
10 Facing the observer (7)
11 Derives the benefits (5)
12 Songbirds (5)
14 Short and stout (5)
15 Large waterbirds (5)
17 Voting compartment (5)
18 Pulls back from (7)
20 Account books (7)
21 Vigorous; strong and healthy (6)
22 ___ interest: a personal reason for involvement (6)

Down

1 Open a wine bottle (6)
2 Lofty peak (8)
3 Tree anchors (5)
5 Ponderously (7)
6 Norse god of thunder (4)
7 Small fasteners (6)
8 Without giving a name (11)
13 Fragrant (8)
14 Disavowals; rebuttals (7)
15 Collect or store (6)
16 Done in stages (6)
17 Form of identification (5)
19 Suppress (4)

PUZZLE 228

Across

1 Aimless (11)
9 E.g. the Thames (5)
10 Animal enclosure (3)
11 Large indefinite quantities (5)
12 ___ Berry: actress (5)
13 Person not accepted by society (8)
16 Noisy and overexcited reaction (8)
18 Titled (5)
21 Mortal (5)
22 One more than five (3)
23 Secluded places (5)
24 Watertight (11)

Down

2 Diacritical marks (7)
3 Act of chasing something (7)
4 Harsh (6)
5 Stagger (5)
6 Flower part; pales (anag.) (5)
7 Insensitivity (11)
8 Amused (11)
14 Shrub with tubular flowers (7)
15 Injurious (7)
17 Make changes to improve something (6)
19 Principle of conduct (5)
20 Compact (5)

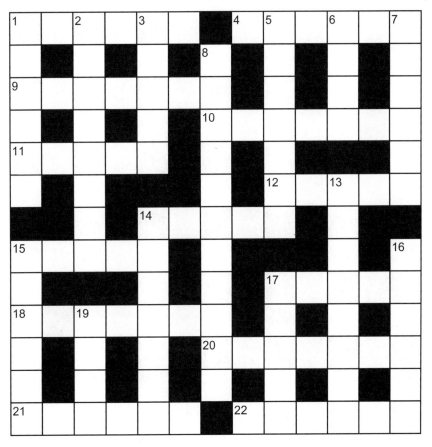

Across
1	Roman military unit (6)
4	Moved at high speed (6)
9	Ragtime (anag.) (7)
10	Risky undertaking (7)
11	Monastery church (5)
12	Brushed clean (5)
14	Pipes (5)
15	Shady spot under trees (5)
17	Sudden attack (5)
18	Arched structure in a garden (7)
20	E.g. from Ankara (7)
21	Cutting or thrusting weapons (6)
22	Advertising catchphrase (6)

Down
1	Musical instrument (6)
2	Intellectual (8)
3	Fully prepared (5)
5	Malady (7)
6	South American country (4)
7	Opposite of a victory (6)
8	Resound (11)
13	Coming out of (8)
14	Marched (7)
15	Go around (6)
16	Punctuation mark (6)
17	Wild and untamed (5)
19	Repeat an action (4)

CROSSWORD

Across

1 Ploys (6)
7 Etiquette (8)
8 Edible mushroom (3)
9 Remove an obstruction from a sink (6)
10 Atop (4)
11 Fastening device (5)
13 Searched clumsily (7)
15 Avoidance (7)
17 Natural underground chambers (5)
21 Chinese dynasty (4)
22 Surface film; coating (6)
23 Auction offer (3)
24 Intellectual (8)
25 Long and very narrow (6)

Down

1 Plan (6)
2 Attribute to (6)
3 Divulge (5)
4 Los Angeles ___ : baseball team (7)
5 State capital of South Carolina (8)
6 Wolflike wild dog (6)
12 Allocated (8)
14 Behave well (7)
16 Expressed something in words (6)
18 Feasible (6)
19 Transmitter (6)
20 Motionless (5)

Across

1 Impel (4)
3 Happened (8)
9 Backdrop; landscape (7)
10 Collection of maps (5)
11 Spiritual nourishment (5)
12 ___ power: energy source (7)
13 Very cold (of weather) (6)
15 Characteristic (6)
17 ___ on: talking repeatedly about (7)
18 Surpass (5)
20 Jewelled headdress (5)
21 United States (7)
22 Musical composition (8)
23 Disgust with an excess of sweetness (4)

Down

1 Uncaring (13)
2 Obtain information from various sources (5)
4 Weeping (6)
5 Not familiar with or used to (12)
6 Release someone from duty (7)
7 Carry editions (anag.) (13)
8 Restore to good condition (12)
14 Free from doubt (7)
16 Struck by overwhelming shock (6)
19 Rotate (5)

PUZZLE 232

Across

1 Type of starch (4)
3 Sanitary (8)
9 Embodiment (7)
10 Where one finds Rome (5)
11 Pop music performance (3)
12 Charming and endearing (5)
13 Hazardous; dangerous (5)
15 Style of Greek architecture (5)
17 Spore-producing organisms (5)
18 Long period of time (3)
19 Confess to (5)
20 Implore (7)
21 Deciphering (8)
22 Heavenly body (4)

Down

1 Legerdemain (7,2,4)
2 Departing (5)
4 Surrenders (6)
5 Distinctive behavioural attribute (12)
6 Least remote (7)
7 Codebreaker (13)
8 Showed not to be true (12)
14 Characterised by constant change (7)
16 Decorative strip of fabric (6)
18 Choose through voting (5)

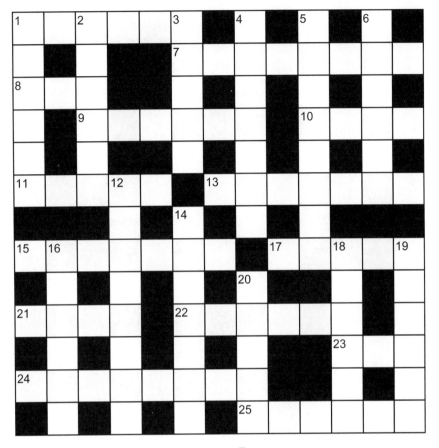

Across

1	Horse-drawn vehicles (6)
7	Round (8)
8	Beam of light (3)
9	Farmer's tool (6)
10	Reverse (4)
11	Rapidity (5)
13	Rubbish (7)
15	Ben ___ : US comedian and actor (7)
17	Escapade (5)
21	Eager (4)
22	Resembling a horse (6)
23	Worn channel (3)
24	Urgent (8)
25	Steers (anag.) (6)

Down

1	Heat; affection (6)
2	Sculptured symbols (6)
3	Make a search (5)
4	Curved structure forming a passage (7)
5	Residential district on the outskirts of a city (8)
6	Small pet canine (6)
12	Loftiness (8)
14	Profit from (7)
16	System of ideas to explain something (6)
18	Penetrate (6)
19	Paths (6)
20	Lump or bump (5)

PUZZLE 234

Across

1 Warships (8)
5 Woodwind instrument (4)
9 Woolly ruminant animal (5)
10 Downwind (7)
11 Starting here (anag.) (12)
14 North American nation (abbrev.) (3)
15 Acquires through merit (5)
16 Violate a law of God (3)
17 Significantly (12)
20 Imitate (7)
22 Enlighten; educate morally (5)
23 Throw a coin in the air (4)
24 Draws quickly (8)

Down

1 E.g. salmon (4)
2 Reluctance to change (7)
3 Pertaining to letters (12)
4 Measure of length (3)
6 Organ situated in the skull (5)
7 Abiding; lasting (8)
8 Second part of the Bible (3,9)
12 Ravine (5)
13 Fastest (8)
16 Concerned just with oneself (7)
18 Words that identify things (5)
19 Extras (cricket) (4)
21 Large deer (3)

Across

1 Be attractive (6)
4 Powerful (6)
9 Chocolate chewy cake (7)
10 Thinks logically (7)
11 Cloudy; not clear (5)
12 Narrow passageway (5)
14 Small canoe (5)
15 Ladies (5)
17 Church farmland (5)
18 Holy place (7)
20 Traditional piano keys (7)
21 Abandon (6)
22 Guard against (6)

Down

1 Collections of photos (6)
2 Announce publicly (8)
3 Irritate (5)
5 Fusion chamber (7)
6 Toon (anag.) (4)
7 Vitreous (6)
8 Streamlined (11)
13 Elks idea (anag.) (8)
14 Needleworker (7)
15 Squandered (6)
16 Hired out (6)
17 Large waterbird (5)
19 Keeps on at (4)

Across

1 OK (2-2)
3 Stated clearly (8)
9 Elevated plain (7)
10 Ascended (5)
11 Quantitative relation (5)
12 Snobbish (7)
13 Migratory grasshopper (6)
15 Nearer (6)
17 Supervise (7)
18 Pale orange tropical fruit (5)
20 ___ Arabia: country in the Middle East (5)
21 Japanese fish dish (7)
22 Craving (8)
23 Soon; shortly (4)

Down

1 In a manner that exceeds what is necessary (13)
2 Stem of an arrow (5)
4 Hesitates (6)
5 Heart specialist (12)
6 Instrument panels (7)
7 Dismay and amazement (13)
8 Act of reclamation (12)
14 Break between words (in verse) (7)
16 Individual (6)
19 Pertaining to birds (5)

Across

1 One of the seven deadly sins (4)
3 Complete (8)
9 Largest anthropoid ape (7)
10 Shallow circular dish (5)
11 Extension (12)
13 Lofts (6)
15 Sound system (6)
17 Not excusable (12)
20 Slender freshwater fish (5)
21 Against the law (7)
22 Plan anew (8)
23 Nuisance plant (4)

Down

1 E.g. Bertrand Russell (8)
2 Sound of an emergency vehicle (5)
4 Planet (6)
5 Monotonously (12)
6 Glitz; allure (7)
7 Dote (anag.) (4)
8 Ordinary dress (5,7)
12 Wore clothes on the catwalk (8)
14 Drinking vessel (7)
16 Getting older (6)
18 Brass instrument (5)
19 Speak indistinctly (4)

Across

1 Desperate Housewives actress (3,8)
9 Pear-shaped fruit (3)
10 Change (5)
11 Fall heavily (5)
12 Foe (5)
13 More attractive (8)
16 Unbarred (8)
18 Ride a bike (5)
20 Character in the musical Oliver! (5)
21 Feudal vassal (5)
22 Statute (3)
23 Huge three-horned dinosaur (11)

Down

2 The prevailing fashion (5)
3 Given to disclosing secrets (5)
4 Closer (6)
5 Sets of clothes (7)
6 Pancreatic hormone (7)
7 Device used to increase thrust (11)
8 Tries out novel ideas (11)
14 Slim (7)
15 Modern type of paint (7)
17 Win over (6)
18 Peak (5)
19 Brace (5)

Across

1   Sweet dessert (4)
3   Name for New York City (3,5)
9   Wavering vocal quality (7)
10 Make a map of (5)
11 Name applied to something (5)
12 State of the USA (7)
13 Mystery (6)
15 Rough shelter (4-2)
17 Hanging drapery (7)
18 Eighth Greek letter (5)
20 Mother-of-pearl (5)
21 Type of cocktail (7)
22 Reserved in advance (3-5)
23 Plant with fronds (4)

Down

1   Public officials (5,8)
2   Skewered meat (5)
4   Line of equal pressure on a map (6)
5   Practice of designing buildings (12)
6   Military unit (7)
7   Act of extending by inference (13)
8   Accepted behaviour whilst dining (5,7)
14 Unlawful (7)
16 Swarmed (6)
19 Join together; merge (5)

CROSSWORD **244**

Across

1 Flash intermittently (6)
4 Bores into (6)
9 Seat of the US Congress (7)
10 Ignorant of something (7)
11 Burning (5)
12 Edgar ___ : French artist (5)
14 Folders (5)
15 Attractive young lady (5)
17 Hit with the fist (5)
18 Excited agreeably (7)
20 Pulling on the heartstrings (7)
21 Recapture (6)
22 Unkempt (of hair) (6)

Down

1 Companionable (6)
2 Act of retaliation (8)
3 Wash one's body in water (5)
5 Drawers (anag.) (7)
6 Capital of Peru (4)
7 Slumbers (6)
8 Of noble birth (4-7)
13 Smiling broadly (8)
14 Part of a horse's leg (7)
15 Superior (6)
16 Impudent (6)
17 Dog (5)
19 US monetary unit (4)

Across

4	Writing implement (6)
7	Mild aversion (8)
8	Long bench (3)
9	Just and unbiased (4)
10	Vent (6)
11	Supplement to a will (7)
12	Small marine fish (5)
15	Precious stone (5)
17	Temporary stay (7)
20	Most pleasant (6)
21	Engrossed (4)
22	Collection of many sheets of paper (3)
23	Excessively self-indulgent (8)
24	Gaming tile with pips in each half (6)

Down

1	Emperor of Japan (6)
2	Infinite time (8)
3	Diffusion of molecules through a membrane (7)
4	Nuisances (5)
5	Person who imprisons another (6)
6	Opposite of highest (6)
13	Extend beyond a surface (8)
14	Act of touching (7)
15	Knocked into (6)
16	Indiscriminate (6)
18	Matures (of fruit) (6)
19	Japanese form of fencing (5)

Across

1	Trying to heal (8)
5	Continent (4)
9	Avoided by social custom (5)
10	Grotesque monster (7)
11	Reckless; ready to react violently (7-5)
13	Sad pot (anag.) (6)
14	Action of making use of something (6)
17	Restrict within limits (12)
20	Garden flower (7)
21	Tawdry (5)
22	Small children (4)
23	Offered (8)

Down

1	Skirt worn by ballet dancers (4)
2	Import barrier (7)
3	Considerately (12)
4	Five cent coin (US) (6)
6	Engross oneself in (5)
7	Considers in detail (8)
8	Joyously unrestrained (4-8)
12	Knight of the round table (8)
15	One who settles a dispute (7)
16	Large property with land (6)
18	Automaton (5)
19	Saw (4)

Across

1 Wisdom (8)
5 Poker stake (4)
8 Liquid essential for life (5)
9 Most unattractive (7)
10 Withdraw from an agreement (4,3)
12 Notes down (7)
14 Avoided a trial (7)
16 Mountain in the Himalayas (7)
18 Cheese on toast (7)
19 Defamatory statement (5)
20 Where bees are kept (4)
21 Publicly recommend (8)

Down

1 Stitched (4)
2 Style of architecture (6)
3 Relating to a company (9)
4 Thick innermost digits (6)
6 Liam ___ : Schindler's List actor (6)
7 Qualified for by right (8)
11 Lowest female singing voice (9)
12 Investigate systematically (8)
13 History play by Shakespeare (5,1)
14 Specified (6)
15 11th Greek letter (6)
17 Piece of evidence (4)

Across

1 Spice (8)
5 Low dull sound (4)
9 Popular flower (5)
10 Business matters (7)
11 Perennial plant with fleshy roots (7)
12 Draw out (5)
13 Took it easy (6)
14 Increase in intensity (4,2)
17 Heals (5)
19 Costing (anag.) (7)
20 River of South East Africa (7)
21 Intense sorrow (5)
22 Spun thread used for knitting (4)
23 Abstinent from alcohol (8)

Down

1 Unconditionally (13)
2 Becomes less severe (7)
3 Foreboding (12)
4 Citrus fruit (6)
6 Verse form (5)
7 Rude (13)
8 An idea that is added later (12)
15 Nationalist (7)
16 Refuse to acknowledge (6)
18 ___ Willis: daughter of Demi Moore (5)

Across

1 Agreement (11)
9 Sound of a cow (3)
10 Unreliable (5)
11 Pilfer (5)
12 Regions (5)
13 Hot pepper (8)
16 In spite of the fact (8)
18 Type of bus (5)
20 Elevated step (5)
21 Move sideways (5)
22 Limb (3)
23 Moved to another place (11)

Down

2 Form of oxygen (5)
3 Faces (anag.) (5)
4 Kigali's country (6)
5 Extremely bad (7)
6 Climbing plant (7)
7 Abashed (11)
8 General guideline (4,2,5)
14 Type of ship (7)
15 Become husky (7)
17 Bob ___ : Irish singer (6)
18 Make less miserable (5)
19 Conscious of (5)

Across

1 Remove contaminants from (6)
4 Create by carving (6)
9 Scorn (7)
10 Excuse (7)
11 Famous cricket ground (5)
12 Grins (anag.) (5)
14 Useful (5)
15 Move to music (5)
17 Strong gust of wind (5)
18 Flower-shaped competition award (7)
20 Repair a vehicle (7)
21 Surgical knife (6)
22 Within this context (6)

Down

1 Foot levers (6)
2 Repress (8)
3 Cooks in fat (5)
5 Superficial (7)
6 Quieten down; send to sleep (4)
7 Large solitary cats (6)
8 Unintelligible (11)
13 Opposite of positive (8)
14 Unit of square measure (7)
15 Come off the tracks (6)
16 Scattered about untidily (6)
17 Brought forth (5)
19 Examine quickly (4)

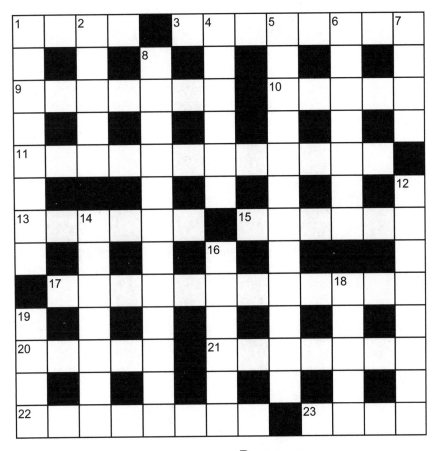

Across

1 Dressed (4)
3 Opposite of a pessimist (8)
9 Single-horned creature (7)
10 Referred to (5)
11 Beginning (12)
13 Saddens (6)
15 Capital of the Bahamas (6)
17 Inharmoniously (12)
20 Relating to birth (5)
21 Support (7)
22 Type of melon (8)
23 Where you are now (4)

Down

1 North African semolina (8)
2 Self-evident truth (5)
4 Takes fright (6)
5 Immeasurably (12)
6 Aims or purposes (7)
7 Clean up (4)
8 Nationally (12)
12 Exempt from tax (4-4)
14 Rich white cheese (7)
16 Fit for cultivation (of land) (6)
18 Levy (5)
19 Unit of linear measure (4)

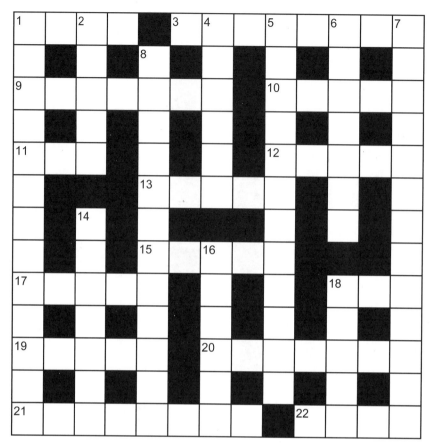

Across

1 Collide with (4)
3 Brings disorder to (8)
9 Plants with unusually shaped flowers (7)
10 Clean feathers (of birds) (5)
11 Self-esteem (3)
12 Correct (5)
13 Savoury meat jelly (5)
15 Sets of six balls in cricket (5)
17 Benefactor (5)
18 ___ Weasley: friend of Harry Potter (3)
19 Bungle (5)
20 Eighth sign of the zodiac (7)
21 Getting away from (8)
22 Unfortunately (4)

Down

1 Capable of being decomposed (13)
2 Piece of code to automate a task (5)
4 Arch of the foot (6)
5 Consequence of an event (12)
6 Promises (7)
7 Holier-than-thou (13)
8 Absolute authority in any sphere (12)
14 Relating to motion (7)
16 Thomas ___ : rival of Nikola Tesla (6)
18 Push back (5)

Across

1 Abdominal exercises (3-3)
4 Substance present in cereal grains (6)
9 Allowing (7)
10 Action of taking away something (7)
11 Divide; separate (5)
12 Vacillate (5)
14 Grips with the teeth (5)
17 Earnings (5)
19 Metal pieces used as money (5)
21 Fell over (7)
23 Throw into disorder (7)
24 Move about restlessly (6)
25 Mythical sea monster (6)

Down

1 Remorse (6)
2 Mate (anag.) (4)
3 Popular saying (7)
5 Stringed instruments (5)
6 Multiplying by three (8)
7 Invalidate; nullify (6)
8 Elucidated by using an example (11)
13 Disappeared (8)
15 E.g. Adam Peaty (7)
16 The back of the neck (6)
18 Unexpected (6)
20 E.g. taste or touch (5)
22 Long and limp (of hair) (4)

Across

1 Plot (8)
5 Round before the final (abbrev.) (4)
8 The entire scale (5)
9 Not subject to a levy (3-4)
10 Have as a part (7)
12 Panacea (4-3)
14 Rest days (7)
16 Affinity (7)
18 Multiplied threefold (7)
19 Arose from slumber (5)
20 Lubricates (4)
21 Gather together in one place (8)

Down

1 Animal enclosure (4)
2 Quantity (6)
3 Male head of a family (9)
4 Sell to the public (6)
6 Reprimand (6)
7 Floating masses of frozen water (8)
11 Bird found in grasslands (9)
12 White crested parrot (8)
13 Imaginary (6)
14 Playing card suit (6)
15 Calmness; composure (6)
17 Fundraising party (4)

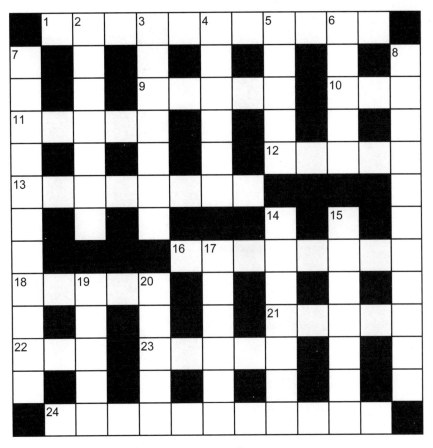

Across

1 Highest class in society (11)
9 Arm joint (5)
10 Large primate (3)
11 Stomach (informal) (5)
12 Pay out money (5)
13 Lacking knowledge (8)
16 Baseless distrust of others (8)
18 Giraffes have long ones (5)
21 Flour and water mixture (5)
22 Drink a little (3)
23 Zodiac sign (5)
24 Respectful (11)

Down

2 Wandering (7)
3 Wood cutters (7)
4 Prayer (6)
5 Assesses performance (5)
6 Pursue in order to catch (5)
7 Lack of being (11)
8 One in charge of a school (4,7)
14 Mobile phone (7)
15 Circular hall (7)
17 Clothing (6)
19 Small woodland (5)
20 Elbow room (5)

Across

1 Denial of something (8)
5 Heat up (4)
8 Elector (5)
9 Opposite of western (7)
10 Adversaries (7)
12 Museum keeper (7)
14 Reaches a destination (7)
16 Solicit votes from (7)
18 Unit of sound in a language (7)
19 Partly melted snow (5)
20 Male children (4)
21 Sample for medical testing (8)

Down

1 Flaring star (4)
2 Assemble (6)
3 Large hairy spider (9)
4 Lead batsman for a team (6)
6 Pertaining to vinegar (6)
7 Curved surface of a liquid in a tube (8)
11 Not part of the essential nature of a thing (9)
12 Abstract ideas (8)
13 Innate (6)
14 Not awake (6)
15 Space devoid of matter (6)
17 Slender (4)

Across

1 Hinged case hung from the neck (6)
7 Dour help (anag.) (8)
8 Stomach (3)
9 Fight divisions (6)
10 Small branch (4)
11 Cuts slightly (5)
13 Intoxicating element in wine (7)
15 Gathering of old friends (7)
17 Aromatic herb (5)
21 Fastens a knot (4)
22 Seaport in N Spain (6)
23 Method; road (3)
24 Permanent inhabitant (8)
25 Listener (6)

Down

1 Isolated inlet of the sea (6)
2 ___ acid: lemon juice constituent (6)
3 Rotates (5)
4 Scottish national emblem (7)
5 Excessive amount of something (8)
6 Sheep known for its wool (6)
12 Position of a male monarch (8)
14 Small stones (7)
16 Left (6)
18 Opposite of faster (6)
19 Legal practitioner (6)
20 Apathy (5)

PUZZLE 254

Across

4	Like vinegar (6)
7	Church rules (5,3)
8	Encountered (3)
9	Mythical creature (4)
10	Cosmetics (4-2)
11	Highly excited (7)
12	This date (5)
15	A moment (5)
17	One's savings for the future (4,3)
20	Narrate a story once again (6)
21	Solicit custom (4)
22	Silent (3)
23	Window in a roof (8)
24	Evades (6)

Down

1	Twist together (6)
2	Unable to appreciate music (4-4)
3	Drop sharply (7)
4	Not asleep (5)
5	Got rid of (6)
6	Easily remembered (6)
13	Surpass (8)
14	Brings to effective action (7)
15	Became stuck (6)
16	Framed (anag.) (6)
18	Socially awkward (6)
19	Dr ___ : US writer (5)

PUZZLE 255

Across

1 Fluent in the use of
   language (8)
5 Creative disciplines (4)
9 Franz ___ : novelist (5)
10 Mechanical keyboard (7)
11 From this time on (12)
14 Having a high temperature (3)
15 Advisory group (5)
16 What we breathe in (3)
17 Stretched out completely (12)
20 Spiral cavity of the inner ear (7)
22 Egg-shaped solid (5)
23 Opposite of won (4)
24 Least quiet (8)

Down

1 Large deer (pl.) (4)
2 Unconventional (7)
3 Intolerable (12)
4 Grip with the teeth (3)
6 Dry red wine (5)
7 Reference point; norm (8)
8 Blasphemous (12)
12 Barrier (5)
13 Pertaining to the body (8)
16 Plant of the buttercup family (7)
18 Moves back and forth (5)
19 Modify (4)
21 Commotion (3)

Across
1 Magnate (6)
4 Fill a balloon with air (4,2)
9 Perfectly (7)
10 In the direction of (7)
11 Exhibited (5)
12 Listens to (5)
14 Indian garments (5)
17 Inferior to (5)
19 Small crude shelter (5)
21 Young hare (7)
23 Cure-all (7)
24 Division of a group (6)
25 Concur (6)

Down
1 Roofing material made of straw (6)
2 Sharp nail as on a cat (4)
3 Weigh down (7)
5 Vegetables related to onions (5)
6 Easy victory (8)
7 Being nosy (6)
8 Relation by marriage (6-2-3)
13 ___ hour: the latest possible moment (8)
15 Turns around (on a chair) (7)
16 E.g. squares and triangles (6)
18 Still existing (6)
20 Passes the tongue over (5)
22 Garden implement (4)

Across

1 Enter a country by force (6)
4 Red wine (6)
9 Pertaining to actuality (7)
10 Appropriateness (7)
11 Small dust particles (5)
12 Bottle (5)
14 Rises (anag.) (5)
15 E.g. from Athens (5)
17 Particle that holds quarks together (5)
18 Reassess financial worth (7)
20 Jumping (7)
21 Number in a cricket team (6)
22 Promotional material (6)

Down

1 Notoriety (6)
2 Grammatical case in Latin (8)
3 Narcotics (5)
5 Portable computers (7)
6 Rank (4)
7 Christmas decoration (6)
8 Intricately (11)
13 Imaginary (8)
14 Visible horizon (7)
15 Motor vehicle storage building (6)
16 Chess piece that can jump (6)
17 Expansive (5)
19 Climbing plant (4)

PUZZLE 258

Across

1 Consisting of fine particles (8)
5 Metal fastener (4)
9 Dispose of (5)
10 Plaintive (7)
11 Cheated someone financially (5-7)
14 What a hen lays (3)
15 Planet on which we live (5)
16 Hurried (3)
17 Connection or association (12)
20 Position in rugby (3,4)
22 Shrewd (5)
23 Rotate (4)
24 Blows up (8)

Down

1 Opposite of pull (4)
2 African wild pig (7)
3 Derived from past events (12)
4 First woman (3)
6 Unspecified object (5)
7 Choosing (8)
8 Highly abstract (12)
12 Ship's load (5)
13 Modify with new parts (8)
16 Ruled (7)
18 Relay (anag.) (5)
19 What you see with (4)
21 Mend (3)

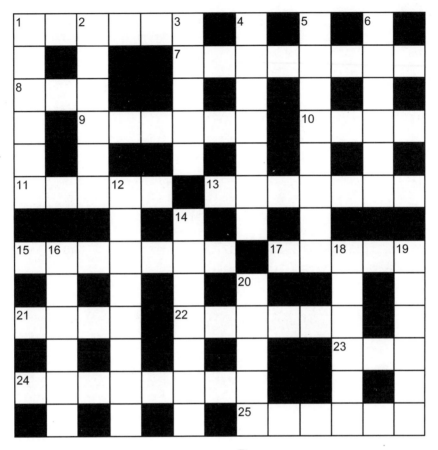

Across

1 Put out of shape (6)
7 Unfurled (8)
8 Mock (3)
9 Turbulence (6)
10 Work hard (4)
11 Snatches (5)
13 Divisions of a group (7)
15 Title appended to a man's name (7)
17 Finely cut straw (5)
21 Strip of leather worn round the waist (4)
22 Closely held back (4-2)
23 Legal ruling (3)
24 Summary (8)
25 Faculties (6)

Down

1 Throughout the course of (6)
2 Leg bone (6)
3 Made silent (5)
4 Shield from harm (7)
5 E.g. plaice (8)
6 Average; moderate (6)
12 Gusty (8)
14 Puzzling and obscure (7)
16 Garment part that covers an arm (6)
18 Popular round fruits (6)
19 Shows displeasure facially (6)
20 Nibbles at (5)

Across

4	Winged child (6)
7	Person who advocates change (8)
8	Piece of wood (3)
9	Cut of beef from the foreleg (4)
10	Make certain of (6)
11	Progress (7)
12	Stead (anag.) (5)
15	Tablets (5)
17	Stands about idly (7)
20	Place that is frequented for holidays (6)
21	Bunch of feathers (4)
22	Remuneration (3)
23	Prevent heat loss (8)
24	Dinner jacket (6)

Down

1	Technique (6)
2	Sudden heavy rain shower (8)
3	Call the validity of a practice into question (7)
4	Crude (5)
5	Slacken (6)
6	Starts (6)
13	In a shrewd manner (8)
14	Dispute or competition (7)
15	Church platform (6)
16	Voice box (6)
18	Prove to be false (6)
19	Leaf of parchment (5)

CROSSWORD

Across

1 Arguments against (4)
3 Political meetings (8)
9 Put in order (7)
10 Health professional (5)
11 Agreed upon by several parties (12)
14 Grandmother (3)
16 Assembly (5)
17 Gone by (of time) (3)
18 Quality of being at hand when necessary (12)
21 Like Catherine Zeta-Jones (5)
22 Volcanic crater (7)
23 Dress clothes (4,4)
24 State of the USA (4)

Down

1 Burrowing ground squirrel (8)
2 Rafael ___ : Spanish tennis star (5)
4 Help (3)
5 Despicable (12)
6 Film directed by Stephen Gaghan (7)
7 Appear to be (4)
8 Device for putting out fires (12)
12 Hawaiian greeting (5)
13 Person of varied learning (8)
15 Short story (7)
19 Not moving (5)
20 Drink greedily (4)
22 Toothed wheel (3)

PUZZLE 262

Across

1 Overweight (6)
4 Decorated with feathers (6)
9 Safe places (7)
10 Approve of publicly (7)
11 Pointed weapon (5)
12 Warming drink (5)
14 Album tracks (5)
17 Decal (anag.) (5)
19 Informs (5)
21 Imprecise (7)
23 Pain in the lower back (7)
24 Hurried (6)
25 Process of increasing in size (6)

Down

1 Best (6)
2 Parched (4)
3 Acts in a disloyal manner (7)
5 Raises up (5)
6 Very attractive (of personality) (8)
7 Wish for (6)
8 Forewarning (11)
13 Certificates of education (8)
15 Secret agent (7)
16 Less fresh (of bread) (6)
18 Disengage (6)
20 Lean or thin (5)
22 Attest (4)

Across

1 Occurring on the surface (11)
9 Fad (5)
10 Trivial lie (3)
11 Arrive at (5)
12 Fairy (5)
13 Cleaning feathers (8)
16 Small-scale musical drama (8)
18 ___ Avenue: NY shopping street (5)
21 Italian cathedral (5)
22 Mountain pass (3)
23 Folded back part of a coat (5)
24 Free from control (11)

Down

2 Modernised (7)
3 Bewitch (7)
4 Large container (6)
5 Crawl (5)
6 Attach (5)
7 Correct to the last detail (4-7)
8 Room used by astronomers (11)
14 Held a baby (7)
15 Piece of furniture (7)
17 Spot (6)
19 Criminal (5)
20 Divide in two (5)

Across

4	Remove weapons from (6)
7	Elation (8)
8	Witch (3)
9	Contented cat sound (4)
10	Sheepskin (6)
11	Express great joy (7)
12	Person staying at a hotel (5)
15	Overly self-confident (5)
17	Fake (7)
20	What a spider spins (6)
21	Doubtful (4)
22	Bed for a baby (3)
23	Registered (8)
24	Be aggrieved by (6)

Down

1	Time that is to come (6)
2	___ Holmes: fictional detective (8)
3	Aperture or hole (7)
4	Meads (anag.) (5)
5	Stick to (6)
6	Item that attracts iron (6)
13	Awkward (8)
14	Thieves (7)
15	Agree (6)
16	Succulent plant (6)
18	Kicked or hit hard (6)
19	Bird sound; chirp (5)

Across

1	Wander (4)
3	Outburst (8)
9	Stammer (7)
10	Vaulted (5)
11	Female singing voice (5-7)
14	Rent out (3)
16	Germaine ___ : Australian author (5)
17	Organ of hearing (3)
18	Able to use the right hand and left hand well (12)
21	___ Lavigne: Canadian singer (5)
22	Polite and refined (7)
23	Royal domains (8)
24	Social insects (4)

Down

1	Look similar to (8)
2	Humming (5)
4	Distant (3)
5	Insuring (12)
6	Vast (7)
7	Dons (anag.) (4)
8	Determined (6-6)
12	Corpulent (5)
13	Stiff coarse hairs (8)
15	Marmoset (7)
19	E.g. Pacific or Atlantic (5)
20	Like the night sky (4)
22	Chewy substance (3)

PUZZLE 266

Across

1 Exhausts (4)
3 Short musical compositions (8)
9 Tapering stone pillar (7)
10 Fourth month (5)
11 Metal container; element (3)
12 Capital of Bulgaria (5)
13 Tuft of hair (5)
15 Tree of the birch family with toothed leaves (5)
17 Track of an animal (5)
18 Enjoyable (3)
19 Swiftly (5)
20 Completely finished (3,4)
21 Small stall at an exhibition (8)
22 Ancient city (4)

Down

1 Meteors (8,5)
2 Hymn of thanksgiving (5)
4 Opposite of an acid (6)
5 Capable of being moved (12)
6 Duties or taxes (7)
7 International organisation (9,4)
8 Squint harder (anag.) (12)
14 Garment worn by dancers (7)
16 Extremely energetic person (6)
18 State of nervous excitement (5)

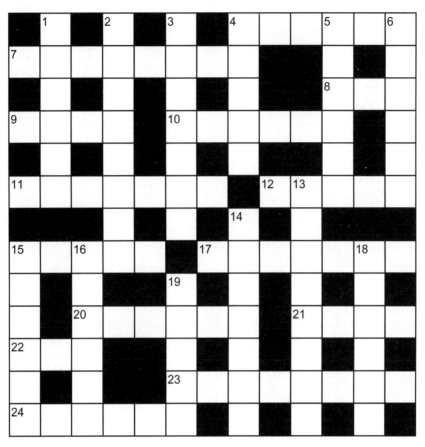

Across

4	Blocks a decision (6)
7	Standards (8)
8	Hairpiece (3)
9	This grows out of follicles (4)
10	Vedic hymn (6)
11	Mends (7)
12	Insanely (5)
15	Welcome (5)
17	Express severe disapproval of (7)
20	Rare (6)
21	Period of imprisonment (4)
22	Wager (3)
23	Proper; apt (8)
24	Blunders (6)

Down

1	Wrinkle (6)
2	Study the night sky (8)
3	Vibrations (7)
4	Show off (5)
5	Ahead (6)
6	Sweet (6)
13	German shepherd dog (8)
14	Nonconformist (7)
15	Speak rapidly (6)
16	Christian festival (6)
18	Seldom (6)
19	Salad plant (5)

Across

1 Elevated off the ground (6)
7 Done away with (8)
8 School of Mahayana Buddhism (3)
9 Cut slightly (6)
10 Public transport vehicle (4)
11 Competes in a speed contest (5)
13 Deprived of food (7)
15 Considerate; diplomatic (7)
17 Sense experience (5)
21 ___ Minnelli: US actress (4)
22 Treelike grass (6)
23 Roll of bank notes (3)
24 Person who hears (8)
25 State of the USA (6)

Down

1 More slothful (6)
2 Small fox with large pointed ears (6)
3 Deducts (5)
4 Eagerness (7)
5 Microorganisms (8)
6 Waste matter (6)
12 Competition participants (8)
14 Tribune (anag.) (7)
16 Reasons for innocence (6)
18 Snarls (6)
19 Book of the Bible (6)
20 Smug smile (5)

PUZZLE 269

Across

1 Ragtime dance (6)
4 Arm strengthening exercise (4-2)
9 Flexible (7)
10 Important church (7)
11 Twenty (5)
12 Jostle and push (5)
14 Gamble (5)
17 Metallic compound (5)
19 Local authority rule (2-3)
21 Type of alcohol (7)
23 Underground prison cell (7)
24 Discontinuance; neglect (6)
25 Playground structure (6)

Down

1 Mashes (anag.) (6)
2 Metallic element (4)
3 The first Gospel (7)
5 Makes well (5)
6 Speculative (8)
7 Filled a suitcase (6)
8 Insanity (11)
13 Rough drafts of a plan (8)
15 Untanned leather (7)
16 Put up with (6)
18 Colour of a lemon (6)
20 Unwanted plants (5)
22 Snoozes (4)

Across

1 Steal livestock (6)
4 Follow closely (6)
9 The ___ : book by Raymond Briggs (7)
10 Blood relative (7)
11 Model figures used as toys (5)
12 Card game (5)
14 Lacking interest (5)
15 Vast multitude (5)
17 Sewage pipe (5)
18 Most important (7)
20 Reticular (7)
21 Powerful (6)
22 French fashion designer (6)

Down

1 Live in (6)
2 Part of the body (8)
3 Devices that emit light (5)
5 Gaunt (7)
6 Statistics and facts (4)
7 Wet (6)
8 Inept (11)
13 Random change (8)
14 Experienced serviceman (7)
15 Keep secret (4,2)
16 Reveal (6)
17 Pertaining to the Netherlands (5)
19 Animal skin (4)

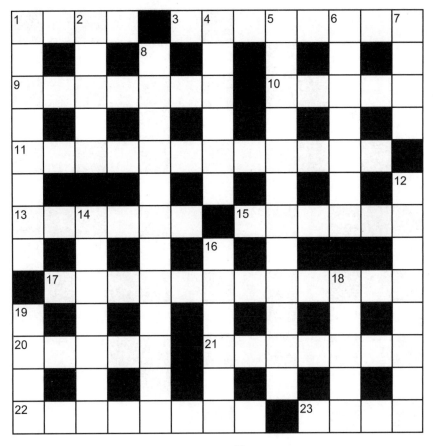

Across

1 Undulating (4)
3 Expensive fungi (8)
9 Satisfy a desire (7)
10 Needing to be scratched (5)
11 Courtesy (12)
13 Moon of the planet Jupiter (6)
15 State of matter (6)
17 Very upsetting (5-7)
20 Australian marsupial (5)
21 Study of the past (7)
22 Innate ability (8)
23 Computer memory unit (4)

Down

1 Squirmed (8)
2 Strong alcoholic drink (5)
4 Sorrowful (6)
5 Amiability (12)
6 Migratory grasshoppers (7)
7 Island of the Inner Hebrides (4)
8 Crucial (3,9)
12 Grotesquely carved figure (8)
14 Bring a law into effect again (2-5)
16 Curved (6)
18 Creamy-white substance (5)
19 Gull-like bird (4)

Across

1   Noises (6)
7   Sparkles (8)
8   Uncooked (of meat) (3)
9   Rubs out (6)
10 Blast of a horn (4)
11 Very strong winds (5)
13 Release; unhook (7)
15 Bicycle stunt (7)
17 Vibrated (5)
21 A Crown document (4)
22 Neither gas nor solid (6)
23 Small abundant insect (3)
24 Sleep disorder (8)
25 Deep serving dish (6)

Down

1   Cord (6)
2   Feeling ill (6)
3   Store in a secret place (5)
4   Express disagreement (7)
5   Playful (8)
6   Extremely courageous (6)
12 Expulsion (8)
14 Using great physical force (7)
16 Wading birds (6)
18 Late time of life (3,3)
19 Young cat (6)
20 Crouch (5)

CROSSWORD

Across

1	Decreasing (8)
5	Melt (4)
8	Opinions (5)
9	Skills (7)
10	Person moved from danger (7)
12	Tinchy ___ : Ghanaian-British rapper (7)
14	Wolfgang ___ Mozart: composer (7)
16	Cultured; elegant (7)
18	Small brownish spot on the skin (7)
19	Try out (5)
20	Young men (4)
21	Strong coffee (8)

Down

1	Talk wildly (4)
2	More profound (6)
3	Guardian (9)
4	Chat (6)
6	Finish a telephone call (4,2)
7	Cowboy films (8)
11	University one attended (4,5)
12	Derisive (8)
13	Cause to feel upset (6)
14	Venomous snakes (6)
15	Moral principles (6)
17	In addition to (4)

Across

1 Cosmetic lacquer (4,7)
9 Action words (5)
10 Strong alkaline solution (3)
11 Thermosetting resin (5)
12 Clean with a brush (5)
13 Set off (8)
16 Representations or descriptions of data (8)
18 Unbuttoned (5)
21 Precipitates (5)
22 Domesticated pig (3)
23 Simple aquatic plants (5)
24 Aristocratic mansion (7,4)

Down

2 Addresses boldly (7)
3 Imposing a tax (7)
4 Hurried (6)
5 We breathe through these (5)
6 Medicinal ointment (5)
7 Battleship (11)
8 Re-evaluation (11)
14 Renew (7)
15 Greatest amount possible (7)
17 Club (6)
19 Any finger or toe (5)
20 Gave out playing cards (5)

Across

1 Short choral compositions (6)
4 Moves slowly (6)
9 Snuggles (7)
10 Provide with food (7)
11 Latin American dance (5)
12 Breadth (5)
14 Small branches (5)
17 Thick woollen fabric (5)
19 Prevent (5)
21 Pasta strips (7)
23 Severe (7)
24 Waterlogged (6)
25 E.g. Iceland (6)

Down

1 Tiny fish (6)
2 Holier than ___ : phrase (4)
3 This evening (7)
5 Corrodes (5)
6 Undomesticated animals (8)
7 Walk nonchalantly (6)
8 Legacy (11)
13 Suave; stylish (8)
15 Caresses (7)
16 Bicycle for two people (6)
18 Removed dirt from (6)
20 Trench (5)
22 ___ Del Rey: singer (4)

PUZZLE 276

Across

1 Displayed freely (6)
7 Intestines of an animal (8)
8 Pitcher (3)
9 Small whirlpools (6)
10 Wild mountain goat (4)
11 Satisfied a desire (5)
13 Opposes (7)
15 Halted (7)
17 Refute by evidence (5)
21 Not stereo (4)
22 Outer layer of the cerebrum (6)
23 Cover with steam (of a glass surface) (3)
24 Hymn or chant (8)
25 Travelled by water (6)

Down

1 Relishes (6)
2 Imperative (6)
3 A payment made (5)
4 Stored away (7)
5 Nautical (8)
6 Articulate; eloquent (6)
12 Daring feats (8)
14 Impressive bird (7)
16 Chest (6)
18 Containerful (6)
19 Swollen; congested (6)
20 Sobs (5)

CROSSWORD

Across

1 Edge (8)
5 Wire lattice (4)
9 Pierces with a horn (5)
10 Give advice to (7)
11 Very determined (6-6)
13 Removed the skin (6)
14 Weakly (6)
17 Withdraw from service (12)
20 Keepsake; reminder (7)
21 Important question (5)
22 Snug (4)
23 About-face (8)

Down

1 Listening devices (4)
2 Country whose capital is Kyiv (7)
3 Conflict of opinion (12)
4 Loud disturbance (6)
6 Became less difficult (5)
7 Vacations (8)
8 Efficient (12)
12 Widespread outbreak (8)
15 Garments worn by women (7)
16 Type of basic aerial (6)
18 Arrives (5)
19 In a good way (4)

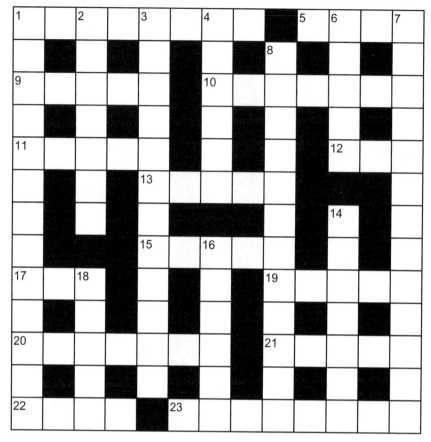

Across

1 User; purchaser (8)
5 Uttered (4)
9 Short letters (5)
10 Frozen water spears (7)
11 Causes great damage (5)
12 State of armed conflict (3)
13 Trimmed (5)
15 Pinkish-red colour (5)
17 Increase the running speed of an engine (3)
19 Remote in manner (5)
20 Recites as a chant (7)
21 Petite (5)
22 Gentle accent (4)
23 Person sent on a special mission (8)

Down

1 Contentious (13)
2 Stylishly (7)
3 Completely unaware of (12)
4 Newspaper chief (6)
6 Radiating light (5)
7 Suspiciously (13)
8 Binoculars (5,7)
14 Proportionately (3,4)
16 Demand from a kidnapper (6)
18 Essential (5)

Across

1 One who tells a story (8)
5 Superhero film based on comic characters (1-3)
9 Attack on all sides (5)
10 Resident (7)
11 Without parallel (6,2,4)
14 Snake-like fish (3)
15 Spring flower (5)
16 Saw (anag.) (3)
17 Fortunate; opportune (12)
20 Winding shapes (7)
22 Animal that uses two legs for walking (5)
23 Great ___ : breed of dog (4)
24 Practise for a later performance (8)

Down

1 Pen points (4)
2 Bertrand ___ : British philosopher (7)
3 Extremely large (12)
4 Not new (3)
6 ___-soprano: singing voice (5)
7 Gibberish (8)
8 Contradictory (12)
12 La ___ Vita: iconic film (5)
13 Hated (8)
16 Sweet covering (7)
18 The Hunter (constellation) (5)
19 Verge (4)
21 That vessel (3)

PUZZLE 280

Across

1 Pieces of jewellery (8)
5 ___ Epps: US actor and rapper (4)
8 Kind of beet (5)
9 European country (7)
10 Sudden desire (7)
12 Out of control (7)
14 Puts out of shape (7)
16 More straightforward (7)
18 Fled from captivity (7)
19 Tremble (5)
20 Stage of twilight (4)
21 Careless (8)

Down

1 Purple-brown colour (4)
2 Close at hand (6)
3 Relating to the stomach (9)
4 Three times (6)
6 Praying ___ : insect (6)
7 Sergeant (anag.) (8)
11 Openly declared to be (of a person) (9)
12 Large cask (8)
13 Hits hard (6)
14 Clear the bed of a river (6)
15 Act of selling on goods (6)
17 Belonging to a woman (4)

Across

1   Small North American lynx (6)
4   Desire for water (6)
9   Outer layer of a hair (7)
10 E.g. from London (7)
11 Seed cases (5)
12 Male monarchs (5)
14 Thin roofing slabs (5)
17 Card game (5)
19 Internal parasites (5)
21 Refills (7)
23 First (7)
24 Took in breath (6)
25 Really cold (6)

Down

1   Decorate (6)
2   Sailing ship (4)
3   Opposed to (7)
5   Emerge from an egg (5)
6   Bag carried on your back (8)
7   Tithes (anag.) (6)
8   Female students (11)
13 Narrowly avoided accident (4,4)
15 Commercial form of zinc (7)
16 Possessing (6)
18 Series of prayers (6)
20 Grin (5)
22 Greek god of war (4)

PUZZLE 282

Across

1 Creative skill (8)
5 Inspired by reverence (4)
9 Humped ruminant (5)
10 Primates (7)
11 Notwithstanding (12)
14 Popular beverage (3)
15 Sacred hymn or song (5)
16 Definite article (3)
17 Generally accepted (12)
20 Piece of research (7)
22 Collection of songs (5)
23 Portion of medicine (4)
24 Household cooling devices (8)

Down

1 Rainbow shapes (4)
2 Painting medium (7)
3 Working for oneself (4-8)
4 Strong drink (3)
6 In what place (5)
7 Catastrophe (8)
8 Coming between two things in time (12)
12 Path to follow (5)
13 ___ for cash: short of money (8)
16 Quiver (7)
18 Is aware of (5)
19 Mischievous fairies (4)
21 Hill (3)

Across

4 Capital of Russia (6)
7 Exaggerated emotion (8)
8 What a spider weaves (3)
9 Feathered creature (4)
10 Dung beetle (6)
11 Additional and supplementary part (7)
12 With cunning (5)
15 Domineering (5)
17 Excavating machines (7)
20 Using all one's resources (3,3)
21 Cash register (4)
22 Craze (3)
23 Urging on (8)
24 Machine that creates motion (6)

Down

1 Indefinitely large number (6)
2 Sports grounds (8)
3 Divide into three parts (7)
4 Parrot (5)
5 Cattle herder (6)
6 Unstable (6)
13 Thing used for tying (8)
14 Simple songs (7)
15 Confuse (6)
16 Veteran sailor (3,3)
18 Controlling (6)
19 Compel (5)

Across

1 Residents of an area (6)
4 Monist (anag.) (6)
9 Porch (7)
10 Called on (7)
11 Sly looks (5)
12 Finds agreeable (5)
14 Reverence for God (5)
15 Moisten meat (5)
17 Picture border (5)
18 Flavouring from a crocus (7)
20 Order (7)
21 Push forcefully (6)
22 ___ Brody: actor in The Pianist (6)

Down

1 Active; energetic (6)
2 Removes errors (8)
3 Touches down (5)
5 Ingenuously (7)
6 Sound of a pig (4)
7 Swaps (6)
8 Upkeep (11)
13 A desert in south-western Africa (8)
14 Noblewoman (7)
15 Common volcanic rock (6)
16 Connective tissue (6)
17 Renowned (5)
19 Anxiety; dread (4)

Across

1 Movable barrier (4)
3 Extremely lovable (8)
9 Game where success is based on luck (7)
10 More delicate (5)
11 Blends; mixtures (12)
14 Kind or sort (3)
16 Bring together (5)
17 Male aristocrat (3)
18 Formal introduction (12)
21 Shaping machine (5)
22 Dilemma (7)
23 War memorial (8)
24 Study assiduously (4)

Down

1 Inconceivably large (8)
2 Motet (anag.) (5)
4 Lacking moisture (3)
5 Cooling device in the kitchen (12)
6 Yellow fruits (7)
7 Book of the Bible (4)
8 Having a tendency to become liquid (12)
12 Extraterrestrial (5)
13 Send a signal (8)
15 Protein found in hair (7)
19 Relation by marriage (2-3)
20 Group of countries in an alliance (4)
22 Bland soft food (3)

PUZZLE 286

Across

1 Belonging to the past (8)
5 Stylish (4)
9 Ask for earnestly (5)
10 Metal similar to platinum (7)
11 Provide a substitute for (7)
12 Teacher (5)
13 Sense of musical time (6)
14 Make better (6)
17 Capital of Japan (5)
19 Insect body segment (7)
20 Country house (7)
21 Welsh breed of dog (5)
22 Tilt to one side (4)
23 Albert ___ : iconic German-born physicist (8)

Down

1 Excessively negative about (13)
2 Precipitously (7)
3 Antique; not modern (3-9)
4 Iridaceous plants (6)
6 Lift up (5)
7 Understanding (13)
8 Easy targets (7,5)
15 Steep in (7)
16 Lapis ___ : blue gemstone (6)
18 John ___ : English romantic poet (5)

CROSSWORD

Across

1 Conjecture (11)
9 Of recent origin (3)
10 Studies a subject at university (5)
11 Find an answer to (5)
12 Cover with liquid (5)
13 Liberties (8)
16 Small flesh-eating mammal (8)
18 Polite and courteous (5)
20 Flat-bottomed boat (5)
21 Backless sofa (5)
22 Very small child (3)
23 Tendency to disintegrate (11)

Down

2 Strength (5)
3 Transport by hand (5)
4 Lender (6)
5 Scuffles (7)
6 One's mental attitude (7)
7 Incalculable (11)
8 Coarse cotton gauze (11)
14 More irate (7)
15 Tedium (7)
17 Cry and sniffle (6)
18 Body of rules (5)
19 Stove (anag.) (5)

Across

1 Top aim (anag.) (6)
4 Go up (6)
9 Late (7)
10 Have a moderating effect on (7)
11 Church council (5)
12 Eat quickly (5)
14 Light downy particles (5)
17 Entices (5)
19 Shed (5)
21 Beseech (7)
23 Enthusiastic reception (7)
24 Pinches sharply (6)
25 Outer parts of bread loaves (6)

Down

1 16 of these in a pound (6)
2 Brass musical instrument (4)
3 Powerful dog (7)
5 Searches for (5)
6 Put at risk (8)
7 Fears greatly (6)
8 Astonishing (11)
13 Unyielding (8)
15 Large swimming shoe (7)
16 Bring into a country (6)
18 Animal carapaces (6)
20 Opposite of thin (5)
22 Belonging to us (4)

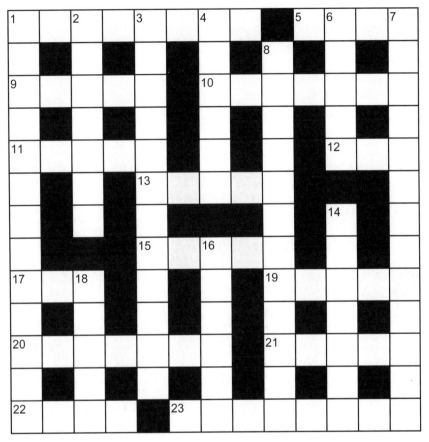

Across

1 Absolute (8)
5 Standard measure (4)
9 Ancient object (5)
10 Comes into view (7)
11 Sequence (5)
12 Born (3)
13 Give rise to (5)
15 Franz ___ : Hungarian composer (5)
17 Primary colour (3)
19 Synthetic fabric (5)
20 Distribute illicitly (7)
21 Game of chance (5)
22 Simple (4)
23 Monotony (8)

Down

1 Irretrievable (13)
2 Plunder (7)
3 Not able to be comforted (12)
4 ___ Staunton: English actress (6)
6 Church instrument (5)
7 Of various types; assorted (13)
8 Clearly evident (12)
14 Hot pepper (7)
16 Mark of disgrace (6)
18 Worthless material (5)

Across

- **1** Loud resonant sound (4)
- **3** Not injured (8)
- **9** Chemical element with atomic number 33 (7)
- **10** Regulations (5)
- **11** Quality of being genuine (12)
- **13** Living room (6)
- **15** Domesticated llama (6)
- **17** Science of space travel (12)
- **20** Customary practice (5)
- **21** Swift-flying songbird (7)
- **22** Height (8)
- **23** Anxious; nervous (4)

Down

- **1** Capable of being endured (8)
- **2** Beginning of something (5)
- **4** Subtle detail (6)
- **5** Relating to farming (12)
- **6** Civilians trained as soldiers (7)
- **7** Fine powder (4)
- **8** Clothing such as a vest (12)
- **12** Raised road (8)
- **14** Pompous person (7)
- **16** In mint condition (6)
- **18** Lazed (5)
- **19** Large US feline (4)

Across

1 Soonest (8)
5 Soothing remedy (4)
9 Underground enlarged stem (5)
10 Juicy fruits (7)
11 Assumed names (7)
12 Cattle-breeding farm (5)
13 Presented the case for (6)
14 Bird with yellow and black plumage (6)
17 Scope or extent (5)
19 Italian rice dish (7)
20 Large Israeli city (3,4)
21 Golf clubs (5)
22 Open the mouth wide when tired (4)
23 To some degree (8)

Down

1 Wastefully; lavishly (13)
2 Stealing (7)
3 Regardless of (12)
4 A husband or wife (6)
6 Inert gas (5)
7 Naughtily (13)
8 Radishes grin (anag.) (12)
15 Furthest away (7)
16 Go from one place to another (6)
18 Under (5)

PUZZLE 292

Across

1 Turn down (6)
7 Hideousness (8)
8 Irritate (3)
9 Slips through the net (6)
10 Sequence of concentric circles (4)
11 Obnoxiously forward (5)
13 Repeats from memory (7)
15 Opportunities (7)
17 The furnishings in a room (5)
21 Pull (4)
22 ___ Margolyes: actress (6)
23 Adult male (3)
24 Occur at the same time (8)
25 Plant of the parsley family (6)

Down

1 Renovate (6)
2 Fist fighters (6)
3 Pays for financially (5)
4 Showed something briefly (7)
5 Passive (8)
6 Aim to achieve something (6)
12 Dealing with (8)
14 Mythical female sea creature (7)
16 Involving direct confrontation (4-2)
18 Widespread (6)
19 Nasal (6)
20 Short and sweet (5)

Across

1 Tehran is the capital here (4)
3 Relating to courts of law (8)
9 From now on (7)
10 Character in Oliver Twist (5)
11 Ski run (5)
12 Italian fast racing car (7)
13 State of the USA (6)
15 Person to whom a lease is granted (6)
17 Greek white wine (7)
18 Approximately (5)
20 Reason for innocence (5)
21 Flamboyant confidence of style (7)
22 Fairness (8)
23 Circular movement of water (4)

Down

1 Not suitable (13)
2 Bottomless pit (5)
4 Unique (3-3)
5 Bubbling (12)
6 Gestures that convey meaning (7)
7 In a thoughtful manner (13)
8 Best starting placement in a motor race (4,8)
14 Wind together (7)
16 Grounds and buildings of a university (6)
19 Competed in a speed contest (5)

Across

1 Shine (4)
3 Formal speeches (8)
9 Vents (7)
10 Hackneyed (5)
11 Friendliness (12)
13 Smile affectedly (6)
15 Boring; hard to digest (6)
17 Adverse (12)
20 Type of coffee (5)
21 Musical wind instrument (7)
22 Fretting (8)
23 Vegetable matter used as fuel (4)

Down

1 Piece of furniture (8)
2 Japanese mattress (5)
4 Rural (6)
5 Dictatorial (12)
6 Left out (7)
7 Ooze or leak slowly (4)
8 Intentionally (12)
12 Always in a similar role (of an actor) (8)
14 Imaginary scary creature (7)
16 Silky case of some insect larvae (6)
18 Woollen material like felt (5)
19 Wolf (anag.) (4)

CROSSWORD

Across

1 Beast with three heads (8)
5 Upper front part of a boot (4)
8 During (5)
9 Fork off (7)
10 Inns (7)
12 Corridor (7)
14 Mediocre (7)
16 Treachery (7)
18 Necessary (7)
19 Carer (anag.) (5)
20 Centre (4)
21 Wild prank (8)

Down

1 Intimidates (4)
2 Periods of rule (6)
3 Massive land mammals (9)
4 Modernise (6)
6 Atmospheric phenomenon (6)
7 Gratification (8)
11 The other way around (4,5)
12 Free from sensual desire (8)
13 Thin decorative coating (6)
14 Fishes (6)
15 ___ Silverstone: US actress in Clueless (6)
17 Not false (4)

Across

- **4** Irrational fear (6)
- **7** All-round view (8)
- **8** Part of a coat (3)
- **9** Bend or coil (4)
- **10** Squirt (6)
- **11** Container releasing a fine spray (7)
- **12** Join together (5)
- **15** Alcoholic beverage (5)
- **17** Ask for (7)
- **20** East ___ : where one finds Norfolk (6)
- **21** Centre of rotation (4)
- **22** Throat of a voracious animal (3)
- **23** Intelligently (8)
- **24** Hit (6)

Down

- **1** Natural fertiliser (6)
- **2** Arduous (8)
- **3** Double-reed instrument (7)
- **4** Sets of two things (5)
- **5** Device pressed by game show contestants (6)
- **6** Relating to high mountains (6)
- **13** Copied (8)
- **14** Periods of ten years (7)
- **15** Ascends (6)
- **16** Storage compartment (6)
- **18** Abilities; talents (6)
- **19** Group of birds (5)

PUZZLE 297

Across

1 Collared ___ : bird (4)
3 Explosively unstable (8)
9 Tuneful (7)
10 Warning of danger (5)
11 Dispute or fight (3-2)
12 Upstart; one who has recently gained wealth (7)
13 Make worse (6)
15 Dwarfed tree (6)
17 One more (7)
18 First Greek letter (5)
20 Annoyed (5)
21 Bathing tub with bubbles (7)
22 Addictive tobacco drug (8)
23 Chess piece (4)

Down

1 Process of taming an animal (13)
2 Personal attendant (5)
4 Hold a position or job (6)
5 Ability to see the future (12)
6 Tidies up (7)
7 Activity of conveying information (13)
8 Firm rebuke (12)
14 Mundane (7)
16 Inhabitant of Troy (6)
19 Popular Italian dish (5)

Across

1 Upsets; agitates (8)
5 Mineral powder (4)
9 Cuts very short (5)
10 Great bravery (7)
11 Seven-a-side game (7)
12 Fragrance (5)
13 Haphazardly (6)
14 Long-legged rodent (6)
17 Asian country (5)
19 Master of ceremonies (7)
20 Leguminous plant also called lucerne (7)
21 Prod with the elbow (5)
22 Beige colour (4)
23 Disperse (anag.) (8)

Down

1 Remove dangerous substances from (13)
2 Soon (7)
3 Untimely (12)
4 See or observe (6)
6 Friend (Spanish) (5)
7 Militant aggressiveness (13)
8 Agreements; plans (12)
15 Overturned (7)
16 Cream-filled pastry (6)
18 Postpone (5)

Across

1 Computer keyboard user (6)
4 Scared (6)
9 Policeman or woman (7)
10 Insult (3-4)
11 Produce as a fruit (5)
12 Number of deadly sins (5)
14 Sisal (anag.) (5)
17 Protective containers (5)
19 Sorceress (5)
21 Dolorous (7)
23 Bring up (7)
24 Saturated with liquid (6)
25 Short-sightedness (6)

Down

1 Entices to do something (6)
2 Breathe hard (4)
3 Large public rooms on ships (7)
5 Ten more than forty (5)
6 People of olden times (8)
7 Mock (6)
8 Gave; donated (11)
13 Dared to suggest (8)
15 Piecemeal and disjointed (7)
16 Moves to-and-fro (6)
18 ___ Plath: author of The Bell Jar (6)
20 Place to live (5)
22 Move wings; flutter (4)

PUZZLE 300

Across

- **1** Lacking confidence (8)
- **5** Land measure (4)
- **9** Torn apart (5)
- **10** Ballroom dance (3-4)
- **11** Clean spiritually (5)
- **12** Criticise strongly (3)
- **13** Small game bird (5)
- **15** Completely correct (5)
- **17** Belgian town (3)
- **19** Avoid (5)
- **20** Fighter (7)
- **21** Run away with a lover (5)
- **22** Currency of France and Germany (4)
- **23** Continues obstinately (8)

Down

- **1** Not capable of being restrained (13)
- **2** Quite a few (7)
- **3** As a result (12)
- **4** Part of the eye (6)
- **6** Chop into pieces (3,2)
- **7** Ebullience (13)
- **8** Entirety (12)
- **14** E.g. spring and summer (7)
- **16** Accumulate over time (6)
- **18** Change (5)

CROSSWORD

Across

1 Large holes in the ground (4)
3 Surround (8)
9 Variety show (7)
10 Challenged (5)
11 A type of error in speech (8,4)
14 Intentionally so written (3)
16 Conceal (5)
17 The sound of a dove (3)
18 Excessively loud (12)
21 South American dance (5)
22 Gathered together (7)
23 Fence of stakes (8)
24 Pottery material (4)

Down

1 Opposition to war (8)
2 Piece of furniture (5)
4 Louse egg (3)
5 Imprudence (12)
6 Pertaining to the heart (7)
7 Ceases (4)
8 Forerunners (12)
12 Heavy iron block (5)
13 Obstinately (8)
15 Water passage (7)
19 Urge into action (5)
20 Pace (4)
22 Superhuman being (3)

Across

4	Laugh boisterously (6)
7	One with another (8)
8	Item of furniture one sleeps on (3)
9	Assist in wrongdoing (4)
10	Quantity you can hold (6)
11	Soaked in liquid (7)
12	Wears well (5)
15	Bodies of water (5)
17	Distances (7)
20	Overseas (6)
21	Joan ___ : Spanish artist (4)
22	Mammal with a bushy tail (3)
23	Pleasantness (8)
24	Yearned for (6)

Down

1	Fighting between armed forces (6)
2	One appreciative of art (8)
3	Less expensive (7)
4	Dirty (5)
5	Legendary tales (6)
6	Increases a gap (6)
13	Heated exchange of views (8)
14	Judgement (7)
15	Legitimate (6)
16	Horn (6)
18	Pester (6)
19	Strike repeatedly (5)

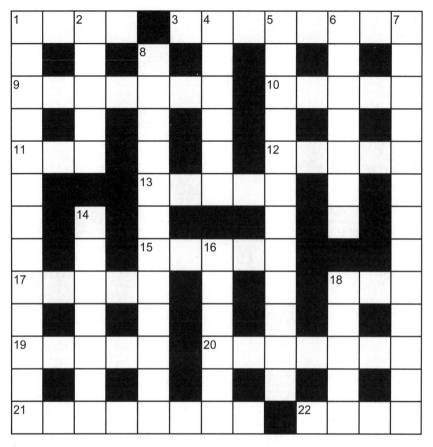

Across

1	Lane (anag.) (4)
3	A division between people (8)
9	Woven woollen fabric (7)
10	Spoken for (5)
11	Cereal plant (3)
12	Cease being awake (5)
13	Incontrovertible evidence (5)
15	Topic (anag.) (5)
17	Insane (5)
18	Bitumen (3)
19	Admirable (5)
20	Flourish (7)
21	Number of holes on most golf courses (8)
22	Relinquish (4)

Down

1	Fizz (13)
2	Decrease; lessen (5)
4	Coarse cloth (6)
5	Adequate (12)
6	Writing fluid holder (7)
7	Absence (13)
8	Joblessness (12)
14	Large cushion for sitting on (7)
16	Multiply by three (6)
18	At that place; not here (5)

Across

1	Structured set of information (8)
5	Barriers to hold back water (4)
8	Strength (5)
9	Dissolution of a marriage (7)
10	Relished (7)
12	Sailing ship (7)
14	In a friendly manner (7)
16	Sophisticated hair style (7)
18	Supply; provide (7)
19	Item of cutlery (5)
20	Engage in spirited fun (4)
21	Distinction (8)

Down

1	Foolish (4)
2	Cause sudden excitement (6)
3	Have profits that equal costs (5,4)
4	Make unhappy (6)
6	Ordered arrangements (6)
7	Delays it (anag.) (8)
11	Thomas ___ : third US President (9)
12	Refined and elegant (8)
13	Correspond to (6)
14	Song of devotion (6)
15	Complain about (6)
17	Leg joint (4)

Across

1 Opposing political progress (11)
9 Cereal grain (3)
10 Sea duck (5)
11 Violent weather (5)
12 Unite in matrimony (5)
13 Number of days in a fortnight (8)
16 Type of employment (4-4)
18 Electrician (5)
20 Venomous snake (5)
21 Milky plant fluid (5)
22 Viscous liquid (3)
23 Fragility (11)

Down

2 Trees (anag.); organic compound (5)
3 Requiring much mastication (5)
4 Blue plant dye (6)
5 Child's room (7)
6 Took away (7)
7 Ordinary (11)
8 Briefly (11)
14 Vessel that cleans rivers (7)
15 Promising actress (7)
17 Pertaining to the mind (6)
18 Pallid (5)
19 Upper coverings of buildings (5)

PUZZLE 306

Across

1	Excellently (8)
5	Yearn for (4)
9	Denim (anag.) (5)
10	Small explosive bomb (7)
11	Long race (5-7)
14	Cohere (3)
15	Willow twig (5)
16	Argument against something (3)
17	Make a guess that is too high (12)
20	Deluge (7)
22	Boldness; courage (5)
23	US pop star who sang I Got You Babe (4)
24	Leaning at an angle (8)

Down

1	Seethe (4)
2	Non-pedigree dog (7)
3	Not found (12)
4	Fall behind (3)
6	Seashore (5)
7	All people (8)
8	Demands or needs (12)
12	___ Eastwood: US actor (5)
13	Uncertain if God exists (8)
16	Provided food for an event (7)
18	Spooky (5)
19	Main acting part (4)
21	One more than one (3)

CROSSWORD

Across

1 Snatch (anag.) (6)
4 Saturated (6)
9 Caresses with the nose (7)
10 Sheriff's officer (7)
11 Remove hair (5)
12 Evil spirit (5)
14 Entrance barriers (5)
17 Chunk (5)
19 Stared into space (5)
21 Information (7)
23 Satisfy; conciliate (7)
24 ___ Schwarzenegger: actor (6)
25 With intensity (6)

Down

1 Restrained (6)
2 Not in favour (4)
3 Moving along the ground (of aircraft) (7)
5 Labyrinths (5)
6 Removed goods from a van (8)
7 Sprints (6)
8 Gained access to surreptitiously (11)
13 Almond paste (8)
15 Wrap in garments (7)
16 Crested lizard (6)
18 With little effort (6)
20 Speak in a slow manner (5)
22 Less than average tide (4)

PUZZLE 308

Across

1 Bound (4)
3 Process of sticking to a surface (8)
9 Trimmed (anag.) (7)
10 ___ Fury: British boxer (5)
11 Terrified or extremely shocked (6-6)
14 Exclamation of amazement (3)
16 Minute pore in a leaf (5)
17 Observe (3)
18 Advantageous; superior (12)
21 Bore into (5)
22 Closing sections of compositions (7)
23 Splashing with water (8)
24 Ancient boats (4)

Down

1 Light axe (8)
2 Senior figure in a tribe (5)
4 Water barrier (3)
5 Amusing (12)
6 E.g. flies and beetles (7)
7 ___ Simone: US singer (4)
8 Regretfully (12)
12 Search rigorously for (5)
13 Appreciates (8)
15 Combatant (7)
19 Lazy person (5)
20 Not evens (4)
22 Cooling tool (3)

CROSSWORD

Across

1 Greenish-blue colour (4)
3 Affecting only the appearance (8)
9 Assemble (7)
10 Hank of wool (5)
11 Saying (5)
12 Absolutely incredible (7)
13 Least young (6)
15 Bodyguard (6)
17 Distant runner-up (4-3)
18 Lover of Juliet (5)
20 Data received (5)
21 Annoying (7)
22 Make; produce (8)
23 Repudiate (4)

Down

1 Easy to deal with (13)
2 Not illuminated (5)
4 Expenditure (6)
5 Very skilful act (12)
6 Quivering singing effect (7)
7 Sweets (13)
8 One who takes part in a protest (12)
14 Standup (anag.) (7)
16 Apply ointment for religious reasons (6)
19 Large deer (5)

PUZZLE 310

Across

1 Rebuke (8)
5 Musical staff sign (4)
9 Covered with water (5)
10 Small piece of fried bread (7)
11 Preliminary (12)
13 Former name of Sri Lanka (6)
14 Long-haired variety of cat (6)
17 Bring together into a mass (12)
20 Helped to happen (7)
21 Roman robes (5)
22 Source of inspiration (4)
23 School pupils (8)

Down

1 Quantity of paper (4)
2 Clearly (7)
3 Dreamy; odd and unfamiliar (12)
4 Large insect (6)
6 Game of chance (5)
7 Male comedian (8)
8 Intense (12)
12 Frozen dessert (3,5)
15 Eight-sided polygon (7)
16 Surrounded by (6)
18 Comes close (5)
19 Requests (4)

Across

1 Prodigal (8)
5 Peel (4)
9 Send money in payment (5)
10 Outsiders (7)
11 Astronomical units (7)
12 Cowboy display (5)
13 Willow twigs (6)
14 Ratio of reflected to incident light (6)
17 ___ John: English singer (5)
19 Persistent problem (7)
20 Shoulder blade (7)
21 Scale (5)
22 Mud grooves (4)
23 Not digital (8)

Down

1 Computer program for writing documents (4,9)
2 Japanese warrior (7)
3 Someone who sets up their own business (12)
4 Furthest; extreme (6)
6 Epic poem ascribed to Homer (5)
7 Causing disgrace (13)
8 Relating to horoscopes (12)
15 Latter part of the day (7)
16 Get hold of (6)
18 Distinguishing characteristic (5)

PUZZLE 312

Across

1 Bone of the forearm (4)
3 Educated people (8)
9 Liberty (7)
10 Bits of meat of low value (5)
11 Type of verse (5)
12 Edible mollusc (7)
13 Security (6)
15 Show servile deference (6)
17 Letter (7)
18 Lubricated (5)
20 Shout of appreciation (5)
21 Art of paper-folding (7)
22 Prayer service (8)
23 Mass of floating ice (4)

Down

1 Incapable of being anticipated (13)
2 Destitute (5)
4 Punctuation marks (6)
5 Use of words that mimic sounds (12)
6 Offend the modesty of (7)
7 25th anniversary of marriage (6,7)
8 Coming from outside (12)
14 Warship (7)
16 Celebrity (6)
19 Exit (5)

Across

1 Strongly (8)
5 Successful move (4)
9 Do extremely well at (5)
10 Wine merchant (7)
11 Currents of air (7)
12 Half of six (5)
13 Person who fails to turn up (2-4)
14 Wiped out (6)
17 In a vertical line (5)
19 Terse (7)
20 Dispensers (7)
21 Perfect (5)
22 Catherine ___ : British comedienne (4)
23 Evaluator (8)

Down

1 Temperature at which water turns to ice (8,5)
2 Breaks out (7)
3 Intense anxiety (12)
4 Sumptuously rich (6)
6 Possessor (5)
7 Upright; vertical (13)
8 Ugly (12)
15 Gloomy (7)
16 Advantages (6)
18 Surprise result (5)

Across

1 Moved (6)
7 On the outer side (8)
8 Popular edible fish (3)
9 Develop (6)
10 Most important point (4)
11 Irritable (5)
13 Rounded domes (7)
15 Husbands or wives (7)
17 Conceals (5)
21 Whip (4)
22 Highly motivated (6)
23 Empty space between two objects (3)
24 Negative aspect (8)
25 Respire with difficulty (6)

Down

1 Wrangle (6)
2 Take away (6)
3 Lure an animal into a trap (5)
4 Sports arena (7)
5 Green vegetable (8)
6 Czech monetary unit (6)
12 Moving (8)
14 Slender stemlike plant appendage (7)
16 Keyboard instruments (6)
18 Hang loosely (6)
19 Maples (anag.) (6)
20 Strong fibrous tissue (5)

Across

4 Be owned by (6)
7 Waste disposal site (8)
8 Chain attached to a watch (3)
9 Type of earring (4)
10 Type of nursery (6)
11 Large ocean (7)
12 Sea crew member (5)
15 Yearns for (5)
17 Brutality (7)
20 Make tidier (6)
21 Money in notes or coins (4)
22 Dishonourable person (3)
23 Mobster (8)
24 Food that is not liquid (6)

Down

1 Eastern temple (6)
2 Tape diva (anag.) (8)
3 Lap of a track (7)
4 Short high-pitched tone (5)
5 Makes available for sale (6)
6 Mel ___ : Braveheart actor (6)
13 Cloudy and dull (8)
14 Cutting back a tree (7)
15 Calculating machine (6)
16 George ___ : composer (6)
18 Adornment of hanging threads (6)
19 Bucks (5)

PUZZLE 316

Across

1 Built (11)
9 Flat-topped conical hat (3)
10 Triangular river mouth (5)
11 Indicate indifference (5)
12 ___ Murphy: US actor and comedian (5)
13 Pristine (5-3)
16 Visionary; utopian (8)
18 Total disorder (5)
20 Gives off (5)
21 Surprising development in a story (5)
22 Don (anag.) (3)
23 Specialist in care for the feet (11)

Down

2 Seeped (5)
3 Grasslike marsh plant (5)
4 Long swelling wave (6)
5 Pursuing (7)
6 Piece of jewellery (7)
7 For all practical purposes (11)
8 The rules of the road (7,4)
14 Revival (7)
15 Wound dressing (7)
17 Economise (6)
18 Despised (5)
19 Veins (anag.) (5)

Across

1 Dominance by one group over others (8)
5 Make a garment using wool (4)
8 Young bird (5)
9 ___ shorts: item of clothing (7)
10 Valence (anag.) (7)
12 Night lights (7)
14 Stingy (7)
16 Nation (7)
18 Obvious (7)
19 Neutral shade (5)
20 Hindu spiritual discipline (4)
21 Stressed (8)

Down

1 Access illegally (4)
2 Stringed instrument (6)
3 Temporary (9)
4 Royal people (6)
6 Type of confectionery (6)
7 Absurd representation of something (8)
11 Police officer (9)
12 Deception (8)
13 Purchasing (6)
14 Occult (6)
15 Oppose (6)
17 Give nourishment to (4)

PUZZLE 318

Across

1 Representative example (8)
5 Mace (anag.) (4)
9 Teams (5)
10 Foot support (7)
11 Now and then (12)
14 Eccentric (3)
15 ___ Federer: tennis star (5)
16 Pub that may provide accommodation (3)
17 Showed (12)
20 Coincide partially (7)
22 Rogue; scoundrel (5)
23 Has to (4)
24 Routine and ordinary (3-2-3)

Down

1 Luxurious (4)
2 Decreased (7)
3 Hopelessly (12)
4 E.g. oxygen (3)
6 Christmas song (5)
7 Evacuating (8)
8 Evening dress for men (6,6)
12 Brick-shaped lump of metal (5)
13 Beetle larva that bores into timber (8)
16 Country whose capital is Reykjavik (7)
18 Encounters (5)
19 Tax (4)
21 Small green vegetable (3)

CROSSWORD

Across

1 Signs for public display (8)
5 Unable to hear (4)
8 Takes part in a game (5)
9 West Indian musical style (7)
10 Worked out logically (7)
12 Easily drawn out into a wire (7)
14 Container for mail (7)
16 Apart; into pieces (7)
18 Uma ___ : US actress (7)
19 Panorama (5)
20 Boring (4)
21 Protect from harm (8)

Down

1 Apple seeds (4)
2 Language (6)
3 Refrained from an action (9)
4 Period of ten years (6)
6 Regard as likely to happen (6)
7 Swamping (8)
11 Passes into a solution (9)
12 Gone (8)
13 Reciprocal (6)
14 Quickly (6)
15 One who manages finances at a college (6)
17 Honoured lady (4)

Across

1	Make room for (11)
9	Borders (5)
10	Degenerate (3)
11	Pond-dwelling amphibians (5)
12	Strain (5)
13	Inhaled (8)
16	Capital of Chile (8)
18	Gestured at (5)
21	Large quantities of paper (5)
22	Annoy constantly (3)
23	Sheep's sound (5)
24	Ghost (11)

Down

2	Packed (7)
3	State of being overweight (7)
4	Bird of the crow family (6)
5	Work tables (5)
6	Steer (anag.) (5)
7	Hard to imagine; astonishing (4-7)
8	Energetically or vigorously (11)
14	Surprise (7)
15	Buildings for storing cars (7)
17	Come into view (6)
19	___ Mortensen: US actor in Crimson Tide (5)
20	First appearance (5)

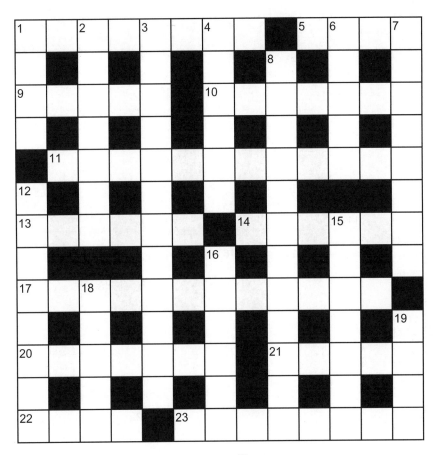

Across

1 Plummet (8)
5 Pass over (4)
9 Dens (5)
10 Abandon one's principles (4,3)
11 Lacking a backbone (12)
13 Relays (anag.) (6)
14 Recluse (6)
17 Decide in advance (12)
20 Examine (7)
21 Bring together (5)
22 Delight (4)
23 Conventional (8)

Down

1 Longest river (4)
2 Small wood (7)
3 Dispirited (12)
4 Goes to see someone (6)
6 Swedish monetary unit (5)
7 People in hospital (8)
8 Gossip (12)
12 Becoming agitated (8)
15 Human beings collectively (7)
16 Volleyball position (6)
18 Follow on from (5)
19 Medium-sized feline (4)

Across

1 Unit of power (4)
3 Large Spanish estate (8)
9 Fourth book of the Bible (7)
10 Tall structure on a castle (5)
11 Was in first place (3)
12 ___ Witherspoon: Legally Blonde actress (5)
13 Leaves out (5)
15 Supernatural skill (5)
17 Popular party dance (5)
18 Sum charged (3)
19 Set of moral principles (5)
20 Carbon ___ : greenhouse gas (7)
21 Move out the way of (8)
22 Spherical objects (4)

Down

1 Boots with pointed toes (6-7)
2 Domesticated (5)
4 Birthplace of St Francis (6)
5 Junction (12)
6 Freshness (7)
7 Pleasantness (13)
8 Renditions (12)
14 Squeezed the skin tightly (7)
16 Belt worn round the waist (6)
18 Member of a Catholic religious order (5)

Across

1 Factual TV program (11)
9 Witty (5)
10 By means of (3)
11 Type of leather (5)
12 Talk (5)
13 Delicate ornamental work (8)
16 Postponement (8)
18 Wanes (anag.) (5)
21 Chopped finely (5)
22 Tyrannosaurus ___ : dinosaur (3)
23 Amends (5)
24 Having power (11)

Down

2 Well-behaved (7)
3 Be subjected to (7)
4 Develop gradually (6)
5 Cash registers (5)
6 Variety show (5)
7 Advance quickly (4-7)
8 E.g. Christmas Day (4,7)
14 Receiver (7)
15 Former Greek monetary unit (7)
17 Whole (6)
19 Plant hormone (5)
20 One of the senses (5)

Across

1 Bulbous perennial herb (8)
5 Vale (4)
9 Smallest amount (5)
10 Platform (7)
11 Bart's father in the Simpsons (5)
12 Ant and ___ : British presenting duo (3)
13 Craftsman who uses stone (5)
15 Area of land (5)
17 Not (anag.) (3)
19 Faint southern constellation (5)
20 No longer in use (7)
21 Sailing ship (5)
22 Spool-like toy (4)
23 An unwelcome person; invader (8)

Down

1 Unenthusiastically (4-9)
2 Shocked (7)
3 Sporadic (12)
4 Throws a coin in the air (6)
6 Implant (5)
7 Compiler of a dictionary (13)
8 Skilled joiner (12)
14 Caused to burn (7)
16 Jane ___ : author of Pride and Prejudice (6)
18 Attractively stylish (5)

Across

1 Enthusiastic approval (11)
9 Fishing stick (3)
10 Remains somewhere (5)
11 Remove paint from a wall (5)
12 Covered with powdery dirt (5)
13 Adolescent (8)
16 Study of animal behaviour (8)
18 Historic nobleman (5)
20 Country in Western Asia (5)
21 Loosen up (5)
22 Small shelter (3)
23 E.g. Queen of Hearts (7,4)

Down

2 Ciphers (5)
3 Entrance hall (5)
4 Centre (6)
5 Throwing a coin in the air (7)
6 Surplus or excess (7)
7 One who held a job previously (11)
8 Divisions of companies (11)
14 Relating to heat (7)
15 Obviously (7)
17 Measure of capacity (6)
18 Poisonous (5)
19 Hate (5)

Across

1 Heavenly (8)
5 Proverbs; cutting tools (4)
8 Woody-stemmed plant (5)
9 Destructive (7)
10 Firm providing flights (7)
12 Most active (7)
14 Mournful poems (7)
16 Evaded (7)
18 Closely packed together (7)
19 Give a solemn oath (5)
20 Court enclosure (4)
21 Great adulation (8)

Down

1 Male children (4)
2 Units of linear measure (6)
3 Broke into pieces (9)
4 Positive and happy (6)
6 Matter (6)
7 Liquids which dissolve other substances (8)
11 Practice session for a performance (9)
12 Well-rounded (8)
13 Of the universe (6)
14 Readied for publication (6)
15 Force fluid into (6)
17 Cafeteria item (4)

Across

1 Mean (5-6)
9 Seed of an apple (3)
10 Exposed (5)
11 Nadir (anag.) (5)
12 Starts off (5)
13 Mounted guns (8)
16 Streams of rain (8)
18 Walks up and down (5)
20 ___ Presley: US singer (5)
21 Desires (5)
22 Female sheep (3)
23 Act of publishing in several places (11)

Down

2 Slight error (5)
3 Absorbent pads (5)
4 Faker (6)
5 Depresses (7)
6 Distinguished (7)
7 Engagement (11)
8 Witches (11)
14 Seriously (7)
15 Restrained (7)
17 Line of latitude (6)
18 Suggest (5)
19 Doctrine; system of beliefs (5)

PUZZLE 328

Across

1 Ready to eat (4)
3 E.g. Heathrow and Gatwick (8)
9 Plant with starchy tuberous roots (7)
10 More than enough (5)
11 Optimism (12)
13 Nudges out of the way (6)
15 Layered cake (6)
17 Productivity (12)
20 Expressed clearly (5)
21 Reddening of the skin (7)
22 Remedy to a poison (8)
23 Primary colour (4)

Down

1 Rebound (8)
2 Outmoded (5)
4 Son of Daedalus in Greek mythology (6)
5 Smooth and easy progress (5,7)
6 Retaliatory action (7)
7 Wets (anag.) (4)
8 Lacking tolerance or flexibility (6-6)
12 Source of annoyance (8)
14 Beetroot soup (7)
16 Compensate for (6)
18 Peer (5)
19 Tiny parasite (4)

Across

4 City in NE England (6)
7 Squid dish (8)
8 Beer container (3)
9 Princess ___ : Star Wars character (4)
10 2002 animated film featuring a woolly mammoth (3,3)
11 Positively charged ions (7)
12 Impudent (5)
15 Brief appearance (5)
17 Male sibling (7)
20 Gathering up leaves in the garden (6)
21 Animate existence (4)
22 Breed of dog (3)
23 Bridge above another road (8)
24 Over there (6)

Down

1 Photographic device (6)
2 Organism that exploits another (8)
3 Not in a hurry (7)
4 Eats a main meal (5)
5 Shrike (anag.) (6)
6 Strong (6)
13 Eland (8)
14 Part of a gun (7)
15 Conform (6)
16 Edge (6)
18 Exude (6)
19 Movable helmet part (5)

Across

1 Pyotr ___ : Russian composer (11)
9 Possessed (3)
10 Contaminate (5)
11 Natural yellow resin (5)
12 Late (5)
13 Remote; cut off (8)
16 Figure of speech (8)
18 Frenzied (5)
20 Passenger ship (5)
21 Negatively charged ion (5)
22 Small truck (3)
23 Calm and sensible (5-6)

Down

2 Programmer (5)
3 Suitably (5)
4 Sharp cutting implements (6)
5 Essentially (7)
6 Collective settlement in Israel (7)
7 Pertaining to office workers (5-6)
8 Greenish (11)
14 Poison (7)
15 Bravery (7)
17 Aloof (6)
18 Ray (5)
19 Flaring stars (5)

Across

1 Hollow pipe (4)
3 Made another excited about (8)
9 Charmer (anag.) (7)
10 Rescues (5)
11 Nevertheless (3)
12 Donor (5)
13 Academy Award (5)
15 Quick (5)
17 Small group ruling a country (5)
18 Muhammad ___ : boxer (3)
19 A number between an eighth and a tenth (5)
20 Open-meshed material (7)
21 Clover-like plant (8)
22 Supportive associate (4)

Down

1 Men In Black actor (5,3,5)
2 Rupture (5)
4 Scandinavian (6)
5 Person studying after a first degree (12)
6 Restoration to life (7)
7 Upsettingly (13)
8 Cameraman (12)
14 A rich mine; big prize (7)
16 Meal eaten in the fresh air (6)
18 A satellite of Uranus (5)

Across

1	Area an aeroplane can fly in (8)
5	Ancient France (4)
9	Firearm (5)
10	Tortilla rolled around a filling (7)
11	Build up again from parts (12)
14	Public transport vehicle (3)
15	Uncertainty (5)
16	Adult males (3)
17	Fully extended (12)
20	Scientific study of life (7)
22	Language of ancient Rome (5)
23	Stained (4)
24	Meddlesome person (8)

Down

1	Askew (4)
2	Roof beams (7)
3	Prerequisite (12)
4	Edible nut (3)
6	Word of farewell (5)
7	A detail to be explained (5,3)
8	Creatively (12)
12	Foam or froth (5)
13	Took in (8)
16	A very skilled performer (7)
18	Store of hoarded wealth (5)
19	Feeling of resentment or jealousy (4)
21	Thee (3)

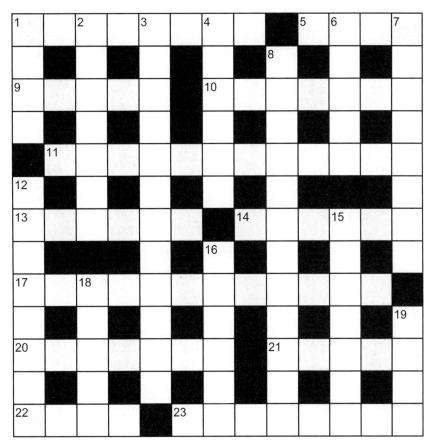

Across

1 Sanctions (8)
5 This covers your body (4)
9 Small firework (5)
10 These follow Sundays (7)
11 Uncomplimentary (12)
13 Measuring sticks (6)
14 Distinctive uniform (6)
17 Luckily (12)
20 Vary the pitch of the voice (7)
21 Tines (anag.) (5)
22 Three feet length (4)
23 Male relation (8)

Down

1 Otherwise (4)
2 Active during the day (7)
3 Troublemaker (6-6)
4 Hostility (6)
6 Service colour of the army (5)
7 Small bunches of flowers (8)
8 Ancient and old-fashioned (12)
12 Cunningly (8)
15 Signs up (7)
16 Part of a motor (6)
18 Send someone to a medical specialist (5)
19 School that Prince William attended (4)

Across

1 Having celebrities in attendance (4-7)
9 Person who steers a boat (3)
10 Hang with cloth (5)
11 Faint (5)
12 Temporary police force (5)
13 Unsubstantiated (8)
16 Quarter note (8)
18 Debate in a heated manner (5)
20 Not in good physical condition (5)
21 Pattern (5)
22 Metal container; is able to (3)
23 Charitable donation (11)

Down

2 Levies (5)
3 Natural elevation (5)
4 Emotional shock (6)
5 Dons clothes (7)
6 Give authority to (7)
7 Type of treatment using needles (11)
8 Large car windows (11)
14 Open air controlled blaze (7)
15 Coal bucket (7)
17 Archimedes' famous cry (6)
18 Detailed assessment of accounts (5)
19 Type of lizard (5)

CROSSWORD

Across

1 Sorcerer (8)
5 ___ Baldwin: US actor (4)
9 Art gallery (5)
10 Crossbar set above a window (7)
11 Hinged surface on an aeroplane wing (7)
12 Fault; mistake (5)
13 Single-celled organism (6)
14 Wellbeing (6)
17 Make law (5)
19 Refrain from (7)
20 Ugly building (7)
21 Dissatisfaction (5)
22 Periodic movement of the sea (4)
23 Interpret in a certain way (8)

Down

1 Ineptitude in running a business (13)
2 Famous Italian astronomer (7)
3 Donation (12)
4 Performing on stage (6)
6 Intense light beam (5)
7 Wide-ranging (13)
8 Failure to act with prudence (12)
15 Novice driver (7)
16 Get by with what is available (4,2)
18 In the lead (5)

PUZZLE 336

Across

1 Adolescent (abbrev.) (4)
3 Recurring at intervals (8)
9 Japanese massage technique (7)
10 Plant spike (5)
11 Excess (5)
12 Underwater projectile (7)
13 Get-up-and-go (6)
15 Imperfection (6)
17 Faster (7)
18 State of the USA (5)
20 Consumed (5)
21 End stations (7)
22 Sit with legs wide apart (8)
23 Component part (4)

Down

1 Blandness (13)
2 Be alive; be real (5)
4 Agree or correspond (6)
5 Middleman (12)
6 Bishop's jurisdiction (7)
7 Acrobat who twists and bends their body (13)
8 Uncurled (12)
14 Termite (anag.) (7)
16 Savage (6)
19 Set straight (5)

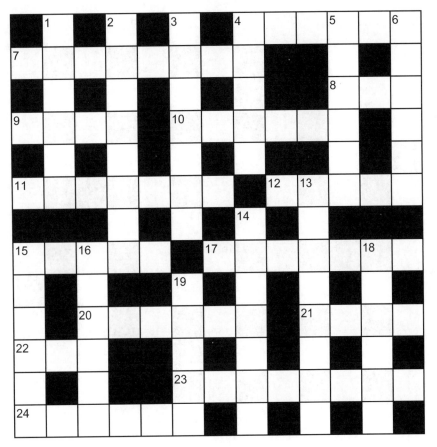

Across

4 Material; textile (6)
7 Notes of a chord played in rapid succession (8)
8 Solemn pledge (3)
9 Very short skirt or dress (4)
10 Bean (6)
11 Swears (7)
12 Grinding machines (5)
15 Really angry (5)
17 Make insane (7)
20 Come into view (6)
21 Electrically charged particles (4)
22 Jolt (3)
23 Excessively emotional (6,2)
24 Crazy person (6)

Down

1 Painter (6)
2 Disease (8)
3 Nimbleness (7)
4 Blacksmith's workshop (5)
5 Expose (6)
6 Escrow (anag.) (6)
13 Pictured (8)
14 Shooting stars (7)
15 Deadlock (6)
16 Swerved (6)
18 Intellectual giant (6)
19 Physical strength (5)

Across

1 Type of state (8)
5 Single article (4)
9 Equip (5)
10 Sheikhdom in the Persian Gulf (7)
11 Fellow plotter (12)
13 Support (6)
14 Outcome (6)
17 Without equal (12)
20 Quantities (7)
21 Big cat (5)
22 Ripped (4)
23 Alienate (8)

Down

1 Long grass (4)
2 Small field (7)
3 Total confusion (12)
4 Drink (6)
6 Browned bread (5)
7 Opposite of majority (8)
8 Chair proctor (anag.) (12)
12 Exultant (8)
15 E.g. fluorine or chlorine (7)
16 Produces an effect (6)
18 Church singers (5)
19 Soft creamy cheese (4)

CROSSWORD

Across

1 Items of value (6)
4 Abandon a plan (6)
9 Agile circus performer (7)
10 Not tidy (7)
11 Direct (5)
12 Turns down (5)
14 Varieties (5)
17 Small hill (5)
19 Public disturbances (5)
21 Attributed to (7)
23 Chilly attitude (7)
24 Flock of geese (6)
25 Author (6)

Down

1 Love affairs (6)
2 Garment for the foot (4)
3 Film starring Jim Carrey (3,4)
5 Aromatic plants (5)
6 Text of an opera (8)
7 Restaurant (6)
8 Patriotism (11)
13 Not giving affection (8)
15 Captain (7)
16 Cooking in hot oil (6)
18 Person staying in another's home (6)
20 Magical incantation (5)
22 Take ___ : band (4)

Across

1 Rebuild (11)
9 Sully or blemish (5)
10 Tack (3)
11 Extravagant dinner (5)
12 Less narrow (5)
13 Pithy saying (8)
16 Not ripe (of fruit) (8)
18 Ordered arrangement (5)
21 Thing of value (5)
22 Grassland (3)
23 Hebrew prophet (5)
24 Freed (11)

Down

2 Understanding of another (7)
3 Bivalve molluscs (7)
4 Climbs (6)
5 Rejuvenate (5)
6 God of love (5)
7 Combustible (11)
8 Increasing gradually by degrees (11)
14 Card game (7)
15 Copious (7)
17 Breakfast food (6)
19 Supply with new weapons (5)
20 Country in the Arabian peninsula (5)

Across

1 Is composed of (8)
5 Quartz-like gem (4)
9 Storage space under the roof (5)
10 Unpredictable (7)
11 Insistently (12)
13 Reddish-brown colour (6)
14 Andre ___ : former US tennis player (6)
17 Creator of film scripts (12)
20 E.g. Evita (7)
21 Opposite of outer (5)
22 Where a bird lays eggs (4)
23 Tidal waves (8)

Down

1 Cajole (4)
2 Concepts (7)
3 Ineptness (12)
4 Written agreement (6)
6 Floral leaf (5)
7 Game of chance (5,3)
8 Knowledge of a future event (12)
12 Male journalists (8)
15 Breastbone (7)
16 Increases in size (6)
18 Flowers given on Valentine's Day (5)
19 ___ and cons: pluses and minuses (4)

Across

1 E.g. trophies and medals (6)
4 Absorbent material (6)
9 Virtuoso solo passage (7)
10 Hugged (7)
11 Soft paste (5)
12 Chambers (5)
14 Dirty (5)
15 Tall and thin (5)
17 Small loose stones (5)
18 Motor-driven revolving spindle (7)
20 Kitchen stoves (7)
21 Holds up (6)
22 Was scared of (6)

Down

1 Consider to be true (6)
2 Interview for an acting role (8)
3 Drab (5)
5 Resembling dust (7)
6 Small metal spike (4)
7 Discharges (6)
8 Food taken to school (6,5)
13 Supervisor (8)
14 Bewilder (7)
15 Fastened shut with a key (6)
16 Served (anag.) (6)
17 Puff on a cigarette (5)
19 Tablet (4)

Across

1 Tip the hat (4)
3 Coloured paper thrown at weddings (8)
9 Feeling of vexation (7)
10 Normal (5)
11 Astonishing; amazing (3-9)
14 Consume food (3)
16 Long tubes (5)
17 Sweet potato (3)
18 Give a false account of (12)
21 Bedfordshire town (5)
22 Tree of the walnut family (7)
23 Enclosed area in a farm (8)
24 Retained (4)

Down

1 Stated emphatically (8)
2 Body of burning gas (5)
4 Possess (3)
5 Fence closure (anag.) (12)
6 Non-attendance (7)
7 Woes (4)
8 Clearness (12)
12 Arise unexpectedly (3,2)
13 Purple quartz (8)
15 Cyclone (7)
19 Wear away over time (5)
20 Heavy stick used as a weapon (4)
22 Female pronoun (3)

Across

1 Property professional (6,5)
9 Hog (3)
10 Musical instrument (5)
11 Breathing organs (5)
12 Trite (5)
13 Dish of rice with fish and eggs (8)
16 Least old (8)
18 Buffalo (5)
20 Quavering sound (5)
21 Leaves (5)
22 What a painter creates (3)
23 Fit to be seen (11)

Down

2 Sweetening substance (5)
3 Sufficiently (5)
4 Pass by (6)
5 Study of rocks (7)
6 Convent (7)
7 Prophetic of the end of the world (11)
8 Scatter widely (11)
14 Accounts inspector (7)
15 Eternal (7)
17 Relating to monkeys (6)
18 ___ Rhymes: US rapper and songwriter (5)
19 Gastropod with a shell (5)

Across

1 Trees that bear acorns (4)
3 Ozzy ___ : Black Sabbath vocalist (8)
9 Vanquish (7)
10 Clever (5)
11 Laudatory (12)
13 Cure-all (6)
15 Maiden (6)
17 Poorly fed (12)
20 Balearic island (5)
21 Pedigree (7)
22 Capital of Uzbekistan (8)
23 Paradise garden (4)

Down

1 Busy (8)
2 Country in East Africa (5)
4 Bad handwriting (6)
5 Perceptions (12)
6 Attains (7)
7 Consumes food (4)
8 The ? symbol (8,4)
12 Short heavy club (8)
14 Slanted letters (7)
16 Lightweight cotton cloth (6)
18 Accumulate; amass (5)
19 River deposit (4)

Across

1 Thing that incurs feeling of hatred (11)
9 Longing (3)
10 Dessert dish (5)
11 ___ Piper: variety of potato (5)
12 Test or examine (5)
13 Deluge (8)
16 Relating to office work (8)
18 Move out of the way (5)
20 Views; observes (5)
21 Therefore (5)
22 Towards the stern (3)
23 Radiant; sumptuous (11)

Down

2 Shelf-like beds (5)
3 Filthy (5)
4 Nerve cell (6)
5 Abounding (7)
6 Lasted longer than expected (7)
7 Energetically (11)
8 Insults (11)
14 Avid follower (7)
15 Zeppelin (7)
17 Geneva (anag.) (6)
18 Staple food (5)
19 Looking tired (5)

Across

1 Large bag (4)
3 Twining plant (8)
9 Protective layers (7)
10 Edge or border (5)
11 Lexicons (12)
13 Short written works (6)
15 Person subject to an attack (6)
17 Exceptional (12)
20 White heron (5)
21 Biting (7)
22 Putting into practice (8)
23 Scarpered (4)

Down

1 Firmness (8)
2 Sceptic (5)
4 Crazy (6)
5 Designed to distract (12)
6 Sincere (7)
7 Hold as an opinion (4)
8 Dimly; not clearly (12)
12 Mimicked (8)
14 Deliver by parachute (7)
16 Discernment (6)
18 Electronic communication (5)
19 Sixth Greek letter (4)

Across

1	Fraudulently (11)
9	Lobed glandular organ (5)
10	Young dog (3)
11	Records (5)
12	Broaden (5)
13	Protected; toughened (8)
16	Undo; loosen (8)
18	Married women (5)
21	Went down on one knee (5)
22	Piece of cloth (3)
23	Take forcibly (5)
24	Enormous (11)

Down

2	Create a positive feeling in a person (7)
3	Gun holder (7)
4	Beginner (6)
5	Spread by scattering (5)
6	Oily organic compound (5)
7	Cooking utensils (11)
8	Dogmatic (11)
14	Top prize (7)
15	Become more precipitous (7)
17	Cloud of dust and gas in space (6)
19	Period of keeping awake to pray (5)
20	Drink noisily (5)

Across

1 Ornamental structure in a pool (8)
5 Select from a large amount (4)
8 Grinding tooth (5)
9 Excess of liabilities over assets (7)
10 Imitating (7)
12 No longer in existence (7)
14 Two-wheeled vehicle (7)
16 Financial supporter (7)
18 Perform repeatedly (7)
19 Small room used as a steam bath (5)
20 Midday (4)
21 Informed upon (8)

Down

1 Renown (4)
2 Raise (6)
3 Lateness (9)
4 Admit to a post (6)
6 Sea ___ : marine echinoderm (6)
7 Take legal action (8)
11 Forerunner (9)
12 The production and discharge of something (8)
13 Lively Spanish dance (6)
14 Zephyr (6)
15 Indistinct (6)
17 A lyric poet (4)

PUZZLE 350

Across

1 Piece of office furniture (4)
3 Marriage ceremony (8)
9 Suggest (7)
10 Peers (5)
11 Made poor (12)
13 Frames used by artists (6)
15 Marble (anag.) (6)
17 Upper chamber in Parliament (5,2,5)
20 Sudden forward thrust (5)
21 Polishing (7)
22 Think deeply for a period of time (8)
23 Marries (4)

Down

1 Prevents from having (8)
2 Tread heavily (5)
4 Rubs (6)
5 Omit too much detail (12)
6 Dreamlike (7)
7 Be at a ___ : be puzzled (4)
8 Recovering from illness (of a person) (12)
12 Portents (8)
14 Derided (7)
16 Australian marsupial (6)
18 Lift up (5)
19 Shut with force (4)

PUZZLE 351

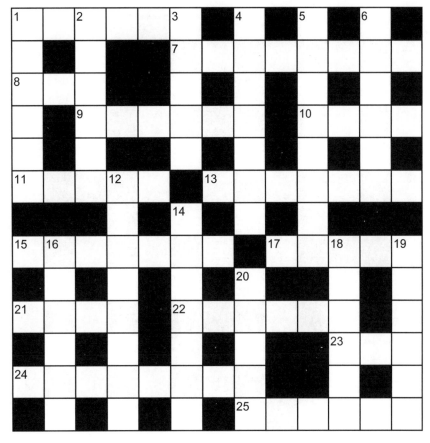

Across

1	Intending (6)
7	Making possible (8)
8	Bird of the crow family (3)
9	Occurring every sixty minutes (6)
10	Subsequently (4)
11	Shy (5)
13	Senior clergyman (7)
15	Char or burn (7)
17	Indoor game (5)
21	Spiritual teacher (4)
22	Help or support (6)
23	Short cylindrical piece of wood (3)
24	Discouraged from doing (8)
25	Quash (6)

Down

1	Modify (6)
2	Havoc (6)
3	Variety or kind (5)
4	Legal practitioners (7)
5	Fleet of ships (8)
6	Arthropod (6)
12	Contained as part of a whole (8)
14	People who are in a club (7)
16	Shrub with glossy leaves (6)
18	Torn (of clothes) (6)
19	Solitary; not married (6)
20	Rushes along (5)

Across

1 Perennial plant (8)
5 Imitated (4)
9 Paved courtyard (5)
10 Suit makers (7)
11 A perfumed liquid (3,2,7)
14 ___ Botham: former England cricketer (3)
15 Relating to sound (5)
16 Cooking utensil (3)
17 Lacking courage (5-7)
20 Steadfast (7)
22 Silly trick (5)
23 Of like kind (4)
24 Uses again (8)

Down

1 Feeling of expectation (4)
2 Learn new skills (7)
3 Airing a TV program (12)
4 Ignited (3)
6 Pointed part of a fork (5)
7 Heading on a restaurant menu (8)
8 List of books referred to (12)
12 Group of activists (5)
13 Spreads out (8)
16 Come out on top (7)
18 ___ Asimov: science fiction author (5)
19 Seek (anag.) (4)
21 Colour or tint (3)

CROSSWORD

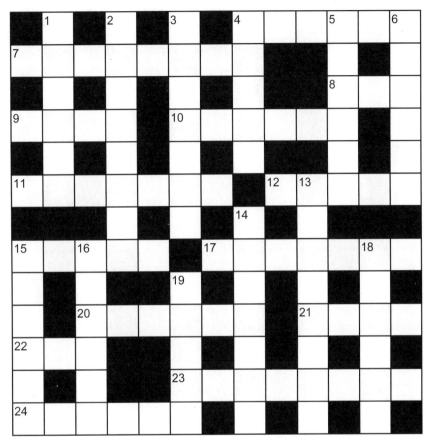

Across

4	Small crustacean (6)
7	Major component of air (8)
8	Dandy (3)
9	First James Bond film (2,2)
10	Immature insects (6)
11	Attack (7)
12	Dislikes intensely (5)
15	Strong currents of air (5)
17	Hermit (7)
20	Nearly (6)
21	Goes wrong (4)
22	Nocturnal mammal (3)
23	Sketching out (8)
24	Constructs a building (6)

Down

1	___ fruit: e.g. orange or lemon (6)
2	Conceited (8)
3	Nimbly (7)
4	Catch; lure (5)
5	Contaminate (6)
6	Students (6)
13	Illnesses (8)
14	In the middle (7)
15	Eat hurriedly (6)
16	Sculptured figure (6)
18	Jumped up (6)
19	Things you buy; effects (5)

PUZZLE 354

Across

1 Offers guidance (8)
5 From a distance (4)
9 Pollex (5)
10 Grassland areas (7)
11 Occult (12)
13 ___ powder: bathroom item (6)
14 Hay-cutting tool (6)
17 Insincere (12)
20 Disparaging remarks (7)
21 Beneath (5)
22 Mob (4)
23 Intrigue (8)

Down

1 Large town (4)
2 Uncommon (7)
3 Next (12)
4 Thin layer of sedimentary rock (6)
6 Fine powdery foodstuff (5)
7 Settles (8)
8 Expensive clothes (5,7)
12 Reading carefully (8)
15 Move slowly (7)
16 Diminish (6)
18 ___ Boyle: Scottish singer (5)
19 Worry about (4)

CROSSWORD

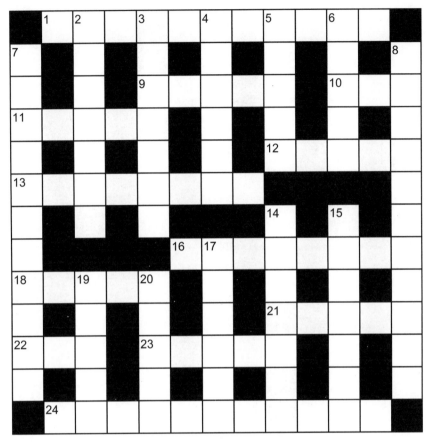

Across

1 Additionally (11)
9 Looked at open-mouthed (5)
10 Vitality (3)
11 Drain away from soil (of a chemical) (5)
12 Skirmish (5)
13 Pounded heavily (8)
16 Cocktail (8)
18 Measures duration (5)
21 Apart from (5)
22 Spoil (3)
23 Singing voice (5)
24 Watching over one's flock (11)

Down

2 Dig out of the ground (7)
3 Become tense (7)
4 Domain (6)
5 Device used to connect to the internet (5)
6 Take great satisfaction in (5)
7 Flared trousers (4-7)
8 Rude (11)
14 Multiplied a number by itself (7)
15 Civilian (7)
17 Street (6)
19 Military walk (5)
20 Establish (3-2)

Across

1 Turning over (8)
5 Turn or slide violently (of a vehicle) (4)
8 Make wavy (5)
9 Game played on a sloping board (7)
10 Explain in detail (7)
12 Urged on (7)
14 Luggage (7)
16 Icy (7)
18 Clear perception (7)
19 Underwater breathing device (5)
20 Secluded narrow valley (4)
21 Dark reddish-brown colour (8)

Down

1 Countenance (4)
2 Frozen water spear (6)
3 Spicy sausage (9)
4 Bit sharply (6)
6 Old measure of distance (6)
7 Thoroughly cooked (of meat) (4-4)
11 Forecast (9)
12 Expelling air abruptly (8)
13 Notable inconvenience (6)
14 Mark on the skin (6)
15 Season after summer (6)
17 ___ Simpson: cartoon character (4)

Across

1 Small pieces (11)
9 Gallivant (3)
10 Long-handled spoon (5)
11 Thin pancake (5)
12 Long pointed teeth (5)
13 Broadcast (8)
16 Hardships (8)
18 Agreeable sound or tune (5)
20 Solids with six equal square faces (5)
21 Spiritual being (5)
22 Pen fluid (3)
23 Uninvited guest (11)

Down

2 Fashions; styles (5)
3 Stories (5)
4 Withstand (6)
5 Voted in to office (7)
6 Greek goddess of retribution (7)
7 Self-centred (11)
8 Easily achieved (5,2,4)
14 Brazilian dance (7)
15 The rubbing of muscles (7)
17 Bigger (6)
18 Thaws (5)
19 Michael ___ : R.E.M. lead singer (5)

Across

1 Revoke a law (6)
4 Physical item (6)
9 Business establishments (7)
10 Humorous drawing (7)
11 Took illegally (5)
12 Father (5)
14 Beasts of burden (5)
17 Renown (5)
19 Greets with enthusiasm (5)
21 Reserved (7)
23 The Windy City (7)
24 Scorched (6)
25 Worshipper (6)

Down

1 Rotten (of food) (6)
2 Having no money (4)
3 Word opposite in meaning to another (7)
5 Polishes (5)
6 Surrounded on all sides (8)
7 Assigned a piece of work (6)
8 Comfort; solace (11)
13 Resolution (8)
15 Lost grip (7)
16 Throws carelessly (6)
18 Higher in rank (6)
20 Sum of money wagered (5)
22 Gelatinous substance (4)

Across

1 Argumentative (11)
9 The Norwegian language (5)
10 Antelope (3)
11 Lives (anag.) (5)
12 Flatten on impact (5)
13 Deep ditches (8)
16 Wide-ranging (8)
18 Fresher (5)
21 Old-fashioned (5)
22 Partly digested animal food (3)
23 Basic units of chemical elements (5)
24 Radically (11)

Down

2 Single-handed (7)
3 Plunder (7)
4 Continent (6)
5 Appears (5)
6 Tycoon (5)
7 Branch of physics (11)
8 Innovative or pioneering (7,4)
14 Salt lake in the Jordan valley (4,3)
15 Handful (7)
17 ___ Goldberg: US actress (6)
19 Long-legged bird (5)
20 Calls out like a lion (5)

PUZZLE 360

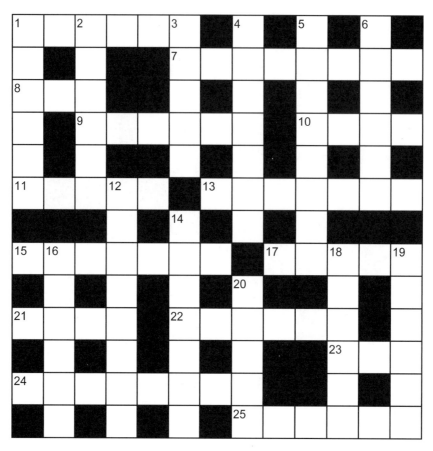

Across

1 Ingenious device (6)
7 E.g. uncle or sister (8)
8 Scientific workplace (abbrev.) (3)
9 Wear away (6)
10 Writing fluids (4)
11 Compositions in verse (5)
13 Exceed (7)
15 Type of cheese (7)
17 Gold measure (5)
21 ___ Moore: Hollywood actress (4)
22 Spreads out and apart (6)
23 In what way (3)
24 Exaggerated masculinity (8)
25 Small carnivorous mammal (6)

Down

1 Ride a horse at pace (6)
2 Lower in value (6)
3 Walk (5)
4 Exuberantly joyful (7)
5 Country in North East Africa (8)
6 Calls forth (6)
12 00:00 on a 24-hour clock (8)
14 Player of an instrument that is low in pitch (7)
16 Dog-like mammals (6)
18 Shares (anag.) (6)
19 Gardening tool (6)
20 Let (5)

Across

1 Engravings (8)
5 Suggestion or tip (4)
8 Small primate (5)
9 Four-stringed guitar (7)
10 Pamphlet (7)
12 100 years (7)
14 Insubstantial (7)
16 Fan (7)
18 Decline gradually (4-3)
19 Research deeply (5)
20 Rough or harsh sound (4)
21 Provided a service (8)

Down

1 ___ Henderson: English singer (4)
2 Meet or find by chance (4,2)
3 Asymmetrical (9)
4 Dirty; grimy (6)
6 Standards to be aimed at (6)
7 Decade from 1920 - 1929 (8)
11 Without fixed limits (4-5)
12 Bowl-shaped strainer (8)
13 Raise in relief (6)
14 Layered dessert (6)
15 Of the eye (6)
17 Upper part of the body (4)

Across

1	Work out logically (6)
4	Sudden pain (6)
9	Puts inside something else (7)
10	Disease carried by mosquitoes (7)
11	Eject lava (5)
12	Desire to hurt someone (5)
14	Dark beer (5)
17	Trudged through water (5)
19	Notices (5)
21	Catches fire (7)
23	Yearbook (7)
24	Shelves (6)
25	Insurgents (6)

Down

1	True skin (6)
2	Business agreement (4)
3	Rushes forward in attack (7)
5	Use inefficiently (5)
6	Brought up; cared for (8)
7	Not real or genuine (6)
8	Fault-finding programs (11)
13	Knowledgeable (8)
15	Shine like a star (7)
16	Tel Aviv's country (6)
18	Pieces of crockery (6)
20	Scorch (5)
22	Story (4)

Across

1 Pays homage to (8)
5 Deciduous trees (4)
8 Lighter (5)
9 Best (7)
10 Compliment unduly (7)
12 Imperfections (7)
14 Hair-cleansing product (7)
16 Most profound (7)
18 Art of public speaking (7)
19 Colour lightly (5)
20 Skit (anag.) (4)
21 Teacher (8)

Down

1 Totally erase (4)
2 Respite (6)
3 Cyclone (9)
4 Trial impressions of pages (in printing) (6)
6 Extremes (6)
7 Broad-brimmed hat (8)
11 Relating to the south polar region (9)
12 Stalemate (8)
13 Meal (6)
14 Remained (6)
15 Celestial body (6)
17 Ale (4)

Across

4 Element with atomic number 6 (6)
7 Trickster (8)
8 Fix the result in advance (3)
9 Freezes over (4)
10 Ursine (anag.) (6)
11 Slow bowler in cricket (7)
12 Potatoes (informal) (5)
15 Private room on a ship (5)
17 Garden lattice (7)
20 By mouth (6)
21 Stirling ___ : racing driver (4)
22 Deep hole in the ground (3)
23 Single eyeglasses (8)
24 Sailing vessels (6)

Down

1 Drinking vessel (6)
2 Capital of Finland (8)
3 Used to one's advantage (7)
4 Smash into another vehicle (5)
5 Writing desk (6)
6 Periods of darkness (6)
13 Art of controversial discussion (8)
14 Speaking to God (7)
15 Rough (of water) (6)
16 Pertaining to life (6)
18 Important topics for debate (6)
19 Purple fruits (5)

SOLUTIONS

CROSSWORD

Puzzle 1
Puzzle 2
Puzzle 3
Puzzle 4
Puzzle 5
Puzzle 6
Puzzle 7
Puzzle 8
Puzzle 9
Puzzle 10
Puzzle 11
Puzzle 12

Puzzle 13

Puzzle 14

Puzzle 15

Puzzle 16

Puzzle 17

Puzzle 18

Puzzle 19

Puzzle 20

Puzzle 21

Puzzle 22

Puzzle 23

Puzzle 24

CROSSWORD

Puzzle 25

```
M A J O R I T Y . S K I M
O I H A M N I
R E T R O . S H Y N E S S
G T D T L U
A C E T O N E . H E L E N
N R D D O D
F O S T E R . C L O T H E
R N A O O R
E B B E D . F I G U R E S
E O R R I O T
M A R C O N I . C A N D O
A O N C A T O
N U N S . R A I L R O A D
```

Puzzle 26

```
C A N A P E . J U I C E S
U E R S N A Q
B A B Y I S H . L V U
I R M A N O D Y N E
S N A K E K C A
M S E K N A C K
. K F U S E S E
C R A W L P R O
A Y E P L A I T
D I P L O M A I T H
D U V R E Q U I T E
I L E E U O R
E X P E R T F E I N T S
```

Puzzle 27

```
. E S S E N T I A L L Y .
A I N R S A B
M I X D R O O P W E
B T E U H A L T S
A P H I D P A E T
S D . R E C L U S E S
S D C T S E
A I R B R U S H L
D E O U F R A I L
O U S T S B I B I
R S S P U R N B U N
S E E R A O G
C R E D I B I L I T Y
```

Puzzle 28

```
. P H O T O G R A P H S .
R Y E C E A
R E G M I N E R D I P
C H I M P E E G P
O E T V S T E V E
G U N M E T A L A
N E D M B S
I I N C I S I V E
T U C K S U N T M
I A T C D E U C E
O U T R I L L S M N
N C O E E E T
. S H O P L I F T I N G .
```

Puzzle 29

```
. F S A Z A M B I A
P R O T O Z O A I L
I O I I S U M
S N A P M A R K E T O N
G P U E R N
P E N A L T Y B R O A D
G H C E L
P A C E D W A L L A B Y
U L B S E L
S A L L E Y S V I O L
H A M I O A O
E M N I C K N A M E
S A Y I N G K T S
```

Puzzle 30

```
C O C K C R O W Z I N C
O O O C C C O
M E L O N C R A N I U M
P L T U P N M
A M A T E U R R O G U E
S G M S I N
S W E E P S S C E N E S
I O O I O U
O L D E R T R O U S E R
N O A T U T A
A L G E R I A S H R U B
T M Y W L I L
E D A M N A V Y B L U E
```

Puzzle 31

```
D E T E C T O R W A R D
U Y O U B M O
K A R A N R A I N B O W
E A S O L N
. I N S U F F I C I E N T
I N L O H I
L A Y T R O P E R I M
L A L M E E
F R O N T I S P I E C E
A R I S I B
T A B L O I D T O T A L
E I N U R A O
D O T S P O L Y G L O T
```

Puzzle 32

```
M G P A B O D E S
W I E L D I N G E E
N A G I B O X
K U D U M I L I E U T
T C E E N O
R E J O I N S W A K E N
M T F B
T E X A S H O A R D E R
O E S R U X
F R E V E R E P L U G
F A X E I T L
E E R E G U L A T E
E N S U E S N Y S
```

Puzzle 33

```
P O R T A L S T A V E S
O E M I A E A
S T A T I O N R E L
E S T T A N T R U M
R O O M Y E I O
S N R S C O R N
E M A R S H V
M E D I A O E P
A R G S E R V E
N A M I B I A T S D
I A L T R O T T E D
L T E E A E L
A T T E S T S T A P L E
```

Puzzle 34

```
P I C K I N G S L U S H
E L L O K L U
S H E L L T O A S T E R
O A U L R R
. A R O M A T H E R A P Y
S E I I I
E R R N O T E D G I N
N A A O R G
S H O O T I N G S T A R
I R I C B S
B E D R O O M O X B O W
L E N U P E I
E A R N A D D E N D U M
```

Puzzle 35

```
K N E E J E R K B A L D
I R A O L E
L U M E N B I V O U A C
N I E B M R
N F E X P A N S E
I C E C O L D L A P
N N E I
J F D C O N C E P T
E P I T A P H T N
C L A I S L
T A M P E R S F A U N A
E E E U E P
D A D S P R E L U D E S
```

Puzzle 36

```
O C T A V E A B L O O M
C R E U U V O
C O A R S E N D E D
U N T E N G O R G E
L O S E S Q E S
T E U T A U N T
C V E I N S P
M I T R E V C A
I S O S N O U T
F R A N T I C P M T
F C I A S I N I N E
E I G L K N N
D O D D E R B E G G E D
```

SOLUTIONS

CROSSWORD

Puzzle 37

```
A R T I S T I C   A C N E
R   R   U   G   C   H   S
G R A S P   L O O S E N S
O   C   E   O   U   A   A
  C H O R E O G R A P H Y
P   E   M   S   A     I
R E A G A N   E G R E S S
O   R   C   E   A   T
B R E A K T H R O U G H
A   L   E   E   U   E   A
B R I T T L E   S C R U M
L   O   S   S   L   L   I
Y E T I   D E W Y E Y E D
```

Puzzle 38

```
  S H O R T C H A N G E
C   A   O   O   U   I   G
I   P   A X I N G   F O R
R O L E S   L   U   T   A
C   E   T   E   R E S I N
U N S T E A D Y     D
M   S   D     P   C   C
S       P A R A B O L A
P A G E S   T   T   N N
E   L   P   O   E N J O Y
C O Y   R E N A L   U O
T   P   E   A   L   R N
  C H E E R L E A D E R
```

Puzzle 39

```
  A G O R A P H O B I C
S   O   U   I   U   N N U
Y A W   S L A N T   S N
M   N   T   Z   B A T E D
P A S T Y   Z   A   A E
A     C A L C U L U S   S
T   B   A   K   L   L
H A R M L E S S     R
E   E   L   K   P O L K A
T E A S E   A   U   O B
I   T   G E T U P   V A L
C   H   R   E   I   E E
R E M O R S E L E S S
```

Puzzle 40

```
E X P I R E   C A T N A P
X   A   E   S   N   I   L
P I R A N H A   A   C A
E   M   T   V A R I E T Y
L E E D S   I   C   E
S   S   N   H E W E R
  A   M U G G Y   R
R I N S E   G   E   C
E   A   R   L U C K Y
P E T U N I A   U   K G
E   R   I   C O N T A I N
N   I   N   E   C   G E
T H O U G H   T H R E A T
```

Puzzle 41

```
  H   M   L   P O S E U R
L E M O N A D E   M U
  I   U   S E   B U G
E G G S   H A V A N A   G
  H   S   I   E   R   E
A T T A I N S   L I K E D
    K   G   M   M
B Y W A Y   C A R P E T S
R   A   L   R   O   H
I   R O B O T S   L O O K
C A B   R   H   I   R
K   L   R O A S T I N G
S T E A D Y   L   E   Y
```

Puzzle 42

```
  C A T C H P H R A S E
S   P   A   A   E   U   A
M O P   D U N E S   M C
A   L   D   I   P L A N K
L A Y B Y   N   R   T N
L     D I C A P R I O   O
M   A   W   Y   A   W
I N S C R I B E     L
N   P   I   L   F O S S E
D E I G N   A   L   I D
E   R   K A Z O O   D O G
D   I   L   E   R   E E
  U N D E R S T A N D S
```

Puzzle 43

```
F A T H E R L Y   D A U B
E   H   N   A   D   O
A C R I D   D I S T O R T
T   O   U   I   R   U
  B   R   N O M I N A L
M U S T A N G   A S   I
N   N   N   N   S
E   S C   U N I F O R M
M A T T E R S   F   B
O O   H   E   O   F
N O W H E R E   S N I P E
I   E   R   T   S   U
C O D E   A S S O R T E D
```

Puzzle 44

```
  O V E R B E A R I N G
I   I   O   L E O   D
N A P   A R I A S   T I
A   E   D   C   C H I P S
D A R E S   I   U   C P
V   E T H E R E A L   E
I C   W   S   S   E
S T O M A C H S     A
A   R   R   O   W A S P S
B I N D S   H   A   I
L   I   H O R S E   F I N
E   C   I   O   A   E G
  T E M P E R A T U R E
```

Puzzle 45

```
M O N G O L I A   S C A R
O   A   L   N   C   H   I
T A S T Y   L O O P I N G
I   C   M   A   O   N   H
O V E R P A Y   R E A C T
N   N   I   S   D   E
P U T S C H   V I R A G O
I   G   T   N   V   U
C O B R A   S H A D O W S
T   A   M   E   T   C   N
U P S W E P T   I N A N E
R   I   S   S   O   D   S
E T N A   R E U N I O N S
```

Puzzle 46

```
  B   A   F   T A T T O O
G R A N U L A R   O   D
  O   T   O   I   A N D
A G U E   W H E E L S   S
U   A   E   S   T   O
G E S T U R E   B O S O N
    E   Y   C   V
H A I R S   W A K E F U L
A   R   S   U   R   N
N   O U T P U T   C H I P
K E N   I   I   O   Q
E   E   E N O R M O U S
R I D G E D   N   E   E
```

Puzzle 47

```
R E V E A L E D   F U N D
I   I   C   F   B   N   I
F R E S H   T R O U P E S
E   T   I   O   I   S
  I N T E L L I G E N C E
C   A   V   I   I   C
O H M   E A G L E   P E T
N   M   H   W   R   S
C O N V E N T I O N A L
E   O   N   O   I   C
D R I F T E D   G I R T H
E   S   S   A   I   I A
D A Y S   A D H E R E N T
```

Puzzle 48

```
C A S K   O F F S H O O T
U   C   C   R   U   R   I
S P A T U L A   B E D I M
H   N   R   U   S   I   E
I N T I M I D A T I N G
O   U   S   A   A   G
N E V A D A   A N G L E R
S   A   G   B   T   E
  U N V E R I F I A B L E
M   E   O   K   A   O   N
A R S O N   I N T E N S E
M   S   L   N   E   G   R
A N A L Y S I S   F O X Y
```

SOLUTIONS

Puzzle 49

	F	B	A		B	I	G	B	E	N	
F	L	O	U	N	D	E	R		E		E
	O		T		V		E		A	S	P
G	R	I	T		E	R	A	S	E	R	H
	A		E		R		K		E		E
C	L	A	R	E	T	S		S	H	R	E	W
		U		S		T		A			
S	O	P	P	Y			E	Y	E	B	R	O	W
I		O		P		P		I		B	
L		S	W	E	R	V	E		T	I	L	T
V	A	T			O		S		A		I
E		E		P	R	E	S	T	I	G	E
R	I	D	G	E	S		T		S		E

Puzzle 50

	F	I	R	E	B	R	I	G	A	D	E	
C		M		R	O		L		Y		A	
O	P		A	R	O	S	E		L	I	P	
M		N		E	I		M	A	N	O	R	
M	A	I	L	S		K		A		A		P
P		N		E		I		M	A	N	O	R
R	E	G	A	R	D	E	D		O		P	
E			E	S			C	A	P			
S			B	E	H	O	L	D	E	R		
S	A	V	E	D		M		N	U	I		
	I		I	E		B		V	O	L	G	A
O	W	L		P	U	L	S	E		A		T
	N		L	O		E		N		T		E
	B	A	D	T	E	M	P	E	R	E	D	

Puzzle 51

L	E	S	S		A	R	A	C	H	N	I	D
U		O		B	E		O		O			A
C	O	N	C	E	I	T		N	E	X	U	S
I			I		L	O		S		I		H
D	E	C	E	L	E	R	A	T	I	O	N	
I			I			T		R		U		A
T	W	A	N	G	S		O	U	T	S	E	T
Y		N	E		O		C					T
	U	N	P	R	O	F	I	T	A	B	L	E
A		U		E		F		I		I		N
C	O	L	O	N		I	G	N	O	R	E	D
E		A		C		C		G		C		E
S	C	R	E	E	N	E	D		S	H	O	E

Puzzle 52

D	U	O	S		C	H	A	I	N	S	A	W
I		W		E		N		T		A		A
A	V	I	G	N	O	N		D	R	A	Y	S
P		N		T		I		R		P		P
A	G	G	R	E	S	S	I	V	E	L	Y	
S			R		T		I		I		O	
O	R	C		F	R	O	N	D		T	I	P
N		A		E		I		U				E
	A	P	P	R	E	C	I	A	T	I	O	N
E		T		E				L	D	I		
P	L	A	I	N		H	A	L	C	Y	O	N
I		I		C		O		Y		L		G
C	O	N	T	E	M	P	T		A	L	E	S

Puzzle 53

T	R	E	M	B	L	E	D		G	A	S	H
A		X		U		N		H	N	O		O
P	I	P	I	T		T	R	O	D	D	E	N
E		R		T		I		P	E		E	
	R	E	L	E	N	T	L	E	S	S	L	Y
P		S		R		Y		L			B	
A	S	S	E	S	S		R	E	F	U	S	E
R			C		T		S		N		E	
A	S	T	R	O	P	H	Y	S	I	C	S	
K		I		T		R		N	I	D		
E	A	R	A	C	H	E		E	N	V	O	Y
E		E		H		S		S		I		E
T	A	S	K		W	H	I	S	T	L	E	S

Puzzle 54

P	E	B	B	L	E		A	V	I	A	T	E
A		U		I		U		I		R		N
R	U	N	D	O	W	N		N		I		T
A		G		N		O	U	T	R	A	G	E
D	R	A	G	S		B		A				R
E		L			S		G	A	S	E	S	
	O		P	I	E	C	E		W			
F	E	W	E	R		R			I		C	
I			O	V		G	E	N	I	E		
G	R	A	N	D	M	A		O		D		A
H		I		U		N	O	D	U	L	E	S
T		M		C		T		L		E		E
S	A	S	H	E	S		H	Y	B	R	I	D

Puzzle 55

D	E	B	A	R	K		S		C		R	
E		U			I	M	P	R	O	V	E	D
J	O	B		C		U		L		A		
E		B	U	N	K	E	R		E	T	C	H
C		L		S		R		S		T		
T	E	E	T	H		R	E	A	L	I	S	M
		E		C		D		A				
F	L	U	M	M	O	X		S	W	O	O	P
	O		P		R		A		R			U
C	I	A	O		S	O	N	A	T	A		P
	T		R	E	G			C	A	P		
R	E	P	A	R	T	E	E		L		E	
	R		L		S		R	U	D	E	S	T

Puzzle 56

S	U	S	P	E	N	S	E		A	B	U	T
O		T		L		U	Q		L			A
D	O	U	S	E		B	O	U	Q	U	E	T
A		N		C		W		I	R		T	
	U	N	A	T	T	A	I	N	A	B	L	E
O		E		R		Y		T		R		R
B	O	D	K	I	N		R	E	S	C	U	E
E			F		S		S	A		D		
D	O	I	T	Y	O	U	R	S	E	L	F	
I		M		I	P		E	L		H		
E	X	P	E	N	S	E		N	O	O	S	E
N		L		G		R		C	U	R		
T	O	Y	S		O	B	S	E	S	S	E	D

Puzzle 57

D	A	H	L	I	A		S	P	R	A	W	L
E		U		N		T		A		P		O
B		M	D		R	E	C	I	P	E	S	
A	M	P	H	O	R	A		K		E		E
R			O		N		S	O	N	A	R	
S	M	E	A	R	S		S			D		S
		X		S	L	A	B	S		I		
S		P			C			T	A	X	E	D
C	E	L	L	S		T		A				U
O		O		T		I	N	T	E	N	D	S
T	O	R	N	A	D	O		U		U		T
C		E		G		N		R		L		E
H	A	S	T	E	N		T	E	L	L	E	R

Puzzle 58

J	E	W	E	L	S		T		L		A	
U		O			C	A	R	R	I	A	G	E
N	I	B		A		A		B		E		
I		B	A	L	L	A	D		R	A	N	T
O		L		D		E		E		T		
R	E	E	L	S		B	R	I	T	I	S	H
		I		I		S		T				
P	E	N	N	A	N	T		R	I	S	E	S
	C		E		T		Y		U		A	
R	H	E	A		E	G	O	I	S	M		W
	O		G		R		U			M	A	Y
D	E	L	E	T	I	O	N		E		E	
	D		S		M		G	A	N	D	E	R

Puzzle 59

	A		C		L		B	L	O	U	S	E
A	B	L	A	T	I	V	E		P		D	
	S		R		G		L		H	U	G	
L	U	D	O		H	A	I	R	D	O		I
	R		T		T		E		L		L	
A	D	H	E	R	E	S		R	U	D	D	Y
		N		R		J	N					
M	O	V	E	D		C	O	B	W	E	B	S
E		I		D		G		I		O		
A		E	N	D	I	N	G		E	X	A	M
N	O	W		V			E	L		S		
L		E		A	C	R	I	D	I	T	Y	
Y	O	D	E	L	S		S		Y		S	

Puzzle 60

	D	E	C	E	I	T	F	U	L	L	Y	
D		R		L		R		N		A		W
E	T	A		E	P	O	C	H		T		O
T		S	G		I			A	F	T	E	R
E	V	E	R	Y		K		P		I		D
R			G	A	Z	P	A	C	H	O		
I		C	L		Y			E				M
O	C	A	R	I	N	A	S					E
R		R	T		T		M	E	T	R	O	U
A	R	I	S	E		O	A		I			U
T		B		R	O	M	A	N		L	O	T
E		O	A		I		G		T			H
	P	U	B	L	I	C	H	O	U	S	E	

Puzzle 61

```
. T R U S T W O R T H Y .
P I T O E A I .
O V . A N O D E . B I N .
S T A R T . D . K . I . G
S . L U E . S A T Y R . R
I R R I T A N T . . . . E
B . Y E . . E . S M D . .
. . . P A S T R A M I . .
L A W N S . P . A . J . E
I . H . E . P . B R O W N
T O O . W H E E L . R . T
Y . O E N . E . . . C . S
. A P H R O D I S I A C .
```

Puzzle 62

```
G A L O S H . S C O L D S
L . A . O R . L . O . T .
O R P . E C U A D O R . E
B E A C H E S . M . E . E
A . . I . I . P O S T S .
L O C H S . G . . T . S .
. . L . M O N T E . A . .
. P . I . A . L A R C H .
H U M I D . T . E . I . .
R . A . I N V I T E S . .
A R T D E C O . A . A . S
S . I . T . N . . T . G E
E X C E S S . B E A S T S
```

Puzzle 63

```
S O M E . C L E A N C U T
C . E R A M . H . . I . .
H O T H E A D . O L I V E
E . A . A . R . C . R . .
D I L A P I D A T I O N .
U . . P . R . I . R . E .
L E G . E X A M S . Y A P
E . A . A . M . A . I . .
. O V E R C A U T I O U S
S . O . A . . I . F . O .
P U T O N . B O O S T E D
U . T . C . E . N . E . E
D E E P E N E D . G N U S
```

Puzzle 64

```
P E R U S E . S K A T E D
L . O A . C I R Y . . . Y
O O T . O U T S I Z E . .
V A T I C A N . E . M . I
E . H . C . S P A I N . N
R O U S E . A . . R . G .
. N . L A T E R . A . . .
O . N N E . . H A N G S .
C L E R K . N O N . . . .
T . E . N . A M M O N I A
E N D M O S T . B . E . Z
T . E W E . U . . A . Z .
S I D I N G . O S P R E Y
```

Puzzle 65

```
. S C R E W D R I V E R .
A . R . L O N S N . . . N
T H Y . G R U F F . T . E
R . P A . B . . A D O P T
O T T E R . L . N . N . H
C . . . . B E S T R I D E
I D O . . . S . . A . . R
O V E R U S E S . . . . L
U . F . T R . . . V I O L A
S H A W L . R I A N . . .
L . C . A M A S S . S A D
Y . T S T . . T I I S . .
. P O R T R A I T I S T .
```

Puzzle 66

```
U R D U . C R O S S B O W
N . A . O . A . H . O . H
D E L I V E R . A B A S E
I . L . E . I . R . R . E
S H Y . R . T . P E D A L
C . I . E G Y P T . E . E
I . P . M . . O . D . . R
P . R . P R A W N . . . D
L E E C H . U . G . P I E
I . C . A . B . U . O . A
N E E D S . U N E Q U A L
E . D . I . R . D . C . E
D R E S S I N G . C H A R
```

Puzzle 67

```
. M . D . H . R O B B E R
M A R I N A D E . . E . U
. D . S R . I . . H U B .
J E E P . M A N G L E . I
. U . E I . S . . S . . E
O P E N I N G . S I T E S
. . . S . G . H . N . . .
R A G E D . L O A D I N G
I . I . B . N . O . I . .
B . V O Y A G E . L A M E
B Y E . N . S . E . B . .
E . R . A C T I N I U M .
D I S P E L . Y . T . S .
```

Puzzle 68

```
W R A N G L E S . I D E A
I . B . O . Y . C R N . N
L A S S O . E R O S I O N
T . C . D . M . E . O . Y
. L O S T P R O P E R T Y
S . N . E U L . . I . . I
P O D . M A M B A . T E N
A . . P . B . C . O . . G
R I O D E J A N E I R O .
K . G R . . N . S . D . .
L A R G E S T . T R I P E
E . E . D A L . O . F . .
R A S H . B U O Y A N C Y
```

Puzzle 69

```
. S U B S T A N T I A L .
C . N . T . R . A . I . O
A . T . A L T A R . M A P
R O W D Y . F . N . E . .
D . I . U . . U . S U D A N
I N S A N E L Y . . . . A
O . T . G . . D . U N . N
G . . . R E N O W N E D .
R U C K S . N . U . K . S
A . H . W . J . B E N C H
P R O . A T O L L . O . U
H . R . R . I . E . W . T
. T E R M I N A T I N G .
```

Puzzle 70

```
D I S M A L . S . S . G .
E . T . . O V E R T U R E
F I R . V . E . R . O . .
T . A E L D E R S . I C O N
L . . R . A . D . V . . .
Y U M M Y . S W E E T E R
. I . L S . N . . . . . .
G L A N C E D . S T A L E
. O . I N . G . R . N . .
A C T S . G A R L I C . A
. A . T T . A . . H E M .
S T A R S H I P . E . E .
. E . Y Y . H A N S E L .
```

Puzzle 71

```
G A R R I S O N . M A D E
R . E . L . A . E O S . .
E A S E L . F O X T R O T
Y . O . E . H . T . I . I
. B U R G L A R A L A R M
C . N . I D U . U . . . A
H I D . T H I N S . S E T
A . . I . O . T U E . . E
I N A D M I S S I B L E .
R . N . A . V . T . W . .
M I N U T I A . E L A T E
A . E . E I L . N . A . .
N E X T . P L A Y B A C K
```

Puzzle 72

```
T E R T I A R Y . Z E B U
R . E . N . A . X . N . N
A I D E D . F L A R E U P
N . O . E . T . M . R . R
S K I M P . E . E . T E E
G . N . E R R E D . . . C
R . G . N . R . D E . . D
E . . . D I T T O . P . .
S O N . E . U . P R O B E
S . A . N . N . P R N . .
I N D U C E D . I N A P T
O . I . E . R . N . M . E
N I R O . V A N G U A R D
```

CROSSWORD

Puzzle 73

```
T E T H E R E D   K I W I
E U L   M E N   N
L I T R E   B A N Q U E T
E O   C O T   R R
M E R I T E D   H Y E N A
A E R   Y   U N
R A D I O S   O S C A R S
K   L   B I G   I
E S S A Y   R E A R I N G
T C S O   S T E
I T A L I A N   T R A I N
N L S   C I T C
G A P E   C O N C R E T E
```

Puzzle 74

```
C O O K   P A N D E M I C
O C O D   I A U
N O T E P A D   S T R U T
C E P   U A T T
A C T O R   C A D D I S H
T E E V A E
E N L I S T   M A G N U M
N O S B N U
A N N U I T Y   T O R U S
T G V G A U T
I M B U E   O R G A N Z A
O O L N E T R
N E W L Y W E D   U S E D
```

Puzzle 75

```
J E R O B O A M   I S L A
O I O D C A T
H A N O I   R E A D M I T
N G L I N B I
  D I S I N F E C T A N T
F N N T E U
E N G A G E   E L A T E D
T P A L S E
C I R R O S T R A T U S
H O I H T N S
I N C E N S E   I M A G O
N K T N O M N
G U Y S   P A I N T I N G
```

Puzzle 76

```
G E R B I L   I M P E L S
I A N U E M P
V M D   N O T A B L E
E A S T E N D   E O A
U P E   S O L A R
P A I N T R D S
  N   H O S T S E
S T C   M E N D S
T E E N S O A E
U R E   R E C I T E D
C O N C A V E K O U
C E L S E F C
O D D E S T   A D J U R E
```

Puzzle 77

```
  A D V E N T U R O U S
I E X A O N O
M A B   P O I S E   S U
P A E L   B O O S T U
R U R A L O U U S
O   P R E C I N C T
V O P K D A
E M B A R K E D N
M L E X   F A C E D
E P I C S H I O I
N Q   S T A R R   W O N
T U E L E E G
  N E W S R E A D E R S
```

Puzzle 78

```
I N C E   S P R I N K L E
N L O A M I X
T H I E V E S   P A S T A
E N E S E S G
N I G E R   E A R N I N G
T I S F N E
I O D I N E   M E R G E R
O E D D C A
N E P T U N E   T E M P T
A R L E I I E
L Y I N G   P R O D D E D
L V E E N G L
Y I E L D I N G   V E R Y
```

Puzzle 79

```
  N O U R I S H M E N T
S U E E A U T
I T   S T A N D   T R Y
N I C H E S A T P
G O R O   M A Y B E
U N M O V I N G W
L E E S M R
A   V I R T U O S I
R U F F S M U R T
I I A P   D R O V E
T A X   B L A D E C R
Y E R C N C S
  O S T E N T A T I O N
```

Puzzle 80

```
D R A W B A C K   A D Z E
A R R A C E V
T O R S O   T H I M B L E
E A T V U R
  E N C H A N T I N G L Y
F G E A L D
A L E   R A I L S   U M A
N I V E N Y
D I S I N T E G R A T E
A C L V R S
N I R V A N A   A C U T E
G A W S N T E
O H M S   T H A T C H E R
```

Puzzle 81

```
C U P S   P A S S P O R T
O A F S H N R
N O R F O L K   O P E R A
T K R I R R N
R E A L M   N A T I O N S
I A G C U P
B A R E L Y   F I E S T A
U E D A R R
T A S T E R S   C H U T E
I I H T U N
O D D L Y   H A I R C U T
N U D M T L L
S K E L E T A L   R E L Y
```

Puzzle 82

```
H I D E A W A Y   A G E D
E O E S C R O
L O S E R   S A R C A S M
P S O U E F I
  K I N D E R G A R T E N
T E Y E T I
H I R I N G   K I M O N O
R A W V C N
I N C O M P E T E N C Y
L U I A N L N
L Y R I C A L   E X U D E
E L S T S D T
R A Y S   W H I S K E R S
```

Puzzle 83

```
  F O R E F A T H E R S
D F X R A O A
O F   H E R T Z   B U D
M A L T A I E I I
E I U V   L I N E N
S I N I S T E R F
T E T T S I
I   S T A R S I G N
C E D E D R U R I
A E O A   S H O U T
T O P   W A I S T C U
E T E N E C M
  C H O L E S T E R O L
```

Puzzle 84

```
I N C L U D E S   T A X I
V H N A P S N
A W A R D   U N R O L L S
N R E E A I
  I M P R O V E M E N T S
A E S E E T
C A R   T I R E D   A Y E
A A S I C D
D I S A F F E C T I O N
E I F A L S
M A G N E T S   T R Y S T
I H D A E T E
C U T S   A C I D T E S T
```

Puzzle 85

```
E N T I C E   G L I D E R
N O A I E O A
C A M E R O N   O D R
A O E   E X P L O R E
G I R L S   F A   F
E R O   F   R U N N Y
  O   C R E E D   E
J E W E L   C   C U P
E A T   P E T E R
J U J I T S U   R R A
U U T   A N O M A L Y
N M E L V L L E
E X P I R Y   L E S S E R
```

Puzzle 86

```
B R A N C H E S   S A G A
E L A X H S C
A D U L T   P S Y C H I C
S M E O P E I
T E N U R E S   O W N E D
O U P E T E
F O S S I L   S H O O I N
B L A E P T
U N T I L   K E T C H U P
R R A I I E R
D I A G R A M   C E L L O
E Y S B A I N
N O S Y   S O U L M A T E
```

Puzzle 87

```
I N N S   N A R R A T E S
N I I S U Y P
C O G E N C Y   N A C H O
O H T L O O N
M E T E R   U P F R O N T
P A M T N A
E T H A N E   C H O S E N
T E S A E E
E M P T I E S   M A C H O
N A G S I U
T I T L E   I S L A N D S
L I N G L C L
Y A C H T I N G   W H E Y
```

Puzzle 88

```
  A B R A C A D A B R A
I I P V C U G
R O B   A F O O T   B O
R L R W U M B E R O
E J E C T A A I D
V   A L F R E S C O
O B D Y H N
C A U T I O U S   B
A F S R   M O T O R
B E F I T S A A O
L A   U N I T Y   M E W
E L R N O E N
  D O U B L E C R O S S
```

Puzzle 89

```
A C C O L A D E   C R A M
L H I E A I
U S I N G   T R A U M A S
M L H E B T
  L T   C E D I L L A
B A Y O N E T I E K
R I S E
A C N   E X P O S E S
C H A N G E S A E
E N C R C M
L U C K I E R   A M U S E
E E O G R S
T A L K   T W E E T E R S
```

Puzzle 90

```
I N P U T S   A C C O R D
N O O R O V O
M I L E A G E L E Z
A O D   S I L E N C E
T I N T S T I N
E E A   D A M P S
C   C A U S E A T
H I K E R R T S
O O A   C R E P T
P O P C O R N A R E
I U K   T E R R I N E
N P E S E A P
G U A R D S   A D D L E S
```

Puzzle 91

```
M O N A R C H Y   A P E S
U E E A B I E
S I T U P   B U R G L A R
K W R I E E E
  C O V E N T G A R D E N
F R S S S A
A N K L E T   S T E W E D
N N A S E E
L E G I T I M A T E L Y
I U I O R F O
G R E E N E R   O P A L S
H S G A K R L
  T E S S   A L T E R E G O
```

Puzzle 92

```
E M B E R S   I   A U
S E I N S O L E N T
C O W L O L W
H   A F L O A T   I B I S
E R S O A S
W E E D Y   S P E N C E R
E B E C
P L O V E R S   L E F T S
O E I P U H
F U E L   S Q U I R M O
D O T M B O W
F L I P F L O P L E
Y S E   S H I E L D
```

Puzzle 93

```
E S P E C I A L   H E R B
A Y O V M D A
S T R U M   E M O T I O N
T A P R U C K
I M P E R S O N A T O R
O I T E T O
B U D G I E   P A R C E L
S S T D I O L
C O N D I T I O N I N G
U E O V S T H
R E V E N U E   I R O N Y
E I S R D R M
D I S H   A T H E R T O N
```

Puzzle 94

```
R E F U G E   A F L A M E
I L R R O M A
G R A N U L E   L E G
H M B   C O L O N E L
T R E K S O O E
S N C L   W A D E S
  C   G I L D S I
P R O W L E S S
E A C   B A C O N
S O L I C I T I I E
T E I   E L L I P S E
L N E D G L R
E X T O R T   R E F E R S
```

Puzzle 95

```
K N O C K I N G   O P U S
I P I O E L H
S T E E L   B E C A U S E
S N L O H M R
  E A V E S D R O P P E R
P I R Y L I
A R R O W S   B O G G L E
C H R C E S
I M M E A S U R A B L E
F O L S T A U
I M P R E S S   I N T E R
E E S I O I N
R O S Y   W A R N I N G S
```

Puzzle 96

```
D E A N   A N G E L I C A
O G B E X D P
W E A P O N S   C H I R P
N I I T H O O
I O N S L   A S T E R
N   T I E I N I T
G S E G C I O
S A   R O U G E O
T E M P O N A   F E N
R O U E B I M
E L V E S   V O L U B L E
E A L E E R N
T A R R Y I N G   L E F T
```

CROSSWORD

Puzzle 97

```
P A Y S . A C A D E M I A
L . A . M . L . R E X . X
U P H E A V E . A N N U L
M . O . N . V . M . A . E
P R O T U B E R A N C E .
I . . F . . R . T . E . M
N E U R A L . F I A S C O
G . N . C . . C . . . . O
. P I T T E R P A T T E R
S . F . U . M . L . U . L
P R I O R . A T L A N T A
A . E . E D . Y . E . N .
R E S I D U A L . G R I D
```

Puzzle 98

```
C A P E R S . H A M M E R
R . H . A . H . D . I . E
A P E L I K E . J . L . A
B . A . N . L A U N D E R
B U S H Y . I . D . . . E
Y . A N . C . G R I N D .
. . N . F R O Z E . M . .
D E T E R . P . . P . P O
O . A . T . J O U S T . T
W R A N G L E . U . T . T
S . U . I . R E D W I N E
E . K . L . S . G . N . R
R A S P E D . W E D G E S
```

Puzzle 99

```
U T T E R S . A . T . S .
P . A . . I M P E R I A L
H O B . N . P . I . D . D
I . L U R K E R . B E D S
L . E . S . O . U . L . .
L O T U S . A V E N U E S
. . N . C . E . A . . . .
H A N D S O N . B L I M P
. D . E . N . B . M . R .
P O U R . D O L L O P . A
R . L . U . I . I . I V Y
M E R I D I A N . S . E .
. D . E . T . D A S H E D
```

Puzzle 100

```
. C O U N T R Y S I D E .
C R . A . E . T . O . C .
R D . T E N S E . Z O O .
E V E N T . P . E . N . .
S . R . W . S E D A N . O
T H E O R I S T . . . . O
F . D . S . . B . S I . .
A . . S C O R C H E S . S
L U R I D . H . E . A . S
L . A . I . I . A G R E E
E L M . S A L A D . P . U
N . P . C . L . T . E . R
. A S T O N I S H I N G .
```

Puzzle 101

```
F O R S W E A R . L A N D
O . A . E . G . C . L . A
R I V A L . E C O N O M Y
M . I . T . N . F . B . .
. I N V E S T I G A T O R
C . . E . R . R . . E . .
H I S . W E A V E . A G A
I . . E . C . G . N . K .
C O R N I S H P A S T Y .
K . A . G . T . H . E . .
P I T C H E R . I D I O M
E . T . E . O . L . . . I
A I D E . G A U N T L E T
```

Puzzle 102

```
S N O W D R O P . C L A P
O . B . I . R . I . E . O
B A L S A . I N R O A D S
S . O . G . E . R . S . I
. I N F R I N G E M E N T
F . G . A . T . S . . . I
A S S U M E . A I R M A N
R . . M . O . S . O . G .
R E S T A U R A T E U R .
I . T . T . I . I . S . E
E V O K I N G . B E S O M
R . R . C . I . L . E . U
S T Y E . I N V E R S E S
```

Puzzle 103

```
P H A R M A C Y . C L A M
E . R . I . O . P E E . E
N A M E S . U N A R M E D
P . B . A . N . T . M . I
Y E A R D O T . H E A R T
P . N . V . S O . . . . E
I N D E E D . P L A C E R
N . . N . U . O . H . . R
C A D E T . N I G E R I A
H . E . U . I . I . O . N
I N V E R T S . C A N O E
N . I . E . O . A . I . A
G O L D . A N G L I C A N
```

Puzzle 104

```
A M B R O S I A . O D E S
R . A . F . N . I . O . E
C L I F F . F U N N I E R
H . L . T . O . H . N . G
. M O T H E R T O N G U E
C . E . M . S . . A . . .
R E T I R E . S P L E E N
E . . E . U . I . G . . T
A N T I C I P A T I O N .
T . U . O . R . A . T . S
I N F E R N O . B U I L T
V . T . D . O . L . S . I
E A S E . S T R E A M E R
```

Puzzle 105

```
. A L T E R C A T I O N .
I . I . V . O . A . P . D
N U B . E T H O S . T . I
T . R . R . E . S K I T S
E X A L T . R . . E . O T
R . R . . R E C L I N E R
R . S . T . . S . S . E S
U N W O R T H Y . . . . S
P . E . U . O . M A S K S
T H E R M . M . I . O . I
E . T . P L I E D . B A N
D . E . E . N . S . E . G
. I N S T I G A T O R S .
```

Puzzle 106

```
U G L Y . S P A C I O U S
N . U . M . A . I . N . E
P A C K A G E . R E G A L
A . C . N . L . R . O . F
S E A . U . L . O P I N E
T . . F R A N C . N . V .
E . C . A . . U . I . I .
U L . C H A S M . U . D .
R O O S T . M . U . D U E
I . I . S U E . L . W . N
S H E E R . L O U D E S T
E . T . E . I . S . L . L
D E S E R T E R . P L A Y
```

Puzzle 107

```
T H E S P I A N . L I D O
O . E . O . V . T . N . N
W O R S T . O U T C A S T
S . I . P . W . L . H . H
. . E . O . E X A M I N E
A G R O U N D . M . C . D
N . . R . S . S . O . . O
T . T R . H O T S P O T .
E V A S I V E . E . E . .
R . B . R . R . R A . F .
O B L I G E D . D I N G O
O . E . E . E . A . U . U
M I S S . O D O M E T E R
```

Puzzle 108

```
D O M E . T W E A K I N G
I . O . T . O . L . G . O
S E C R E T E . L I N E D
P . H . M . . I . E . S .
E X A S P E R A T I O N .
R . . E . A . E . U . A .
S O W . R O V E R . S O P
E . H . A . E . A . . . O
. D I S T I N C T N E S S
S . S . U . . I . D . T .
P I P E R . G E O R G I A
A . E . E . N . A . T . .
T I R E S O M E . E R N E
```

Puzzle 109

```
L A S E R S   S L U M P S
A   O   E   C   O   A   P
P   L   P   R E V E L R Y
T R O L L E Y   E   A   I
O   E   A   P   D O Y E N
  P E T T Y   T     S   G
  O   S K I R L   I
S   B     C   A V A I L
L O O T S   A   R       A
O   G   H   L O C A T E D
P I G T A I L   E   A   D
E   A   M   Y   N   R   E
S I N N E R   O Y S T E R
```

Puzzle 110

```
I N T A C T   P   E   T
N   H   H A L L M A R K
F E W   I   A   B   I
I   A S T R A Y   A L P S
R   R   R   D   E   L
M O T H S   T R O T T E R
  E   G   S   L
A P P A R E L   G E R M S
  R   D   Y   G   A   L
T I N A   S M I T E S   A
  S   C   E   D   C U T
B O T H E R E D   A   E
  N   E   S   Y E L L E D
```

Puzzle 111

```
M O U T H F U L   L O C O
A   N   Y   N   S   D   V
L E T U P   R O U T I N E
I   A   O   O   B   U   R
C O M I C   L   C   M R S
I   E   H E L L O   A
O   D O     N   B   T
U   N O D E S   E   E
S U E   A     C R A T E
N   X   R   I   I   R   M
E L U S I O N   O C H R E
S   L   A   T   U   U   N
S I T E   E Y E S I G H T
```

Puzzle 112

```
O B S E S S   O C T A N T
D   C   P   C   R   K   E
D I R T I E R   I   A   A
I   I   C   E X T E N D S
T A B B Y   D   I     E
Y   B   E   C U B E D
  L   S I N G S   A
S W E A T   T     S   P
T   U   I   S W I R L
A L G E B R A   A   L   I
N   R   B   L O D G I N G
Z U L     S   L   C   H
A M B L E D   T Y R A N T
```

Puzzle 113

```
H I N D M O S T   J A W S
O   E   A   U   V   U
S T I C K   N A P K I N S
E   G   E   K   A   P
  H   S   E N F O R C E
C I S T E R N   O   Y   N
A   I   N   R   N   D
M   B S   K E E P E R S
P R O T E G E   S   N
A   U   R   I   C   J
I N G R A I N   G L O B E
G   H   E   H   D   T
N O T E   F L A T T E N S
```

Puzzle 114

```
  A B R   D O U B T S
A L K A L I N E   A   T
L   C   C   R     B A Y
B U C K   H O B N O B   L
R   F   E   Y     L   E
R E A L I S T   S T E E D
  I   T   T     I
R A S P Y   T W I N N E D
A   L   V   I   N   F
M   O P T I C S   I N F O
O W   C   T   T     E
E   E   A D E Q U A C Y
D O D G E R   D   S   T
```

Puzzle 115

```
A L M S   P E R M E A T E
F   E   C   A   E   N   A
F E R V O U R   R A D A R
L   I   U   W   R   A   L
I N T E N S I F Y I N G
C   T   G   G   T   A
T E S T E D   N O V E L S
S   T   R   A   R     S
  D I S C O N S O L A T E
O   G   L   I   U   S   S
G A M M A   M I N U T E S
L   A   I   A   D   I   E
E N S E M B L E   I R I S
```

Puzzle 116

```
D A I S   A T L A N T I S
E   O   P   R   U   R   E
S A N G R I A   T R A W L
T   I   E   G   H   V   F
R E C A P   I K E B A N A
U   O   O   C   N   I   W
C A S I N G   S T E L L A
T   P   D   A   I   R
I C E B E R G   C H O S E
V   C   R   R   A   V   N
E V I T A   E X T R E M E
L   A   N   E   N   S
Y U L E T I D E   U S E S
```

Puzzle 117

```
A P A T H Y   S U R G E S
L   M   E   L   R   I   A
S U B S I D E   G   S   N
A   I   R   G R E E T E D
C I T E S   E   N     A
E   I   R   C A N A L
  O   B A D L Y   O
D I N E R   E     F   T
E   E   M   P O R C H
M A S C A R A   U   I   E
U   H   K   I M P A L E S
R   O   E   N   A   L   I
E X P O R T   M E S S E S
```

Puzzle 118

```
A L W A Y S   T   H   M
T   A   A I R L I N E S
H A Y   N   I   T   R
E   L A N D E D   H O L E
N   A   Y   E   E   I
S T Y L E   S N A R I N G
  I   B   T   T
T R A C T O R   F O R U M
  E   E   X   F   I   U
C L A N   W A L L O P   M
  O   S   O   U   P U B
C A M E R O O N   L   L
  D   S   D   G R I E V E
```

Puzzle 119

```
S O L E C I S M   F I R M
A   A   O   A   U   S   E
R U N I N   V A N I L L A
K   K   S   I   D   E   N
  D I S C O N T E N T E D
S   E   R   G   T   E
T O R P I D   K E E P E R
A   P   S   C   R   S
C O N S T I T U T I O N
C   A   I   A   V   S
A C T I O N S   B L I N K
T   T   N   I   L   S   I
O N Y X   A S T E R O I D
```

Puzzle 120

```
C O M E D I A N   R U L E
O   A   I   U   R   N   X
P U T T S   K N E E C A P
Y   I   I   C   U   E
  U N I N T E R E S T E D
P   E   F   A   P     I
R O E   E I G H T   M A T
O   E   C   E   I   E
C O U N T E R P O I N T
E   N   I   N   T   T
P O T I O N S   I C I L Y
T   I   U   S   O   P
S P E D   I N S T A N C E
```

CROSSWORD

Puzzle 121

Puzzle 122

Puzzle 123

Puzzle 124

Puzzle 125

Puzzle 126

Puzzle 127

Puzzle 128

Puzzle 129

Puzzle 130

Puzzle 131

Puzzle 132

Puzzle 133

```
O R G A N I S M ▢ E M M A
R ▢ R ▢ I ▢ A ▢ C A P ▢
C L A N G ▢ G R O W N U P
A ▢ N ▢ H ▢ N ▢ I ▢ E ▢
▢ M A T T E R O F F A C T
D ▢ R ▢ C ▢ O ▢ O ▢ ▢ ▢
I C Y ▢ L U N A R ▢ H A T
S ▢ ▢ O ▢ D ▢ M ▢ E ▢ E
Q U E S T I O N A B L E ▢
U ▢ A ▢ H ▢ ▢ T ▢ P ▢ T
I N S T E A D ▢ I N F E R
E ▢ E ▢ S ▢ E ▢ O ▢ U ▢ O
T E S T ▢ ▢ D W I N D L E D
```

Puzzle 134

```
▢ A B S T R A C T I O N ▢
A ▢ U ▢ A ▢ F ▢ U ▢ R ▢ B
B A R ▢ R I F T S ▢ B ▢ U
B ▢ N ▢ R ▢ E ▢ S W I F T
R E T R Y ▢ C ▢ O ▢ T ▢ T
E ▢ ▢ T ▢ S T O C K A D E
V ▢ T ▢ C ▢ K ▢ L ▢ ▢ R
I S O L A T E S ▢ ▢ ▢ F
A ▢ O ▢ T ▢ N ▢ M O D E L
T I L D E ▢ T ▢ E ▢ I ▢ I
E ▢ B ▢ R A R E R ▢ V I E
D ▢ O ▢ E ▢ A ▢ Y ▢ O ▢ S
▢ E X T R A P O L A T E ▢
```

Puzzle 135

```
M U S I C I A N ▢ A B L E
A ▢ T ▢ L ▢ W ▢ F ▢ U ▢ X
C H I N O ▢ E N L A R G E
H ▢ F ▢ S ▢ Y ▢ M ▢ G ▢ ▢
▢ A F F E C T I O N A T E
A ▢ E ▢ M ▢ I ▢ N ▢ ▢ S
N U N ▢ O U G H T ▢ P H I S
A ▢ U ▢ ▢ H ▢ H ▢ E ▢ S
C O N S T I T U E N C Y ▢
O ▢ O ▢ H ▢ W ▢ K ▢ N
N E W Y E A R ▢ A M I D E
D ▢ I ▢ D ▢ L ▢ S ▢ R
A N N E ▢ ▢ B A L L Y H O O
```

Puzzle 136

```
S W A G ▢ M I S S O U R I
I ▢ E ▢ S ▢ M ▢ U ▢ N ▢ N
D E S K T O P ▢ B E R E T
E ▢ O ▢ R ▢ A ▢ S ▢ A ▢ E
S E P I A ▢ R E C O V E R
P ▢ ▢ T ▢ T ▢ R ▢ E ▢ E
L E P T O N ▢ F I E L D S
I ▢ E ▢ S ▢ T ▢ P ▢ ▢ T
T R A I P S E ▢ T E M P I
T ▢ S ▢ H ▢ M ▢ I ▢ O ▢ N
I M A G E ▢ P R O L O N G
N ▢ N ▢ R ▢ L ▢ N ▢ N ▢ L
G A T H E R E D ▢ E S P Y
```

Puzzle 137

```
G I F T E D ▢ S E S ▢ S
O ▢ L ▢ I M P O S I N G
T O Y ▢ O ▢ I ▢ O ▢ A
H E R O D E D ▢ T O R O
A ▢ R ▢ E ▢ E ▢ E ▢ E
M I S T S ▢ A R M R E S T
▢ A S S ▢ S I ▢
S C R I P T S ▢ A C O R N
H ▢ L ▢ E ▢ S ▢ C A ▢
P O L O ▢ L U C E N T ▢ M
R ▢ R ▢ L ▢ R ▢ A T E
N U M E R A T E ▢ N ▢ L
▢ S ▢ D ▢ R ▢ W I S E L Y
```

Puzzle 138

```
▢ L K W ▢ F O R B I D
J U D I C I A L ▢ E ▢ A
X ▢ L ▢ C ▢ I ▢ L O P
O U Z O ▢ K U N G F U ▢ P
R ▢ W ▢ E ▢ G ▢ ▢ G ▢ L
D Y N A S T Y ▢ A G A T E
▢ ▢ T ▢ S ▢ O ▢ R ▢
S E C T S ▢ A R T I S A N
U ▢ R ▢ M ▢ D ▢ D ▢ C
R ▢ I G N I T E ▢ L O A M
R A T ▢ X ▢ A ▢ O ▢ C
E ▢ I ▢ E C L E C T I C
Y U C C A S ▢ S ▢ K A
```

Puzzle 139

```
P I L L A R ▢ U S A G E S
A ▢ I ▢ N ▢ D ▢ E ▢ U ▢ E
R A T ▢ I N V O I C E ▢ U
S P R A W L S ▢ E ▢ D ▢ T
E ▢ ▢ E ▢ T ▢ R O A C H
C L E A R ▢ I ▢ N ▢ E
▢ L ▢ P A N G S ▢ C
A ▢ E ▢ G ▢ K N E E S ▢
D I V E D ▢ U ▢ Y ▢ ▢ I
O ▢ A ▢ R ▢ I N H U M A N
R I T U A L S ▢ I ▢ O ▢ E
E ▢ E ▢ K ▢ H ▢ G O W
S Y D N E Y ▢ S H A R E S
```

Puzzle 140

```
S W A T C H ▢ O B E Y E D
P ▢ C ▢ H ▢ A ▢ E ▢ U ▢ R
R E T R E A T ▢ L ▢ L ▢ E
U ▢ I ▢ S ▢ M A I D E N S
C O V E T ▢ O ▢ E ▢ S ▢ S
E ▢ I ▢ S ▢ S ▢ F U S S Y
▢ I S ▢ G A P E S ▢ N
J U M B O ▢ H ▢ U ▢ C
E ▢ D ▢ E ▢ P A G E R
T R A I L E R ▢ H ▢ N ▢ A
S M E ▢ I N A N E L Y ▢
A ▢ I S ▢ C ▢ S ▢ S ▢ O
M O R A S S ▢ N E L S O N
```

Puzzle 141

```
▢ V E N T U R E S O M E ▢
W ▢ Q ▢ I ▢ E ▢ P ▢ A ▢ A
A U ▢ C O P R A ▢ J I G
T R A C K ▢ U ▢ S ▢ O ▢ G
E ▢ B ▢ L ▢ T ▢ M O R A L
R E L I E V E D ▢ ▢ ▢ O
M ▢ E ▢ S ▢ ▢ B ▢ P ▢ M
E ▢ ▢ C A R E F R E E ▢
L E V E R ▢ D ▢ T ▢ I ▢ R
O ▢ E ▢ I ▢ A ▢ W A N D A
N O R ▢ V A G U E ▢ T ▢ T
S ▢ V ▢ E ▢ I ▢ E ▢ E ▢ E
▢ W E S T C O U N T R Y ▢
```

Puzzle 142

```
Q U A Y ▢ A N G S T R O M
U ▢ L ▢ A ▢ E ▢ U ▢ O ▢ O
A M I A B L E ▢ L I M I T
D ▢ V ▢ S ▢ D ▢ F ▢ O ▢ H
R U E ▢ O E ▢ L O U S E
I ▢ ▢ L O D G E ▢ R ▢ C
L A ▢ U ▢ S ▢ S ▢ C O
A ▢ I ▢ T A S K S ▢ ▢ O
T R A D E ▢ T ▢ N ▢ E M U
E ▢ D ▢ Z ▢ A ▢ E ▢ L ▢ N
R E U S E ▢ D I S R U P T
A ▢ C ▢ R ▢ I ▢ S ▢ D ▢ R
L I T T O R A L ▢ D E W Y
```

Puzzle 143

```
O F F I C E R S ▢ E V E R
V ▢ O ▢ O ▢ U ▢ B I ▢ E
A P R O N ▢ G R A N D P A
L ▢ E ▢ F ▢ C ▢ E ▢ B
▢ O S T E N T A T I O U S
C ▢ E ▢ C ▢ H ▢ E ▢ O
O N E ▢ T H E I R ▢ P A R
M ▢ I ▢ F ▢ I ▢ L ▢ B
P R O P O R T I O N A L
U ▢ B ▢ N ▢ L ▢ C ▢ A
T R A D E I N ▢ O V E R T
E ▢ M ▢ R I G ▢ B ▢ O
R O A R ▢ P L A Y R O O M
```

Puzzle 144

```
A V I D ▢ E G Y P T I A N
D ▢ B ▢ M ▢ E ▢ E ▢ M ▢ O
M Y S T E R Y ▢ R I P E N
I ▢ E ▢ A ▢ S ▢ S ▢ I ▢ A
N I N E S ▢ E X P L O I T
I ▢ U ▢ R ▢ I ▢ U ▢ T
S U L T R Y ▢ C R U S O E
T ▢ E ▢ E ▢ A ▢ N ▢ ▢
R E G I M E S ▢ T E P I D
A ▢ E ▢ C ▢ I ▢ A ▢ A
T E N O N ▢ U T O P I A N
O ▢ D ▢ T ▢ D ▢ N ▢ L ▢ C
R E S I S T O R ▢ I S L E
```

Puzzle 145

D	E	R	I	S	I	V	E		A	S	H	E
E		E		U		O		W		C		N
T	I	M	E	R		I	N	H	E	R	I	T
E		O		P		C		E		U		E
R	E	V	E	R	I	E		E	M	B	E	R
M		E		I		S		L				T
I	N	S	I	S	T		I	B	E	R	I	A
N				I		S		A		E		I
A	D	D	O	N		C	A	R	A	V	A	N
T		O		G		O		R		E		M
I	N	S	U	L	A	R		O	U	N	C	E
O		E		Y		E		W		G		N
N	O	S	E		C	R	E	S	C	E	N	T

Puzzle 146

	C	A	R	T	O	G	R	A	P	H	Y	
M		N		H		A		M		E		P
O		A	E	T	U	D	E		A	W	L	
L	A	G	E	R		C		N		R		A
L		R		E		H		D	O	D	G	Y
Y	E	A	R	B	O	O	K					G
C		M		Y			C		F		R	
O			W	E	L	L	T	O	D	O		
D	O	D	O	S		S		O		R		U
D		O		K		C		S	T	E	R	N
L	I	Z		A	M	A	Z	E		R		D
E		E		T		P		S		U		S
	I	N	T	E	R	E	S	T	I	N	G	

Puzzle 147

T	R	A	M	P	S		S	I	E	V	E	S
A		B		I		O		M		I		H
C	O	N	G	E	A	L		A		S		R
K		O		R		I	N	G	R	A	T	E
L	U	R	K	S		V		E				W
E		M			E		R	E	A	R	S	
		A		B	O	B	B	Y		E		
B	U	L	L	Y		R			R		U	
U			A		A		C	R	O	O	N	
M	E	L	A	N	I	N		O		T		S
P		O		D		C	O	M	P	O	S	T
E		L		B		H		F		I		E
R	E	L	A	Y	S		C	Y	C	L	E	D

Puzzle 148

M	O	P	S		O	U	T	D	A	T	E	D
O		I		R		E		Y		A		A
D	O	L	P	H	I	N		S	U	P	E	R
E		E		A		C		I		E		R
R	E	S	E	R	V	E	P	R	I	C	E	
A		P		V		I		A				R
T	A	B		S	N	O	O	P		L	I	E
E		R		H		K		T		L		L
	D	I	S	O	B	E	D	I	E	N	C	E
L		T		O			O		Y		A	
A	W	A	I	T		C	I	N	E	M	A	S
M		I		E		U		S		P		E
B	A	N	K	R	U	P	T		C	H	A	D

Puzzle 149

R	E	N	O	U	N	C	E		C	H	U	M
O		A		N		O		T		A		A
L	I	T	H	E		M	A	I	L	I	N	G
L		A		X		P		T		T		N
E	C	L	I	P	S	E		T	R	I	B	E
R		I		E		L		L				T
C	L	E	N	C	H		G	E	M	I	N	I
O				T		E		T		N		C
A	D	D	L	E		S	L	A	C	K	E	N
S		A		D		P		T		L		O
T	I	T	U	L	A	R		T	R	I	E	R
E		U		Y		I		L		N		T
R	I	M	S		S	T	R	E	N	G	T	H

Puzzle 150

T	I	C	K	E	T		A	S		I		
O		A		R	E	T	I	C	E	N	T	
M	O	B		E		H		E		N		
T		I	M	P	E	D	E		N	E	A	T
O		N		S		I		A		T		
M	U	S	T	Y		U	S	U	R	P	E	D
		I		P		T		I				
D	A	W	D	L	E	R		C	O	O	E	D
	B		N		B		R		E			
W	A	R	N		D	A	R	T	E	D		P
	T		E		I		I			A	R	E
S	E	A	S	O	N	E	D			I		N
	S		S		G		E	A	R	N	E	D

Puzzle 151

S	U	N	S	H	I	N	E		S	T	E	M
T		E		A		O		N		H		E
E	Q	U	I	P		O	C	U	L	I	S	T
R		T		P		D		R		G		A
E	A	R	L	Y		L		S		H	U	M
O		A		G	R	E	B	E				O
T		L		O			R		A	R		R
Y			L	A	I	T	Y		Q	P		
P	E	P		U		N		R	O	U	G	H
I		L		C		F		H	A		O	
C	H	U	C	K	L	E		Y	E	T	I	S
A		M		Y		R		M		I		I
L	I	E	S		E	S	S	E	N	C	E	S

Puzzle 152

S	T	O	R	M	Y		S	Q	U	A	L	L
W		M		A		R	U	G		I		I
A		E		M		E	L	A	T	I	O	N
M	I	N	I	M	U	M		S		T		K
P				O		E		H	E	A	V	E
S	P	E	N	T		M		T				D
		X		H	O	B	B	Y		O		
P	E		E		R		R		T	O	R	C	H
R	I	G	I	D		A		T				U
O		E		A		N	A	R	R	O	W	S
B	O	T	A	N	I	C		I		H		T
E		I		D		E		U	I		L	
D	A	C	T	Y	L		I	M	P	O	S	E

Puzzle 153

I	N	S	T	I	N	C	T		Y	O	G	I
M		C		L		A		E		D		N
P	E	R	I	L		L	I	F	T	O	F	F
R		A		U		L		F		U		I
A	E	G	I	S		U		O		R	U	N
C		G		T	A	P	E	R				I
T		Y		R		T		T		T		T
I			A	W	F	U	L		H	E		E
C	U	B		T		R		E	V	E	N	S
A		A		I		E		S		R		I
B	U	T	T	O	N	S		S	T	E	A	M
L		C		N		C		L		S		A
E	C	H	O		P	O	N	Y	T	A	I	L

Puzzle 154

	E	S	T	A	B	L	I	S	H	E	D	
O		A		B		A	T		R		D	
V	E	T		E	N	T	R	Y		R		I
E		I		T		E		L	E	A	K	S
R	A	N	T	S		L		I		T		A
A				D	Y	E	S	T	U	F	F	
C		S		C		H		M				F
H	O	T	P	L	A	T	E					E
I		R		O		E		C	I	V	I	C
E	R	E	C	T		A		L		E		T
V		T		H	E	S	S	E		I	C	E
E		C		E		A		L	D			
	G	H	O	S	T	L	I	N	E	S	S	

Puzzle 155

M	O	A	N		W	R	E	S	T	L	E	R
A		L		O	U	I		A		E		E
S	W	O	L	L	E	N		M	I	N	I	M
S		N		D		W		T		T		O
A	N	G	S	T		A	I	L	M	E	N	T
C		E		Y		Y		A		R		E
H	O	N	E	S	T		I	R	O	N	I	C
U		U		T		W		I				O
S	O	P	R	A	N	O		T	A	L	O	N
E		T		M		N		I		I		T
T	W	I	N	E		D	R	E	A	M	E	R
T		A		N	E		S		B			O
S	O	L	I	T	A	R	Y		T	O	L	L

Puzzle 156

B	A	C	K	S	E	A	T		F	E	N	S
O		O		T		L		L		A		A
W	I	P	E	R		C	R	O	Q	U	E	T
L		I		A		O		D		U		U
	E		T		V	E	R	M	E	E	R	
H	Y	D	R	A	T	E		A		D		A
A		Y		G		I						T
Y		G	E		W	E	L	C	O	M	E	
M	A	R	I	M	B	A		R		V		
A		O			F		O		E		T	
K	I	C	K	O	F	F		A	R	R	O	W
E		E		L		D		D		O		
R	A	R	E		V	E	R	S	I	O	N	S

Puzzle 157

```
ONUS HOMEMADE
V  S A  P X E V
EXHIBIT  PURSE
R  E S      A N
CARBOHYDRATE
A     L E I E C
MAD UNARM DYE
E   E T S E   R
 IMPERTINENCE
C  O N    T O B
HINGE REACTOR
U  I S I L C  U
BACKSIDE SHAM
```

Puzzle 158

```
CAKEWALK LOKI
O E A E  N A N
NASAL TOOLKIT
S T K T  N U E
CARBIDE FEMUR
I E  N R L
EULOGY FASCIA
N   S A M H  T
TACIT ZAMBEZI
A I A I A V  O
OPTICAL BARON
U E K E L O  A
SARI PATERNAL
```

Puzzle 159

```
AUDI ARRANGED
N U M H P A  O
TOPIARY PILAU
I E  I M R L B
BASED EYEBALL
A  O D H  N E
CARAFE HECTIC
T I  H A N   R
ENVIOUS SALVO
R U N S I E  S
IGLOO OBVIOUS
A E U R E  N E
LITERATI PAIR
```

Puzzle 160

```
SANCTIFY GLAD
U A R U C O  I
PANDA SPONGES
E N N S  I I C
REISSUE NICER
L E M D C   E
ASSAIL WILLED
T  S E D  I I
IDOLS SHERBET
V C I T  N E A
ENCLOSE THROB
L U N E A T  L
YORK EMPLOYEE
```

Puzzle 161

```
SOMEBODY CALM
U A R I S D  I
MAGMA SQUALLS
O E I O R I  D
 UNANSWERABLE
E T W N O   E
DRAMAS GUIDED
U  S F N A S
CRASHLANDING
A C I L I G  E
TITANIC NYLON
E E G O G E  I
SUDS ONESIDED
```

Puzzle 162

```
AUNT BACCARAT
M O E M R I  U
ENVELOP OBOES
N E E  S T K
DELICATESSEN
I   T R S R F
NAB ROUTE SKI
G  U O M C
HIPPOPOTAMUS
T L L  I A  U
HYDRA STOPPER
U E T A N L  E
SERPENTS WETS
```

Puzzle 163

```
 EMBROIDERER
C O I N A N  P
HIT SITAR D I
R I E E SEGUE
OFFER R H A  I
N  UNCOMMON
O C F   T E T
GLORIOUS   T H
R M N N FABLE
APPLE T I U S
P L SLING YAK
H E S E H E  Y
 EXPENDITURE
```

Puzzle 164

```
MADRIGAL BULB
O E N S C N  A
BASIC KNOWING
S T O  N O U
 SIGNIFICANCE
C N V E I  T
ANY EXTOL SIT
P  O C I C E
STRAIGHTAWAY
I E E  T N A
CLEANUP INDEX
U F T E O A  E
MIST WRINKLED
```

Puzzle 165

```
T I T GREBES
GRANDEUR A  E
O F A I  TUX
CUBA CODDLE T
G M H S  A E
CHOOSES SPURT
U  R M R
TRUST TUNEFUL
H N S  S S N
E TIPPLE EBBS
FUR I  U R  E
T U REMOVING
STEPPE S E  T
```

Puzzle 166

```
ANTECEDE OVID
P R O E A E  I
PRISM AWNINGS
R V M C T O  A
ORINOCO ARMED
X A N G  A V
INLAWS CORONA
M  E S N V N
ACCRA WHITEST
T H L A S R  A
INEPTLY TWANG
O A H E I C  E
NUTS EDUCATED
```

Puzzle 167

```
REALLY C F F
A N ECONOMIC
DAY A P R  N
I WHERRY MIEN
A A S I E  L
LOYAL OSPREYS
N  P T L
SCRIBES MYTHS
R M B P H  T
AURA BOOBOO U
M T L K  RIP
OBSOLETE  N I
S R S DOUSED
```

Puzzle 168

```
T S T SCREAM
CONCERTI F A
B R A N  FED
PAPA CUCKOO A
G M I E R  M
COMBING BETTE
L G T  A
RIDES WRESTLE
O R S I T  A
U ORATOR WISE
SEW U E A  T
E S NUMERALS
DRYING E D  Y
```

Puzzle 169

Puzzle 170

Puzzle 171

Puzzle 172

Puzzle 173

Puzzle 174

Puzzle 175

Puzzle 176

Puzzle 177

Puzzle 178

Puzzle 179

Puzzle 180

Puzzle 181

Puzzle 182

Puzzle 183

Puzzle 184

Puzzle 185

Puzzle 186

Puzzle 187

Puzzle 188

Puzzle 189

Puzzle 190

Puzzle 191

Puzzle 192

CROSSWORD

Puzzle 193

```
S T G   S L I D E S
H I G H J U M P   E A
  L A Z O   B I T
L E A N   Z E U G M A   U
  N K L   T   T   R
S T A F F E D   Q U E E N
  U   R V N
S I L L Y   C A D E N C E
L Y   S R V R
A   N O R W A Y   E V E S
L A X   A I N E
O E   P E N E L O P E
M A S S E S   G Y Y Y
```

Puzzle 194

```
B A S H E S   W R A S S E
U   T A E U P D
R O S   V E N D I N G   I
R E P L E T E   G T   I
O   O R   S H E E N
W H I F F L   F   F G
  T   F L A K E   U
S E   E   S   T O L L S
L A M B S   T C   T
I I   W   I N H A L E R
C U S H I O N   I O I
E E N G   N V P
D E S I G N   A G R E E S
```

Puzzle 195

```
T I M E L Y   S C   B
I A   O U T C R I E S
P R Y   U E U R   R
O   D A L T O N   C O L D
F A   H C I   I
F O Y E R   B I G B A N G
  N A L L
E D U C A T E   F E T E S
O O T S E L
S L I D   A W H I L E   L
L I C A   T A N
L A U N C H E D   E G
R G E   Y E A R N S
```

Puzzle 196

```
  B T S   P E E P E D
B O N H O M I E   H A
  N U A A   O R B
L O O M   R O C K E T   B
  B B T E   O L
R O O S T E R   W I N C E
  U N B N
W R A P S   H A R V E S T
I L M N O H
G   I M P E N D   L O I N
W A G   D A V F
A N   A U G M E N T S
M I S S A L   E D Y
```

Puzzle 197

```
O C C I D E N T   M A T S
N H A I   B O
C A I R N   B O U R B O N
E N G B E I
T E   L I A I S O N
B I Z A R R E   P S L
O O O   A
W S U   H A C K S A W
S A T I S F Y   R T
P Y Y S Y A N
R E M A I N S   P U R E E
I I O H C R
T E E S   S P L A S H E D
```

Puzzle 198

```
S A S H   P E D E S T A L
H U P X   M A I
O B S E R V E   B E F O G
R H O M A F H
T H I E F   P E R F E C T
E T T R T F
E N M E S H   S A F A R I
M A S F S N
P O R T I C O   S L A N G
E R O R I N E
R E I G N   M O N I K E R
E E A A G L E
D E S O L A T E   S E N D
```

Puzzle 199

```
S C R A P E   O W N E R S
P U I M I L Y
I S E   A P P L I E S
C O H A B I T   E G T
E A R   S U I T E
S N A R L I B M
B   D U M P S L
B U O   W I E L D
R I N K S N A I
I D P   I N G R E S S
G R A N O L A   G L M
H N O L E L A
T A T T L E   C R U S T Y
```

Puzzle 200

```
  C A L C U L A T O R S
C T O O E O O
O E   P O U T S   T U B
R A L L Y V T O S
R I C R   S U R G E
O P E R A T E S S
B R T O K S
O   G R A F F I T I
R O B E S E F D V
A A I P   L A N C E
T U N   G U A N O E L
E J H I A Y Y
  H O R S E R A D I S H
```

Puzzle 201

```
D E R E L I C T   H A S P
E U I U S M R
T O N I C   P I C C O L O
E N K O R N P
R E E V E L I   G O O
I R   T R A M P R
O S Y T A T
R   S T R A W U I
A R C P E   R A D I O
T A L G I I N
I T C H I N G   T I B I A
O H T A E L T
N O E L   R E P R I E V E
```

Puzzle 202

```
E F F I C A C Y   I D O L
A O O L W U I
R E R U N   I N H I B I T
S E G C O A I
  O V E R W H E L M I N G
O E A E E A
B E R E T S   T H R O W N
D U G E R T
U N B E L I E V A B L E
R R A N R A A
A P O S T L E   T U N I C
C I E R E D H
Y A L E   H A R D C O P Y
```

Puzzle 203

```
I T C H   S P E C T R U M
N U H A O E A
C A S H I E R   N A V E L
O H E I S E A
N A Y R S   E L A N D
S O T H E R L M
I C G V S I
D O   L I B Y A O
E B O N Y O T   P S I
R L P N O H S
A B A S H   B U R N O U T
T N I O Y T E
E N T I C I N G   H O U R
```

Puzzle 204

```
B R A N C H E D   D A N K
A G E N B E
C R E A M   F I C T I V E
K N E O D P
  D N   L I T T E R S
P L A N T E D   E S A
R I C K
O S N   A T H L E T E
T H O U G H T N X
E R T I H M
C O R S I C A   Q U O T A
T E I U R C
S I L L   U N S E T T L E
```

Puzzle 205

```
I N C O M E   A R I S E S
N   H   A   T   U   C   P
C R A C K E R   F   A   E
I   R   E   A F F A B L E
T A I L S   N   I   D
E   S   S   A E O N S
    M   J A P A N   F
F L A R E   A   F   W
A   A   R   P R I Z E
D E V A L U E   O   C   I
I   A   O   N I P P I N G
N   L   U   T   P   A   H
G R E A S Y   E Y E L E T
```

Puzzle 206

```
S A L A D S   P A Y O F F
E   A   I   S   L   R   I
C   R   S   E L I C I T S
R A D I C A L   A   G   H
E   U   F   S P I C E
T O N G S   C   N   S
O   S T O C K   A
S   V   N   R I L E D
H E E L S   T   Y   I
U   M   O   R E P R E S S
T O B A C C O   T   X   C
U   E   K   L   O   P   O
P E R I S H   A N N O Y S
```

Puzzle 207

```
C I N N A B A R   S O F A
A   U   C   M   P   M   N
M I M I C   A M U L E T S
E   E   I   Z   R   G   W
  P R I D E O F P L A C E
S   A   E   N   O   R
O I L I N G   P S Y C H E
L   I   T   S   E   H   D
D I S S A T I S F I E D
I   P   L   E   U   E   S
E N A B L E S   L A R V A
R   D   Y   T   L   I   N
S E E S   B A B Y H O O D
```

Puzzle 208

```
C A C H E S   S C H I S T
A   A   G   R   A   N   R
R   V   O   E X P U N G E
P L A S T I C   E   U   N
E   I   T   D R E A D
L I V E S   A   N   S
  A   T O N E S   D
S   R   G   A B O D E
T Y I N G   U   G   V
A   A   O   L E G I B L E
L I B E R I A   I   O   N
K   L   E   R   N   N   E
S T E E D S   A G E O L D
```

Puzzle 209

```
R E A R   O P T I O N A L
E   I   C   R   N   I   O
A S S U A G E   T I T U S
S   L   R   L   E   R   E
S W E E T W I L L I A M
E   O   M   L   T   D
S L U D G E   C I N E M A
S   T   R   S   G   Y
  D I S A P P O I N T E D
S   L   P   E   B   W   R
W E I G H   A L L T I M E
A   T   E   K   Y   L   A
M A Y O R E S S   G L U M
```

Puzzle 210

```
O B S I D I A N   S C A M
U   T   I   T   R   A
T H U D S   O P U L E N T
S   D   H   N   D   I
  I   O   E L I S I O N
F R O W N E D   D   T   E
O   O   O   E   E
O   S   U   B E N C H E S
L I T U R G Y   T   U
S   R   P   I   B   P
C H E R V I L   C A B L E
A   E   A   A   U   G
P O T S   S Y L L A B U S
```

Puzzle 211

```
S A B R E S   A B O U N D
U   E   E   U   U   P   E
N A R   N E G A T E S
H A R P I S T   G   H   I
A   E   H   Y A R D S
T I C K S   I   U   T
  H   T A N K S   S
S   I   K   L A T C H
W A L E S   A   I   A
I   D   T   B I T T E R N
V I R T U A L   H   R   G
E   E   N   E   E   G   A
L E N G T H   A R B O U R
```

Puzzle 212

```
W I C K   F L A T M A T E
I   U   D   U   O   R   P
N U R S I N G   G O R S E
D   V   S   E   I   E
P R E S C R I P T I V E
I   O   T   H   E   O
P O P   N I E C E   D U B
E   A   M   R   S
  U N R E A S O N A B L E
A   N   C   E   E   S
J O I S T   D O S A G E S
A   N   E   O   S   I   E
R I G I D I T Y   O N E S
```

Puzzle 213

```
A M B U S H   C   S   V
B   O   A T H L E T I C
J A B   V   A   M   O
E   B I S E C T   O N L Y
C   I   N   T   L   E
T U N E D   M E D I A T E
  S   C   L   N
C O N C E R N   W A L K S
N   A   O   T   O   E
D I L L   C A S I N O   P
O   A   H   A   F A T
K N I T W E A R   A   E
S   E   T   S A C H E T
```

Puzzle 214

```
  A F G H A N I S T A N
A   R   I   E   E   N   H
B U Y   R O U N D   Y   E
S   U   E   T   U M B R A
T A P E D   E   C   O   V
R       F R I E N D L Y
A   R   S   S   Y   H
C E I L I N G S   A
T   N   D   A   V E G A N
A N G L E   M   O   A   D
R   L   C U B I C   F O E
T   E   A   I   A   F   D
  S T O R Y T E L L E R
```

Puzzle 215

```
  C O O P E R A T I V E
D   P   E   O   U   A   S
E   P   R E C U R   L E E
R O O K S   O   F   V   L
M   S   I   C   S H E L F
A V E R S I O N   A
T   D   T   S   P   S
O     O R C H A R D S
L A C E S   I   I   E   U
O   A   T   N E V E R
G A B   U R G E D   E
Y   A   D   E   I   N   D
  P L A Y W R I G H T S
```

Puzzle 216

```
B E S I D E   S W A T H E
R   P   E   D   E   E   N
I S O L A T E   I   N   Z
N   O   R   T I G H T L Y
G E N E S   E   H   M
S   F   R   T R A C E
  U   H Y M N S   C
A L L A Y   I   C   S
R   D   N   C L O U T
M A Z U R K A   O   R   U
I   O   A   T H U N D E R
N   N   N   E   T   E   D
G R E E T S   S H O D D Y
```

SOLUTIONS

387

Puzzle 217

```
C U B E   T E R R I B L E
H   I   A   S   E   E   A
I N J U R E S   P A N I C
T   O   I   A   R   E   H
C O U N T R Y W O M A N
H     H   S   D   T     C
A L A R M S   B U S H E L
T   N   E   V   C       U
  I N S T R U C T I O N S
S   E   I   L   I   U   T
L I L A C   C H O R T L E
I   A     A   N   E     R
M E D D L I N G   O R E S
```

Puzzle 218

```
C L O U D I N G   M A G I
R   V   I   O   M   R   N
O B E Y S   D E A D E N D
S   R   P   D   S   N   E
S Q U E E Z E   S T A F F
C   S   N   D   P       A
U N E A S Y   P R E S E T
L   A   U   O   T       I
T E N E T   P A D D I N G
U   A   I   D   U   M   A
R A V I O L I   C R U M B
A   A   N   K   E   L   L
L I L Y   H E A D L I N E
```

Puzzle 219

```
H A R D B A C K   O R A L
E   E   I   H   M   E   A
L I N G O   A C E R B I C
T   E   G   S   L   E   K
E D G E R   E   O   L O A
R   S   A D D E D   S   D
S   S   P       R   S   A
K     H O S T A   H     I
E B B   I   A   M E A L S
L   O   C   L   A   R   I
T O C C A T A   T O P I C
E   C   L   M   I   E   A
R U E D   V I S C E R A L
```

Puzzle 220

```
B E C O M I N G   B A C H
U   L   A   U   M   A   A
S T A V E   R A C C O O N
T   I   L   S   U   D   S
  M   S   E R R A N D S
V I S I T E D   E   T   O
E   E   R   I   I   M   M
N   M O   F I N A N C E
G R A M M A R   S   A   F
E   L   I   T   T   T   L
F O L D I N G   A B I D E
U   E   H   T   V   L   L
L A T E   S T E E P E S T
```

Puzzle 221

```
C R E E P S   E M I G R E
A   X   I   A   A   O   X
S H E L T E R   S   N   I
T   C   C   T A T T E R S
L A U G H   I   E   T   T
E   T   C   R O P E S   A
  O   B L U E S   A   C
P E R K Y   L   T   C
A   G   A   S W E L L   L
S U P P O R T   A   N   O
S   U   N   E X C I T E S
E   F   E   D   K   E   E
D E F U S E   A S C E N T
```

Puzzle 222

```
I N D E N T E D   A D A M
N   U   O   X   D   A   A
E L L E N   C O O K I N G
X   L   A   U   M   R   I
P E A R L   S   E   Y E S
E   R   C H E S S   T   T
R   D   O   T   S   E   R
I     H E I D I   U   R
E R G   O   N   C A P R I
N   L   L   D   A   P   A
C H O R I Z O   T R O L L
E   O   C   O   E   S   L
D U M P   D R U D G E R Y
```

Puzzle 223

```
F A W N   C A B B A G E S
O   A   D   I   R     E
R A G T I M E   O V A T E
E   O   S   D   P   D
B A N T A M W E I G H T
O     S   R   V   I   J
D U D   T H O S E   C U E
E   E   R   N   R   T   T
  D E C O N G E S T A N T
E   P   U   I   V   I
V A S E S   B A T T E N S
I   E   L   O   Y   R   O
L E A P Y E A R   S T U N
```

Puzzle 224

```
P A R R O T   O   V   D
U   E   R E D D E N E D
S O B   I   Y   R   C
H   O G R E S S   T R A P
E   O   D   S   E   Y
D I T T Y   V E R B O S E
  I   H   Y   R
S C A M P E R   P A C T S
  A   O   R   V   U L
S E A R   S A I L O R   I
  S   O   E   N   D U G
C A S U A L T Y   L   H
  R   S   F   L A T E N T
```

Puzzle 225

```
  C   O   S   P O N C H O
T A S M A N I A   Y   R
  J   I   T   B A G
L O G S   P O T A T O   A
  L   S   P   Y   R   N
D E C I D E D   R A G E S
  O   T   J   R
K I L N S   H O R M O N E
E   E   B   I   C   E
P E N S I G N   H A W K
L O W   L   T   A   T
E   A   L O L L I P O P
R H Y M E S   Y   R   N
```

Puzzle 226

```
A G E N C I E S   P L E A
P   X   A   I   U   Y   R
P O I N T   G E N E R I C
L   G   A   H   I   I   H
I D E A S   T V   C H I
C   N   T H Y M E   P   T
A B     R   R P   E   E
B   O V A L S   E   C
I R K   P   L   I N L E T
L   N   H   L   T   U   U
I T E M I S E   I N C U R
T   A   C   G   E   A
Y O D A   S E A S O N A L
```

Puzzle 227

```
A V O N   S T R E T C H Y
N   L   G   O   X   O   A
T A D P O L E   T H R U M
I   E   O   R   D   S
P E N N S Y L V A N I A
H   E   E   V   A   E
O A R   P L A Z A   L I V
N   O   I   R   G   A
  C O M M E N D A T I O N
S   F   P   N   N   E
H O T E L   N O Z Z L E S
E   O   E   O   A   A C
D E P O S I T S   H Y P E
```

Puzzle 228

```
U M P I R E   W H I T E S
N   I   O   A   E   H   C
C O N J O I N   A   O   R
O   N   T   O B V E R S E
R E A P S   N   I     W
K   C   Y   L A R K S
  L   D U M P Y   E
G E E S E   O     D   P
A   N   U   B O O T H
R E C O I L S   A   L   A
N   U   A   L E D G E R S
E   R   L   Y   G   N   E
R O B U S T   V E S T E D
```

Puzzle 229

```
P U R P O S E L E S S
C  M   U   E   U   E   E
A L   R I V E R   P E N
L O A D S   E   C   A   T
L   U   U   R   H A L L E
O U T S I D E R       R
U   S   T   F   H   T
S       B R O U H A H A
N A M E D   E   C   R   I
E   A   E   F   H U M A N
S I X   N O O K S   F   E
S   I   S   R   I   U D
  I M P E R M E A B L E
```

Puzzle 230

```
C O H O R T   Z I P P E D
Y   I   E   R   L   E   E
M I G R A T E   L   R   F
B   H   D   V E N T U R E
A B B E Y   E   E   A
L   R   O   R   S W E P T
  O   T U B E S   M
B O W E R   E   E   H
Y   O   R   F O R A Y
P E R G O L A   E   G   P
A   E   P   T U R K I S H
S   D   E E   A   N   E
S W O R D S   S L O G A N
```

Puzzle 231

```
T R I C K S   D   C   C
A   M   P R O T O C O L
C E P   I   D   L   Y
T   U N C L O G   U P O N
I   T   L   E   M   T
C L E A T   G R U B B E D
  S   C   S   I
E V A S I O N   C A V E S
O   I   M   S   I   E
M I N G   P A T I N A
  C   N   O   I   B I D
C E R E B R A L   L   E
D   D   T   L I N E A R
```

Puzzle 232

```
U R G E   O C C U R R E D
N   L   R   N   E   I
S C E N E R Y   A T L A S
Y   A   H   I   C   I   C
M A N N A   N U C L E A R
P   B   G   U   V   E
A R C T I C   A S P E C T
T   E   L   A   T   I
H A R P I N G   O U T D O
E   T   T   H   M   W   N
T I A R A   A M E R I C A
I   I   T   S   D   R
C O N C E R T O   C L O Y
```

Puzzle 233

```
S A G O   H Y G I E N I C
L   O   C   I   D   E   R
E P I T O M E   I T A L Y
I   N   N   L   O   R   P
G I G   T   D   S W E E T
H   R I S K Y   S   O
T   D   A   N   T   G
O   Y   D O R I C   R
F U N G I   I   R   E R A
H   A   C   B   A   L   P
A D M I T   B E S E E C H
N   I   E   O   Y   C   E
D E C O D I N G   S T A R
```

Puzzle 234

```
W A G O N S   A   S   L
A   L   C I R C U L A R
R A Y   O   C   B   P
M   P L O U G H   U N D O
T   H   T   W   R   O
H A S T E   G A R B A G E
  A   B   Y   I
S T I L L E R   C A P E R
  H   L   N   B   I   O
K E E N   E Q U I N E   U
O   E   F   L   R U T
P R E S S I N G   C   E
Y   S   T   E S T E R S
```

Puzzle 235

```
F R I G A T E S   O B O E
I   N   L   L   N   R   N
S H E E P   L E E W A R D
H   R   H   W   I   U
  S T R A I G H T E N E R
Q   I   B   O   E   I
U S A   E A R N S   S I N
I   T   G   T   E   G
C O N S I D E R A B L Y
K   O   C   M   F   B
E M U L A T E   E D I F Y
S   N   L   L   N   E
T O S S   S K E T C H E S
```

Puzzle 236

```
A P P E A L   S T R O N G
L   R   N   A   O   N   L
B R O W N I E   K   T   A
U   C   O   R E A S O N S
M I L K Y   O   M   S
S   A   D   A L L E Y
  I   K A Y A K   A
W O M E N   N   K   L
A   I   A   G L E B E
S A N C T U M   O   S   A
T   A   T   I V O R I E S
E   G   E   C   S   D   E
D E S E R T   D E F E N D
```

Puzzle 237

```
S O S O   S P E C I F I C
U   H   R   A   A   A   O
P L A T E A U   R I S E N
E   F   P   S   D   C   S
R A T I O   E L I T I S T
F   S   S   O   A   E
L O C U S T   C L O S E R
U   A   E   P   O   N
O V E R S E E   G U A V A
U   S   S   R   I   V   T
S A U D I   S A S H I M I
L   R   O   O   T   A   O
Y E A R N I N G   A N O N
```

Puzzle 238

```
L U S T   O U T R I G H T
O   I   P   R   E   L   O
G O R I L L A   P L A T E
I   E   A   N   E   M   D
C O N T I N U A T I O N
I   N   S   I   U   M
A T T I C S   S T E R E O
N   A   L   A   I   D
  U N F O R G I V A B L E
S   K   T   E   E   U   L
L O A C H   I L L E G A L
U   R   E   N   Y   L   E
R E D E S I G N   W E E D
```

Puzzle 239

```
  E V A L O N G O R I A
A   O   E   E   U   N   E
F I G   A D A P T   S   X
T   U   K   R   F L U M P
E N E M Y   E   I   L   E
R       P R E T T I E R
B   S   A   S   N   I
U N L O C K E D   M
R   E   R   N   C Y C L E
N A N C Y   D   R   L   N
E   D   L I E G E   A C T
R   E   I   A   S M   S
  T R I C E R A T O P S
```

Puzzle 240

```
C A K E   B I G A P P L E
I   E   T   S   R   L   X
V I B R A T O   C H A R T
I   A   B   B   H   T   R
L A B E L   A R I Z O N A
S   E   R   T   O   P
E N I G M A   L E A N T O
R   L   A   T   C   L
V A L A N C E   T H E T A
A   I   N   E   U   L   T
N A C R E   M A R T I N I
T   I   R   E   E   D   O
S E T A S I D E   F E R N
```

CROSSWORD

Puzzle 241

```
S T R O B E . D R I L L S
O . E . A . B . E . I . L
C A P I T O L . W . M . E
I . R . H . U N A W A R E
A F I R E . E . R . . . P
L . S . A . B . D E G A S
. . . A . F I L E S . R .
B E L L E . O . . . I . C
E . . T . O . P U N C H
T I C K L E D . O . N . E
E . . E . O . E M O T I V E
N . . C . D . C . N . K
R E T A K E . S H A G G Y
```

Puzzle 242

```
. M . E . O . P E N C I L
D I S T A S T E . A . O .
. K . E . M . S . P E W .
F A I R . O U T L E T . E
. D . N . S . S . O . S .
C O D I C I L . S P R A T
. . . T . S . C . R . . .
B E R Y L . S O J O U R N
U . A . K . N . T . . . .
M . N I C E S T . R A P T
P A D . N . A . U E . . .
E . O . D E C A D E N T .
D O M I N O . T . E . S .
```

Puzzle 243

```
T R E A T I N G . A S I A
U . M . H . I . H . T . N
T A B O O . C H I M E R A
U . A . U . K . G . E . L
. T R I G G E R H A P P Y
L . G . H . L . S . . . S
A D O P T S . U P T A K E
N . . F . . I . R . S .
C I R C U M S C R I B E .
E . O . L . T . I . I . E
L O B E L I A . T A T T Y
O . O . Y . T . E . E . E
T O T S . T E N D E R E D
```

Puzzle 244

```
S A G A C I T Y . A N T E
E . O . O . H . E . N .
W A T E R . U G L I E S T
N . H . P . M . S . . . I
. . I . O . B A C K O U T
R E C O R D S . O . N . L
E . A . . A . N . . . E
S . H . T . S E T T L E D
E V E R E S T . R . A .
A . N . . A . A . M . C
R A R E B I T . L I B E L
C . Y . . E . T . D . U
H I V E . A D V O C A T E
```

Puzzle 245

```
C A R D A M O M . T H U D
A . E . P . R . A . A . I
T U L I P . A F F A I R S
E . E . R . N . T . K . R
G I N S E N G . E D U C E
O . T . H . E . R . . . S
R E S T E D . S T E P U P
I . . N . I . H . A . E
C U R E S . G N O S T I C
A . U . I . N . U . R . T
L I M P O P O . G R I E F
L . E . N . R . H . O . U
Y A R N . T E E T O T A L
```

Puzzle 246

```
. C O N C O R D A N C E .
E . Z . A . W . B . R . R
M O O . F L A K Y . E . U
B . N . E . N . S T E A L
A R E A S . D . M . P . E
R . . . J A L A P E N O .
R . S . H . . . L . R . F
A L T H O U G H . . . . T
S . E . A . E . C O A C H
S T A I R . L . H . W . U
E . M . S I D L E . A R M
D E E . O . E . R . B
. T R A N S F E R R E D .
```

Puzzle 247

```
P U R I F Y . S C U L P T
E . E . R . M . U . U . I
D E S P I S E . R . L . G
A . T . E . A B S O L V E
L O R D S . N . O . . . R
S . I . . A . I . R I N G S
. . I . H A N D Y . E .
D A N C E . G . G . G . S
E . . C . L . B L A S T
R O S E T T E . O . T . R
A . C . A . S E R V I C E
I . A . R . S . N . V . W
L A N C E T . H E R E I N
```

Puzzle 248

```
C L A D . O P T I M I S T
O . X . D . A . N . I
U N I C O R N . C I T E D
S . O . M . I . O . E . Y
C O M M E N C E M E N T .
O . S . S . P . T . D .
U P S E T S . N A S S A U
S . T . I . A . R . T
. D I S C O R D A N T L Y
I . L . A . B . I . F
N A T A L . B O L S T E R
C . O . L . L . Y . H . E
H O N E Y D E W . H E R E
```

Puzzle 249

```
B U M P . D I S R U P T S
I . A . D . N . E . L . A
O R C H I D S . P R E E N
D . R . C . T . E . D . C
E G O . T . E . R I G H T
G . R . K . A S P I C . I
R . K . T . . . U . S . M
A . I . O V E R S . . . O
D O N O R . D . S . R O N
A . E . S . I . I . E . I
B O T C H . S C O R P I O
L . I . I . O . N . E . U
E S C A P I N G . A L A S
```

Puzzle 250

```
S I T U P S . G L U T E N
O . E . R . I . U . R . E
R . A . O . L E T T I N G
R E M O V A L . E . P . A
O . . E . U . S P L I T .
W A V E R . S . . . I . E
. . A . B I T E S . N .
S . N . R . W A G E S . S
C O I N S . A . I . . . U
R . . S . E . T U M B L E D
U N H I N G E . M . A . D
F . E . S . D . E . N . E
F I D G E T . K R A K E N
```

Puzzle 251

```
C O N S P I R E . S E M I
A . U . A . E . A . C .
G A M U T . T A X F R E E
E . B . R . A . . . F . B
. . E . I . I N C L U D E
C U R E A L L . O . L . R
O . . R . . . R . . . G .
C . U . C . S U N D A Y S
K I N S H I P . C . P .
A . . R . A . R . L . F
T R E B L E D . A W O K E
O . A . . E . K . M . T
O I L S . A S S E M B L E
```

Puzzle 252

```
. A R I S T O C R A C Y .
N . O . A . R . A . H . H
O . A . W R I S T . A P E
T U M M Y . S . E . S . A
H . I . E . O . S P E N D
I G N O R A N T . . . . T
N . G . S . . . H . R . E
G . . . . . P A R A N O I A
N E C K S . T . N . T . C
E . O . P . T . D O U G H
S I P . A R I E S . N . E
S . S . C . R . E . D . R
. D E F E R E N T I A L .
```

SOLUTIONS

Puzzle 253

Puzzle 254

Puzzle 255

Puzzle 256

Puzzle 257

Puzzle 258

Puzzle 259

Puzzle 260

Puzzle 261

Puzzle 262

Puzzle 263

Puzzle 264

CROSSWORD

Puzzle 265

```
  F S O  DISARM
EUPHORIA   D   A
 T E I M   HAG
PURR FLEECE   N
 R L I S   R  E
REJOICE  GUEST
  C  E R  N
COCKY  FORGERY
O A  T B  A  I
N COBWEB  IFFY
COT   E  E  L
 U  U ENROLLED
RESENT   S Y  D
```

Puzzle 266

```
ROAM EFFUSION
E B S A N  M O
STUTTER DOMED
E Z R   E E  S
MEZZOSOPRANO
B   N B W S  B
LET GREER EAR
E A W   S I  U
  AMBIDEXTROUS
D A L   I C  T
AVRIL GENTEEL
R I E  U G A  E
KINGDOMS  ANTS
```

Puzzle 267

```
SAPS  CANTATAS
H A H L  R A  A
OBELISK  APRIL
O A N A  N I  V
TIN D L  SOFIA
I  QUIFF  F  T
N L U   E S  O
G E ALDER  L
SPOOR Y  A FUN
T T T N B  E  A
APACE  ALLOVER
R R R M  E M
SIDESHOW  TROY
```

Puzzle 268

```
 C S T VETOES
CRITERIA   N U
 E A E U  WIG
HAIR MANTRA  A
 S G O T   R R
REPAIRS  MADLY
  Z S H   L
GREET  CENSURE
A A  C R A  A
B SCARCE  TERM
BET  E T  I
L E  SUITABLE
ERRORS  C N  Y
```

Puzzle 269

```
LIFTED  ABS
A E   OBVIATED
ZEN  C I C  W
I NICKED  TRAM
E E  S I E  G
RACES  STARVED
  N T Y   I
TACTFUL  TASTE
 L R R S  C X
LIZA BAMBOO O
 B N I I   WAD
LISTENER  L U
 S S E  KANSAS
```

Puzzle 270

```
SHIMMY  CHINUP
H R A E  O A
A O T ELASTIC
MINSTER  L I K
E H A  SCORE
SHOVE   N N D
  U WAGER  A
A T   E  ALLOY
BYLAW M W   E
I I E  ETHANOL
DUNGEON  I A L
E E D T  D P O
DISUSE  SEESAW
```

Puzzle 271

```
RUSTLE  SHADOW
E H A  I A A  A
SNOWMAN  G T  T
I U P  COGNATE
DOLLS  O A   R
E D M  RUMMY
 E VAPID  U
HORDE  E  T U
U  T T DRAIN N
SUPREME U T  V
H E R NETLIKE
U L A T  C O  I
POTENT  CHANEL
```

Puzzle 272

```
WAVY  TRUFFLES
R O A U R O  K
INDULGE  ITCHY
G K L F E U  E
GRACIOUSNESS
L  M L D T  G
EUROPA  PLASMA
D E O A I   R
 HEARTRENDING
S N T C E V  O
KOALA  HISTORY
U C N E S R  L
APTITUDE  BYTE
```

Puzzle 273

```
SOUNDS  D S H
T N   TWINKLES
RAW  A S I  R
I ERASES  TOOT
N L  H E T  I
GALES  UNHITCH
  J V T S
WHEELIE  SHOOK
E C O S  L  I
WRIT  LIQUID T
O I E U   ANT
INSOMNIA  G E
S N T  TUREEN
```

Puzzle 274

```
REDUCING  THAW
A E U A   A E
VIEWS TALENTS
E P T T  G  T
 E O EVACUEE
STRYDER  L P R
C  I M   R N
O O A AMADEUS
REFINED  M T
N F  D A H  A
FRECKLE  TRIAL
U N  R E C  S
LADS ESPRESSO
```

Puzzle 275

```
NAILVARNISH
D C E B O A  R
R C VERBS LYE
EPOXY U E V  A
A S I P SWEEP
DETONATE   P
N S G  R M  R
O   SCHEMATA
UNDID U F X  I
G I E D RAINS
HOG ALGAE M A
T I L E S U  L
STATELYHOME
```

Puzzle 276

```
MOTETS  CRAWLS
I H O I  U I  A
NON NESTLES
O N G  T D  H
NOURISH  SALSA
 E G E  R I  Y
 E TWIGS F
T B  T  TWEED
AVOID A R   U
N N I NOODLES
DRASTIC  K A  T
E I C E   N  E
MARSHY  ISLAND
```

Puzzle 277

```
E X U D E D . S . M . F
N . R . E N T R A I L S
J U G . B . A . R . U .
O . E D D I E S . I B E X
Y . N . T . H . T . N .
S A T E D . R E S I S T S
. X . P . D . M .
S T O P P E D . R E B U T
. H . L . A . C . O . U
M O N O . C O R T E X . R
. R . I . O . I . F O G
C A N T I C L E . . U . I
. X . S . K . S A I L E D
```

Puzzle 278

```
B O U N D A R Y . M E S H
U . K . I . A . B . A . O
G O R E S . C O U N S E L
S . A . A . K . S . E . I
. S I N G L E M I N D E D
E . N . R . T . N . A .
P E E L E D . F E E B L Y
I . E . D . S . L . S .
D E C O M M I S S I O N .
E . O . E . P . L . U . W
M E M E N T O . I S S U E
I . E . T . L . K . E . L
C O S Y . R E V E R S A L
```

Puzzle 279

```
C O N S U M E R . S A I D
O . A . N . D . F . G . I
N O T E S . I C I C L E S
T . T . U . T . E . O . T
R U I N S . O . L . W A R
O . V . L . P A R E D . U
V . E . Y . E . G . P . S
E . . C O R A L . R . T
R E V . T . A . A L O O F
S . I . I . N . S . R . U
. I N T O N E S . S M A L L
A . A . G . O . E . L .
L I L T . E M I S S A R Y
```

Puzzle 280

```
N A R R A T O R . X M E N
I . U . S . L . I . E . O
B E S E T . D E N I Z E N
S . S . R . C . Z . S .
. S E C O N D T O N O N E
D . L . N . O . M . N .
E E L . O X L I P . W A S
S . M . C . A . R . E .
P R O V I D E N T I A L .
I . R . C . I . P . E .
S P I R A L S . B I P E D
E . O . L . H . L . E .
D A N E . R E H E A R S E
```

Puzzle 281

```
P E N D A N T S . O M A R
U . E . B . H . A . E .
C H A R D . R O M A N I A
E . R . O . I . T . G .
. B . M . C A P R I C E
H A Y W I R E . R . S . N
O . . N . A . O . T
G . S . A . D E F O R M S
S I M P L E R . E . E .
H . A . E . S . S . H
E S C A P E D . S H A K E
A . K . G . E . L . R
D U S K . H E E D L E S S
```

Puzzle 282

```
B O B C A T . T H I R S T
E . R . G . S . A . U . H
D . I . A . C U T I C L E
E N G L I S H . C . K . I
C . . N . O . H U S K S
K I N G S . T . . A . T
. E . T I L E S . C .
O . A . G . P O K E R
W O R M S . I . E . . O
N . M . M . R E L O A D S
I N I T I A L . T . R . A
N . S . L . S . E . . R
G A S P E D . F R O S T Y
```

Puzzle 283

```
A R T I S T R Y . A W E D
R . E . E . U . I . H . I
C A M E L . M O N K E Y S
S . P . F . . T . R . A
. N E V E R T H E L E S S
S . R . M . R . R . . T
T E A . P S A L M . T H E
R . . L . I . E . R . R
A C K N O W L E D G E D .
P . N . Y . . I . M . I
P R O J E C T . A L B U M
E . W . D . O . T . L . P
D O S E . F R E E Z E R S
```

Puzzle 284

```
. M . S . T . M O S C O W
H Y S T E R I A . O . O .
. R . A . I . C . W E B .
B I R D . S C A R A B . B
. A . I . E . W . O . L .
A D J U N C T . S L Y L Y
. . M . T . D . I . . .
B O S S Y . D I G G E R S
A . E . F . T . A . U .
F . A L L O U T . T I L L
A . D . R . I . U . I .
L . O . C H E E R I N G .
E N G I N E . S . E . G .
```

Puzzle 285

```
L O C A L S . I N M O S T
I . O . A . M . A . I . R
V E R A N D A . I . N . A
E . R . D . I N V O K E D
L E E R S . N . E . . E
Y . C . T . . L I K E S
. T . P I E T Y . A . .
B A S T E . N . . L . T
A . . E . A . F R A M E N
S A F F R O N . A . H . N
A . E . E . C O M M A N D
L . A . S . E . E . R . O
T H R U S T . A D R I E N
```

Puzzle 286

```
G A T E . A D O R A B L E
A . O . D . R . E . A . Z
L O T T E R Y . F I N E R
A . E . L . R . A . A .
C O M B I N A T I O N S .
T . Q . L . G . A . T .
I L K . U N I T E . S I R
C . E . E . R . A .
. P R E S E N T A T I O N
B . A . C . T . N . S .
L A T H E . P R O B L E M
O . I . N . A . R . A .
C E N O T A P H . S W O T
```

Puzzle 287

```
H I S T O R I C . C H I C
Y . T . L . R . S . O . O
P L E A D . I R I D I U M
E . E . F . S . T . S . P
R E P L A C E . T U T O R
C . L . S . S . I . . E
R H Y T H M . E N R I C H
I . . I . L . G . M . E
T O K Y O . A B D O M E N
I . E . N . Z . U . E .
C H A T E A U . C O R G I
A . T . D . L . K . S . O
L I S T . E I N S T E I N
```

Puzzle 288

```
. S P E C U L A T I O N .
I . O . A . O . U . U . C
N E W . R E A D S . T . H
E . E . R . N . . O . E
S P R A Y . E . L . O . S
T . . . . F R E E D O M S
I . A . B . . S . K . E C
M O N G O O S E . . . . C
A . G . R . N . C I V I L
B A R G E . A . O . O . O
L . I . D I V A N . T O T
E . E . O . E . O . H .
. C R U M B L I N E S S .
```

SOLUTIONS

Puzzle 289

```
O P T I M A ■ A S C E N D ■ R
U ■ U ■ A ■ C ■ E ■ N ■ R
N ■ B ■ S ■ O V E R D U E ■
C H A S T E N ■ K ■ A ■ A ■
E ■ ■ I ■ F ■ S Y N O D ■
S C O F F ■ O ■ G ■ S ■ ■
■ B ■ F L U F F ■ E ■ ■ ■
I ■ D ■ N ■ L U R E S ■ H
M O U L T ■ D ■ I ■ ■ H ■
P ■ R ■ H ■ I M P L O R E
O V A T I O N ■ P ■ U ■ L
R ■ T ■ C ■ G E R L ■ L ■
T W E A K S ■ C R U S T S
```

Puzzle 290

```
I M P L I C I T ■ N O R M
R ■ I ■ N ■ M ■ D ■ R ■ I
R E L I C ■ E M E R G E S
E ■ L ■ O ■ L ■ M ■ A ■ C
C H A I N ■ D ■ O N E E ■
O ■ G ■ S P A W N ■ S ■ ■
V ■ E ■ O ■ ■ S ■ C L A ■
E ■ ■ L I S Z T ■ A ■ A ■
R E D ■ A ■ T ■ R A Y O N
A ■ R ■ B I A ■ A ■ E ■ E
B O O T L E G ■ B I N G O
L ■ S ■ E ■ M ■ L ■ N ■ U
E A S Y ■ S A M E N E S S
```

Puzzle 291

```
B O O M ■ U N H A R M E D
E ■ N ■ U ■ I ■ G ■ I ■ U
A R S E N I C ■ R U L E S
R ■ E ■ D ■ E ■ I ■ I ■ T
A U T H E N T I C I T Y ■
B ■ ■ R ■ Y ■ U ■ I ■ C ■
L O U N G E ■ A L P A C A
E ■ P ■ A ■ U ■ T ■ U ■ ■
■ A S T R O N A U T I C S
P ■ T ■ M ■ U ■ R ■ D ■ E
U S A G E ■ S W A L L O W
M ■ R ■ N ■ E ■ L ■ E ■ A
A L T I T U D E ■ E D G Y
```

Puzzle 292

```
E A R L I E S T ■ B A L M
X ■ O ■ R ■ P ■ H ■ R ■ I
T U B E R ■ O R A N G E S
R ■ B ■ U ■ I ■ O ■ C ■ ■
A L I A S E S ■ R A N C H
V ■ N ■ P ■ E ■ D ■ ■ I ■
A R G U E D ■ O R I O L E
G ■ ■ C ■ T ■ E ■ U ■ V ■
A M B I T ■ R I S O T T O
N ■ E ■ I ■ A ■ S ■ M ■ U
T E L A V I V ■ I R O N S
L ■ O ■ E ■ E ■ N ■ S ■ L
Y A W N ■ S L I G H T L Y
```

Puzzle 293

```
R E B U F F ■ F ■ I ■ A ■
E ■ O ■ U G L I N E S S ■
V E X ■ N ■ A ■ A ■ P ■ ■
A ■ E L U D E S ■ C O I L
M ■ R ■ S ■ H ■ T ■ R ■ ■
P U S H Y ■ R E C I T E S
■ A ■ M ■ D ■ V ■ ■ ■ ■ ■
C H A N C E S ■ D E C O R
■ E ■ D ■ R ■ B ■ O ■ H ■
H A U L ■ M I R I A M ■ I
■ D ■ I ■ A ■ I ■ ■ M A N
C O I N C I D E ■ O ■ A ■
■ N ■ G ■ D ■ F E N N E L
```

Puzzle 294

```
I R A N ■ F O R E N S I C
N ■ B ■ P ■ N ■ F ■ I ■ O
A N Y M O R E ■ F A G I N
P ■ S ■ L ■ O ■ E ■ N ■ S
P I S T E ■ F E R R A R I
R ■ ■ P ■ F ■ V ■ L ■ D ■
O R E G O N ■ L E S S E E
P ■ N ■ S ■ C ■ S ■ ■ R ■
R E T S I N A ■ C I R C A
I ■ W ■ T ■ M ■ E ■ A ■ T
A L I B I ■ P A N A C H E
T ■ N ■ O ■ U ■ T ■ E ■ L
E V E N N E S S ■ E D D Y
```

Puzzle 295

```
B U F F ■ O R A T I O N S
O ■ U ■ D ■ U ■ O ■ M ■ E
O U T L E T S ■ T R I T E
K ■ O ■ L ■ T ■ A ■ P ■ ■
C O N V I V I A L I T Y ■
A ■ B ■ C ■ I ■ E ■ T ■ ■
S I M P E R ■ S T O D G Y
E ■ O ■ R ■ C ■ A ■ ■ P ■
■ U N F A V O U R A B L E
F ■ S ■ T ■ C ■ I ■ A ■ C
L A T T E ■ O C A R I N A
O ■ E ■ L ■ O ■ N ■ Z ■ S
W O R R Y I N G ■ P E A T
```

Puzzle 296

```
C E R B E R U S ■ V A M P
O ■ E ■ L ■ P ■ U ■ L ■ ■
W H I L E ■ D I V E R G E
S ■ G ■ P ■ A ■ O ■ A ■ ■
■ N ■ H ■ T A V E R N S ■
P A S S A G E ■ I A ■ U ■
L ■ N ■ C ■ ■ ■ N ■ C ■ R
A ■ V ■ T ■ A V E R A G E
T R E A S O N ■ V ■ L ■ ■
O ■ N ■ ■ G ■ E ■ I ■ T ■
N E E D F U L ■ R A C E R
I ■ E ■ E ■ E ■ S ■ I ■ U
C O R E ■ E S C A P A D E
```

Puzzle 297

```
■ M ■ T ■ B ■ P H O B I A
P A N O R A M A ■ U ■ L ■
■ N ■ I ■ S ■ I ■ Z I P ■
C U R L ■ S P R I T Z ■ I
■ R ■ S ■ O ■ S ■ E ■ N ■
A E R O S O L ■ M E R G E
■ ■ M ■ N ■ D ■ M ■ ■ ■ ■
C I D E R ■ R E Q U E S T
L ■ R ■ F ■ C ■ L ■ K ■ ■
I ■ A N G L I A ■ A X I S
M A W ■ O ■ D ■ T ■ L ■ ■
B ■ E ■ C L E V E R L Y ■
S T R U C K ■ S ■ D ■ S ■
```

Puzzle 298

```
■ D O V E ■ V O L C A N I C
O ■ A ■ A ■ L ■ E ■ O ■ ■
M E L O D I C ■ A L A R M
E ■ E ■ M ■ U ■ I ■ T ■ M
S E T T O ■ P A R V E N U
T ■ N ■ Y ■ V ■ N ■ N ■ ■
I M P A I R ■ B O N S A I
C ■ R ■ S ■ T ■ Y ■ ■ C ■
A N O T H E R ■ A L P H A
T ■ S ■ M ■ O ■ N ■ I ■ T
I R A T E ■ J A C U Z Z I
O ■ I ■ N ■ A ■ E ■ Z ■ O
N I C O T I N E ■ P A W N
```

Puzzle 299

```
D I S T U R B S ■ T A L C
E ■ H ■ N ■ E ■ A ■ M ■ O
C R O P S ■ H E R O I S M
O ■ R ■ E ■ O ■ R ■ G ■ B
N E T B A L L ■ A R O M A
T ■ L ■ S ■ D ■ N ■ ■ T ■
A N Y H O W ■ A G O U T I
M ■ ■ N ■ E ■ E ■ P ■ ■ N
I N D I A ■ C O M P E R E
N ■ E ■ B ■ L ■ E ■ N ■ N
A L F A L F A ■ N U D G E
T ■ E ■ E ■ I ■ T E ■ S ■
E C R U ■ P R E S I D E S
```

Puzzle 300

```
T Y P I S T ■ A F R A I D
E ■ A ■ A ■ C ■ I ■ N ■ E
M ■ N ■ L ■ O F F I C E R
P U T D O W N ■ T ■ I ■ I
T ■ ■ O ■ T ■ Y I E L D ■
S E V E N ■ R ■ ■ N ■ E ■
■ E ■ S A I L S ■ T ■ ■ ■
S ■ N ■ ■ B ■ C A S E S ■
W I T C H ■ U ■ R ■ ■ Y ■
I ■ U ■ O ■ T E A R F U L
N U R T U R E ■ P ■ L ■ V
G ■ E ■ S ■ D ■ P ■ A ■ I
S O D D E N ■ M Y O P I A
```

Puzzle 301

```
I N S E C U R E ▮ A C R E
R ▮ E ▮ E ▮ C U X ▮ ▮
R I V E N ▮ T W O S T E P
E ▮ E ▮ S ▮ I ▮ M ▮ U ▮ A
P U R G E ▮ I N ▮ P ▮ P A N
R ▮ A ▮ Q U A I L ▮ ▮ S
E ▮ L ▮ U ▮ ▮ E ▮ S ▮ I
S ▮ ▮ E X A C T ▮ E ▮ V
S P A N ▮ C ▮ E V A D E
I ▮ L ▮ T ▮ C ▮ N ▮ S ▮ N
B A T T L E R ▮ E L O P E
L ▮ E ▮ Y ▮ U ▮ S ▮ N ▮ S
E U R O ▮ P E R S I S T S
```

Puzzle 302

```
P I T S ▮ E N C I R C L E
A ▮ A ▮ P ▮ I ▮ N ▮ A ▮ N
C A B A R E T ▮ D A R E D
I ▮ L ▮ E ▮ I ▮ D ▮ ▮ S
F R E U D I A N S L I P
I ▮ ▮ E ▮ N ▮ C ▮ A ▮ D
S I C ▮ C O V E R ▮ C O O
M ▮ H ▮ E ▮ I ▮ ▮ E ▮ G
▮ E A R S P L I T T I N G
S ▮ N ▮ S ▮ I ▮ M ▮ E
T A N G O ▮ G R O U P E D
E ▮ E ▮ R ▮ O ▮ N ▮ E ▮ L
P A L I S A D E ▮ C L A Y
```

Puzzle 303

```
▮ C ▮ A ▮ C ▮ G U F F A W
T O G E T H E R ▮ A ▮ I
▮ M ▮ S ▮ E ▮ I ▮ ▮ B E D
A B E T ▮ A R M F U L ▮ E
▮ A ▮ H ▮ P ▮ Y ▮ E ▮ N
S T E E P E D ▮ L A S T S
▮ ▮ T ▮ R ▮ V ▮ R
L A K E S ▮ L E N G T H S
A ▮ L ▮ P ▮ R ▮ U ▮ A
W ▮ A B R O A D ▮ M I R O
F O X ▮ U ▮ I ▮ E ▮ A
U ▮ O ▮ ▮ N I C E N E S S
L O N G E D ▮ T ▮ T ▮ S
```

Puzzle 304

```
E L A N ▮ S C I S S I O N
F ▮ B ▮ U ▮ A ▮ N ▮ O
F L A N N E L ▮ T A K E N
E ▮ T ▮ E ▮ I ▮ W ▮ A
R Y E ▮ M ▮ C ▮ S L E E P
V ▮ ▮ P R O O F ▮ L ▮ P
E ▮ B ▮ L ▮ A ▮ L ▮ E
S ▮ E ▮ O P T I C ▮ A
C R A Z Y ▮ R ▮ T ▮ T A R
E ▮ N ▮ M ▮ E O H ▮ A
N O B L E ▮ B U R G E O N
C ▮ A ▮ N ▮ L ▮ Y ▮ R ▮ C
E I G H T E E N ▮ C E D E
```

Puzzle 305

```
D A T A B A S E ▮ D A M S
A ▮ H ▮ R ▮ A ▮ R ▮ T
F O R T E ▮ D I V O R C E
T ▮ I ▮ A ▮ D ▮ A ▮ A
▮ L ▮ K ▮ E N J O Y E D
G A L L E O N ▮ E ▮ S ▮ I
R ▮ ▮ V ▮ F ▮ L
A ▮ M E ▮ A F F A B L Y
C H I G N O N ▮ E ▮ E
E ▮ R ▮ T ▮ R M K
F U R N I S H ▮ S P O O N
U ▮ O ▮ E ▮ O A E ▮ E
L A R K ▮ E M I N E N C E
```

Puzzle 306

```
▮ R E A C T I O N A R Y
C ▮ S ▮ H ▮ N ▮ U E ▮ M O
O A T ▮ E I D E R ▮ M ▮ O
M ▮ E ▮ W ▮ I ▮ S T O R M
M A R R Y ▮ G E V E ▮
O ▮ N ▮ ▮ F O U R T E E N
N ▮ D ▮ S ▮ Y D ▮ T
P A R T T I M E ▮ ▮ A
L ▮ E ▮ A ▮ E W I R E R
A D D E R ▮ N A ▮ O ▮ I
C ▮ G ▮ L A T E X ▮ O I L
E ▮ E ▮ E ▮ A ▮ E ▮ F Y
▮ B R I T T L E N E S S
```

Puzzle 307

```
F A M O U S L Y ▮ A C H E
U ▮ O ▮ N ▮ A R O ▮ V
M I N E D ▮ G R E N A D E
E ▮ G ▮ I ▮ Q ▮ S R
▮ C R O S S C O U N T R Y
A ▮ E C L ▮ I ▮ O
G E L ▮ O S I E R ▮ C O N
N ▮ V ▮ N E A E
O V E R E S T I M A T E
S ▮ E R ▮ E ▮ E L
T O R R E N T ▮ N E R V E
I ▮ I D W T E A
C H E R ▮ L O P S I D E D
```

Puzzle 308

```
C H A N T S ▮ I M B U E D
U ▮ N ▮ A ▮ I A N A ▮ A
R ▮ T X ▮ N U Z Z L E S
B A I L I F F ▮ E O ▮ H
E ▮ ▮ I I ▮ S H A V E
D E M O N L ▮ D S
▮ A ▮ G A T E S ▮ E
I ▮ R ▮ R ▮ W E D G E
G A Z E D ▮ A A ▮ A
U ▮ I R ▮ T I D I N G S
A P P E A S E ▮ D E ▮ I
N ▮ A W ▮ D L A L
A R N O L D ▮ D E E P L Y
```

Puzzle 309

```
T I E D ▮ A D H E S I O N
O ▮ L ▮ R ▮ A N N ▮ I
M I D T E R M ▮ T Y S O N
A ▮ E ▮ M ▮ E E ▮ A
H O R R O R S T R U C K
A ▮ R C T T R
W O W ▮ S T O M A ▮ S E E
K A E U I ▮ A
▮ P R E F E R E N T I A L
O ▮ R U ▮ I D ▮ I
D R I L L ▮ F I N A L E S
D O L A G E E
S P R A Y I N G ▮ A R K S
```

Puzzle 310

```
A Q U A ▮ C O S M E T I C
C ▮ N ▮ D U A R O ▮ O
C O L L E C T ▮ S K E I N
O ▮ I ▮ M L T M ▮ F
M O T T O ▮ A W E S O M E
M ▮ N ▮ Y R L C
O L D E S T ▮ E S C O R T
D ▮ U ▮ T A T I
A L S O R A N ▮ R O M E O
T ▮ T A O O O N
I N P U T ▮ I R K S O M E
N ▮ A O N E S R
G E N E R A T E ▮ D E N Y
```

Puzzle 311

```
R E P R O A C H ▮ C L E F
E ▮ L T I ▮ C O U
A W A S H ▮ C R O U T O N
M ▮ I E A N T ▮ N
▮ I N T R O D U C T O R Y
I ▮ L W A E ▮ M
C E Y L O N ▮ A N G O R A
E ▮ E R A T C N
C O N G L O M E R A T E
R ▮ E D I A A A
E N A B L E D ▮ T O G A S
A ▮ R Y S E O K
M U S E ▮ S T U D E N T S
```

Puzzle 312

```
W A S T E F U L ▮ R I N D
O ▮ A ▮ N T A L ▮ I
R E M I T ▮ M I S F I T S
D ▮ U R O T A ▮ H
P A R S E C S ▮ R O D E O
R ▮ A P T O ▮ N
O S I E R S ▮ A L B E D O
C ▮ O O V U
E L T O N ▮ B U G B E A R
S ▮ R E T I N A
S C A P U L A ▮ C L I M B
O ▮ I R I A N L
R U T S ▮ A N A L O G U E
```

CROSSWORD

Puzzle 313

```
U L N A   S C H O L A R S
N   E   A   O   N   F   I
F R E E D O M   O F F A L
O   D   V   M   M   R   V
R H Y M E   A B A L O N E
E       N   S   T   N   R
S A F E T Y   K O W T O W
E   R   I   R   P       E
E P I S T L E   O I L E D
A   G   I   N   E   E   D
B R A V O   O R I G A M I
L   T   U   W   A   V   N
E V E N S O N G   B E R G
```

Puzzle 314

```
F I E R C E L Y   C O U P
R   S   O   A   U   W   E
E X C E L   V I N T N E R
E   A   L   I   A   E   P
Z E P H Y R S   T H R E E
I   E   W   H   T       N
N O S H O W   E R A S E D
G       B   P   A   U   I
P L U M B   L A C O N I C
O   P   L   U   T   L   U
I S S U E R S   I D E A L
N   E   S   E   V   S   A
T A T E   A S S E S S O R
```

Puzzle 315

```
B U D G E D   S   B   K
I   E   E X T E R I O R
C O D   C   A   O   R
K   U N F O L D   C R U X
E   C   Y   I   C   N
R A T T Y   C U P O L A S
O   T   M   L
S P O U S E S   H I D E S
I   C   N   S   A
L A S H   D R I V E N   M
N   I   R   N   G A P
D O W N S I D E   L   L
S   G   L   W H E E Z E
```

Puzzle 316

```
  P   A   C   B E L O N G
L A N D F I L L   F   I
  G   A   R   E   F O B
H O O P   C R E C H E   S
  D   T   U   P   R   O
P A C I F I C   B O S U N
  V   T   P   V
A C H E S   C R U E L T Y
B   A   S   U   R   A
A   N E A T E N   C A S H
C A D   A   I   A   S
U   E   G A N G S T E R
S O L I D S   G   T   L
```

Puzzle 317

```
  C O N S T R U C T E D
E   O   E   O   H   A   H
F E Z   D E L T A   R   I
E   F   G   L   S H R U G
E D D I E   E   I   I   H
C       B R A N D N E W
T   R   P   G   G   A   Y
I D E A L I S T
V   B   A   C   H A V O C
E M I T S   R   A   I   O
L   Y   T W I S T   N O D
Y   T   E   M   E   E   E
  C H I R O P O D I S T
```

Puzzle 318

```
H E G E M O N Y   K N I T
A   U   A   O   O   R
C H I C K   B E R M U D A
K   T   E   L   G   V
  A   S   E N C L A V E
T O R C H E S   O   T   S
R   I   N   T
I   B   F   M I S E R L Y
C O U N T R Y   T   E
K   Y   S   A   S   F
E V I D E N T   B E I G E
R   N   I   L   S   E
Y O G A   A C C E N T E D
```

Puzzle 319

```
P A R A D I G M   A C M E
O   E   E   A   D   A   M
S I D E S   S T I R R U P
H   U   P   N   O   T
  O C C A S I O N A L L Y
W   E   I   N   E   I
O D D   R O G E R   I N N
O   I   O   J   C   G
D E M O N S T R A T E D
W   E   G   C   L   L
O V E R L A P   K N A V E
R   T   Y   E   E   N   V
M U S T   D A Y T O D A Y
```

Puzzle 320

```
P L A C A R D S   D E A F
I   R   B   E   X   L
P L A Y S   C A L Y P S O
S   B   T   A   E   O
I   I A   D E D U C E D
D U C T I L E   I   T   I
E   E   N   S   T   I   N
P   M   E   P O S T B A G
A S U N D E R   O   U
R   T   T   O L R D
T H U R M A N   V I S T A
E   A   T   E   A   M
D U L L   C O N S E R V E
```

Puzzle 321

```
  A C C O M M O D A T E
M   R   B   A   E   S
I   O   E D G E S   R O T
N E W T S   P   K   S   R
D   D   I   I   S I E V E
B R E A T H E D
L   D   Y   S   G   U
O       S A N T I A G O
W A V E D   P   A   R   U
I   I   E   P   R E A M S
N A G   B L E A T   G   L
G   G   U   A   L   E   Y
  P O L T E R G E I S T
```

Puzzle 322

```
N O S E D I V E   S K I P
I   P   I   I   B   R   A
L A I R S   S E L L O U T
E   N   H   I   A   N   I
  I N V E R T E B R A T E
F   E   A   S   B       N
L A Y E R S   H E R M I T
A   T   S   R   A   S
P R E D E T E R M I N E
P   N   N   T   O   K   L
I N S P E C T   U N I F Y
N   U   D   E   T   N   N
G L E E   O R T H O D O X
```

Puzzle 323

```
W A T T   H A C I E N D A
I   A   P   S   N   E   G
N U M B E R S   T O W E R
K   E   R   I   E   N   E
L E D   F   S   R E E S E
E       O M I T S   S   A
P   P   R   E   S   S   B
I   I   M A G I C   T
C O N G A   I   T   F E E
K   C   N   R   I   R   N
E T H I C   D I O X I D E
R   E   E   L   N   A   S
S I D E S T E P   O R B S
```

Puzzle 324

```
  D O C U M E N T A R Y
F   R   N   V   I   E   B
A   D   D R O L L   V I A
S U E D E   L   L   U   N
T   R   R   V   S P E A K
F I L I G R E E       H
O   Y   O   H   D   O
R       D E F E R R A L
W E A N S   N   A   A   I
A   U   M   T   D I C E D
R E X   E D I T S   H   A
D   I   L   R   E   M   Y
  I N F L U E N T I A L
```

Puzzle 325

H	Y	A	C	I	N	T	H		D	E	L	L
A		L		N		O		C		M		E
L	E	A	S	T		S	O	A	P	B	O	X
F		R		E		S		B		E		I
H	O	M	E	R		E		I		D	E	C
E		E		D		M	A	S	O	N		O
A	R		D		I			E		I	G	R
R			T	R	A	C	T		G		R	
T	O	N		T		U		M	E	N	S	A
E		I	E	S		A		I			P	
D	E	F	U	N	C	T		K	E	T	C	H
L		T		T		E	E	E		E		E
Y	O	Y	O		I	N	T	R	U	D	E	R

Puzzle 326

	A	C	C	L	A	M	A	T	I	O	N	
P		O		O		I		O	V		D	
R	O	D		B	I	D	E	S		E		E
E		E	B		D			S	T	R	I	P
D	U	S	T	Y		L		I		A		A
E			C		T	E	E	N	A	G	E	R
C		T		C		G		G		E		T
E	T	H	O	L	O	G	Y					M
S		E		E		A		T	H	A	N	E
S	Y	R	I	A		L	O		B			N
O		M		R	E	L	A	X		H	U	T
R	A	L		O		O		I	O			S
	P	L	A	Y	I	N	G	C	A	R	D	

Puzzle 327

B	L	I	S	S	F	U	L		S	A	W	S
O		N		H		P		F		O		
Y	U	C	C	A		B	A	N	E	F	U	L
S		H		T		E		A				V
		E	T		A	I	R	L	I	N	E	
B	U	S	I	E	S	T		E		R		N
A			R		H		E		E			T
L	C	E		E	L	E	G	I	E	S		
A	V	O	I	D	E	D		A		N		J
N	S					I		R	J		T	
C	O	M	P	A	C	T		S	W	E	A	R
E		I			E		E		A		C	A
D	O	C	K		I	D	O	L	A	T	R	Y

Puzzle 328

	C	L	O	S	E	F	I	S	T	E	D	
A		A		W		O		A		M		S
P	I	P		A	I	R	E	D		I		O
P		S	B		G		D	I	N	A	R	
O	P	E	N	S		E		E			C	
I				O	R	D	N	A	N	C	E	
N		G		L		S		T		R		E
T	O	R	R	E	N	T	S			E		
M		A		A		R		P	A	C	E	S
E	L	V	I	S		O		O		R		S
N		E			H	O	P	E	S		E	W	E
T			L	E			I		I	D		S
	S	Y	N	D	I	C	A	T	I	O	N	

Puzzle 329

R	I	P	E		A	I	R	P	O	R	T	S
I		A		N		C		L	I			T
C	A	S	S	A	V	A		A	M	P	L	E
O		S		R		R		I		O		W
C	H	E	E	R	F	U	L	N	E	S	S	
H			O		S		S	T			N	
E	L	B	O	W	S		G	A	T	E	A	U
T		O		M		O		I				I
	F	R	U	I	T	F	U	L	N	E	S	S
F		S		N		I		Q		A		
L	U	C	I	D		S	U	N	B	U	R	N
E		H		E		E		G		A		C
A	N	T	I	D	O	T	E		B	L	U	E

Puzzle 330

	C		P		P		D	U	R	H	A	M
C	A	L	A	M	A	R	I		I			I
	M		R		T		N		K	E	G	
L	E	I	A		I	C	E	A	G	E		H
	R		S		E		S		S		R	T
C	A	T	I	O	N	S		S	A	S	S	Y
			T			T		T		N		
C	A	M	E	O		B	R	O	T	H	E	R
O		A		V		I		E		F		
M	R	A	K	I	N	G		L	I	F	E	
P	U	G		S		G		O		U		
L		I			O	V	E	R	P	A	S	S
Y	O	N	D	E	R		R		E		E	

Puzzle 331

	T	C	H	A	I	K	O	V	S	K	Y	
W		O		P		N		I		I		V
H	A	D		T	A	I	N	T		B		I
I		E		L		V		A	M	B	E	R
T	A	R	D	Y		E		L		U		I
E			I	S	O	L	A	T	E	D		
C		C		C			Y		Z		E	
O	X	Y	M	O	R	O	N				S	
L		A		U		F		M	A	N	I	C
L	I	N	E	R		F		A		O		E
A			A	N	I	O	N		V	A	N	
R		D		G		S		T		A		T
	L	E	V	E	L	H	E	A	D	E	D	

Puzzle 332

T	U	B	E		I	N	S	P	I	R	E	D
O		U		P		O		O		E		I
M	A	R	C	H	E	R		S	A	V	E	S
M		S		O		D		T		I		T
Y	E	T		T		I		G	I	V	E	R
L			O	S	C	A	R		A	E		
E		B		G		A		L	L	S		S
E		O		R	A	P	I	D				
J	U	N	T	A		I		U		A	L	I
O		A		P		C	A	R		R		N
N	I	N	T	H		N	E	T	T	I	N	G
E		Z	E			E		I		E	E	L
S	H	A	M	R	O	C	K		A	L	L	Y

Puzzle 333

A	I	R	S	P	A	C	E		G	A	U	L
W		A		R		O		A		D		O
R	I	F	L	E		B	U	R	R	I	T	O
Y		T		C				T		E		S
	R	E	C	O	N	S	T	I	T	U	T	E
A		R		N		P		S		E		
B	U	S		D	O	U	B	T		M	E	N
S			I			M		I	A		D	
O	U	T	S	T	R	E	T	C	H	E	D	
R		R		I			A		S		E	
B	I	O	L	O	G	Y		L	A	T	I	N
E		V		N		O	L		R		R	V
D	Y	E	D		B	U	S	Y	B	O	D	Y

Puzzle 334

E	N	D	O	R	S	E	S		S	K	I	N
L		I		A		N		A		H		O
S	Q	U	I	B		M	O	N	D	A	Y	S
E		R		B		I		T		K		E
	U	N	F	L	A	T	T	E	R	I	N	G
C		A		E		Y		D		A		
R	U	L	E	R	S		L	I	V	E	R	Y
A		O		S		L		N		S		
F	O	R	T	U	I	T	O	U	S	L	Y	
T		E		S		A		V		I		E
I	N	F	L	E	C	T		I	N	S	E	T
L		R		O		A		T		O		
Y	A	R	D		G	R	A	N	D	S	O	N

Puzzle 335

	S	T	A	R	S	T	U	D	D	E	D	
A		A		I		R		R		M		W
C	O	X		D	R	A	P	E		P		I
U		E		G		U		S	W	O	O	N
P	O	S	S	E		M		S		W		D
U				B	A	S	E	L	E	S	S	
N		B		S			S		R			C
C	R	O	T	C	H	E	T					R
T		N		U		U		A	R	G	U	E
U	N	F	I	T		R	U	E				E
R		I		T	R	E	N	D		C	A	N
E		R		L		K	I	K	S			
	B	E	N	E	F	A	C	T	I	O	N	

Puzzle 336

M	A	G	I	C	I	A	N		A	L	E	C
I		A		O		C		C		A		O
S	A	L	O	N		T	R	A	N	S	O	M
M		I		T		I		R		E		P
A	I	L	E	R	O	N		E	R	R	O	R
N		E		I		G		L				E
A	M	O	E	B	A		H	E	A	L	T	H
G		U		M		S		E		E		E
E	N	A	C	T		A	B	S	T	A	I	N
M		H		I		K		N		R		S
E	Y	E	S	O	R	E		E	N	N	U	I
N		A		N		D		S		E		V
T	I	D	E		C	O	N	S	T	R	U	E

CROSSWORD

Puzzle 337

```
T E E N   P E R I O D I C
A   X   S   Q   N   I   O
S H I A T S U   T H O R N
T   S   R   A   E   C   T
E X T R A   T O R P E D O
L   I   E   M   S   R
E N E R G Y   D E F E C T
S   M   H   B   D   I
S W I F T E R   I D A H O
N   T   E   U   A   L   N
E A T E N   T E R M I N I
S   E   E   A   Y   G   S
S T R A D D L E   U N I T
```

Puzzle 338

```
  A   B   A   F A B R I C
A R P E G G I O   E   O
  T   R   I   R   V O W
M I N I   L E G U M E   E
  S   B   I   E   A   R
A T T E S T S   M I L L S
  R   Y   M   M
L I V I D   D E R A N G E
O   E   B   T   G   E
G   E M E R G E   I O N S
J A R   A   O   N   I
A   E   W O R K E D U P
M A D M A N   S   D   S
```

Puzzle 339

```
R E P U B L I C   I T E M
E   A   E   M   C   O   I
E N D O W   B A H R A I N
D   D   I   I   S   O
  C O L L A B O R A T O R
J   C   D   E   O   I
U P K E E P   U P S H O T
B   R   C   R   A   Y
I N C O M P A R A B L E
L   H   E   U   C   O   B
A M O U N T S   T I G E R
N   I   T   E   O   E   I
T O R N   E S T R A N G E
```

Puzzle 340

```
A S S E T S   S H E L V E
M   O   H   N   E   I   A
O   C   E   A C R O B A T
U N K E M P T   B   R   E
R   A   I   S T E E R   Y
S N U B S   O   T   T
  N   K I N D S   T
F   L   A   K N O L L
R I O T S   L   I   O
Y   V   P   I M P U T E D
I C I N E S S   P   H   G
N   N   L   M   E   A   E
G A G G L E   W R I T E R
```

Puzzle 341

```
  R E C O N S T R U C T
I   M   Y   C   E   U   I
N   P   S T A I N   P I N
F E A S T   L   E   I   C
L   T   E E   W I D E R
A P H O R I S M   E
M   Y   S   C   F   M
M   I M M A T U R E
A R R A Y   U   N   L   N
B   E   E E   A S S E T
L E A   M O S E S   O   A
E   R   E L T   M L
  E M A N C I P A T E D
```

Puzzle 342

```
C O N S I S T S   O P A L
O   O   N   R   P   E   U
A T T I C   E R R A T I C
X   I   O   A   E   A   K
  D O G M A T I C A L L Y
P   N   P   Y   O   D
R U S S E T   A G A S S I
E   E   T   S   N   T   P
S C R E E N W R I T E R
O   N   E   T   R   P
M U S I C A L   I N N E R
E   E   E   L   O   U   O
N E S T   T S U N A M I S
```

Puzzle 343

```
A W A R D S   S P O N G E
C   U   I   P   O   A   X
C A D E N Z A   W   I   U
E   I   G   C U D D L E D
P U T T Y   K   E   E
T   I   E   R O O M S
  I O   M U D D Y   V
L A N K Y   L   E   V
O   O   S   U   S C R E E
C A P S T A N   M   S   R
K   I   I   C O O K E R S
E   L   F   H   K   E   E
D E L A Y S   F E A R E D
```

Puzzle 344

```
D O F F   C O N F E T T I
E   L   T   W   L   R   L
C H A G R I N   U S U A L
L   M   A   O   A   S
A W E I N S P I R I N G
R   S   O E   C   A
E A T   P I P E S   Y A M
D   W   A   U   C   E
  M I S R E P R E S E N T
C   S   E   N   R   H
L U T O N   H I C K O R Y
U   E   C   E   E   D   S
B A R N Y A R D   K E P T
```

Puzzle 345

```
  E S T A T E A G E N T
A   U   M   L   E   U   D
P I G   P I A N O   N   I
O   A   L   P   L U N G S
C O R N Y   S   O   E   S
A       K E D G E R E E
L   A   A   Y   Y   M
Y O U N G E S T   I
P   D   E   I   B I S O N
T R I L L   M   U   N   A
I   T   E X I T S   A R T
C   O   S   A   T   I   E
  P R E S E N T A B L E
```

Puzzle 346

```
O A K S   O S B O U R N E
C   E   Q   C   B   E   A
C O N Q U E R   S M A R T
U   Y   E   A   E   C   S
P R A I S E W O R T H Y
I   T   L   V   E   B
E L I X I R   D A M S E L
D   T   O   M   T   U
  M A L N O U R I S H E D
S   L   M   S   O   O   G
I B I Z A   L I N E A G E
L   C   R   I   S   R   O
T A S H K E N T   E D E N
```

Puzzle 347

```
  A B O M I N A T I O N
D   U   U   E   E   V   D
Y E N   C O U P E   E   I
N   K   K   R   M A R I S
A S S A Y   O   I   R   R
M       I N U N D A T E
I   D A   G   N   S
C L E R I C A L   P
A   V   R   V   B U D G E
L O O K S   E R R   R   C
L   T   H E N C E   A F T
Y   E   I   G A W S
  R E S P L E N D E N T
```

Puzzle 348

```
S A C K   B I N D W E E D
O   Y   I   N   I   A   E
L I N I N G S   V E R G E
I   I   D   A   E   N   M
D I C T I O N A R I E S
I   S   E   S   S   I
T R A C T S   V I C T I M
Y   I   I   A   O
  T R A N S C E N D E N T
Z   D   C   U   A   M   A
E G R E T   M O R D A N T
T   O   L   E   Y   I   E
A P P L Y I N G   F L E D
```

Puzzle 349

Puzzle 350

Puzzle 351

Puzzle 352

Puzzle 353

Puzzle 354

Puzzle 355

```
C O U N S E L S   A F A R
I   N   U   A   H   L   E
T H U M B   M E A D O W S
Y   S   S   I   U   U   O
  S U P E R N A T U R A L
S   A   Q   A   E     V
T A L C U M   S C Y T H E
U   E   L   O   R   S
D I S I N G E N U O U S
Y   U   T   S   T   N   F
I N S U L T S   U N D E R
N   A   Y   E   R   L   E
G A N G   I N T E R E S T
```

Puzzle 356

```
  F U R T H E R M O R E
B   N   I   M   O   E   I
E   E   G A P E D   V I M
L E A C H   I   E   E   P
L   R   T   R   M E L E E
B A T T E R E D       R
O   H   N     S   C   T
T     D A I Q U I R I
T I M E S   V   U   T   N
O   A   E   E   A S I D E
M A R   T E N O R   Z   N
S   C   U   U   E E T
  S H E P H E R D I N G
```

Puzzle 357

```
F L I P P I N G   S L E W
A   C   E   I     E   E
C R I M P   P I N B A L L
E   C   P   P     G   L
    L   E   E X P O U N D
C H E E R E D   R   E   O N
O   O     O   O     N
U   H   N   B A G G A G E
G L A C I A L   N   U
H   S   O   O   T   B
I N S I G H T   S C U B A
N   L   C   I   M   R
G L E N   C H E S T N U T
```

Puzzle 358

```
  S M I T H E R E E N S
E   O   A   N   L   E   P
G A D   L A D L E   M   I
O   E   E   U   C R E P E
T U S K S   R   T   S   C
I         T E L E V I S E
S   L   M   D   S   O   F
T R A V A I L S       F
I   M   S   A   M U S I C
C U B E S   R   E   T   A
A   A   A N G E L   I N K
L   D   G   E   T   P   E
  G A T E C R A S H E R
```

Puzzle 359

```
R E P E A L   O B J E C T
A   O   N   C   U   N   A
N   O   T   O F F I C E S
C A R T O O N   F   L   K
I   I   N   S   S T O L E
D A D D Y   O       S   D
    E   M U L E S   E
C   C   A   K U D O S
H A I L S   T   I   E
U   S   T   I N D R A W N
C H I C A G O   D   G   I
K   O   K   N   E A O
S I N G E D   A D O R E R
```

Puzzle 360

```
  Q U A R R E L S O M E
E   N   A   U   E   O   C
L   A   N O R S E   G N U
E V I L S   O   M   U   T
C   D   A   P   S P L A T
T R E N C H E S       I
R   D   K     D   F   N
O         S W E E P I N G
N E W E R   H   A   S   E
I   A   O   O   D A T E D
C U D   A T O M S   F   G
S   E   R   P   E U E
  D R A S T I C A L L Y
```

Puzzle 361

```
G A D G E T   G   E   E
A   E   R E L A T I V E
L A B   E   E   H   O
O   S   D   F   O   E
P O E M S   S U R P A S S
    I   B   L   I
C H E D D A R   C A R A T
  Y   N   S   A   A   R
D E M I   S P L A Y S   O
  N   G   I   L   H O W
M A C H I S M O   E   E
  S   T   T   W E A S E L
```

Puzzle 362

```
E T C H I N G S   H I N T
L   O   R   R   D   W
L E M U R   U K U L E L E   N
A   E   E   B   A   N
  O   G   B O O K L E T   I
C E N T U R Y   P   S   E
O   L   E   E
L   E   A   T E N U O U S
A D M I R E R   E   C   H
N   B   I   N   U
D R O P O F F   D E L V E
E   S   L   E   A   A
R A S P   R E N D E R E D
```

Puzzle 363

```
D E D U C E   T W I N G E
E   E   H   D   A   U   R
R   A   A   I N S E R T S
M A L A R I A   T   T   A
I   G   G   E R U P T
S P I T E   N   R   Z
  N   S T O U T   E
I   F   S   W A D E D
S P O T S   T   I   I
R   R   I   I G N I T E S
A L M A N A C   K   A   H
E   E   G   S   L   L   E
L E D G E S   R E B E L S
```

Puzzle 364

```
W O R S H I P S   E L M S
I   E   U   R   I   O
P A L E R   O P T I M U M
E   I   R   O   I   B
    E   I   F L A T T E R
D E F E C T S   N   S   E
E   A   T   R
A   R   N   S H A M P O O
D E E P E S T   R   L
L   P   A   C   A   B
O R A T O R Y   T I N G E
C   S   E   I   E   E
K I T S   E D U C A T O R
```

Puzzle 365

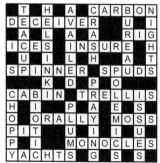

```
  T   H   A   C A R B O N
D E C E I V E R   U   I
  A   L   A   A   R I G
I C E S   I N S U R E   H
  U   I   L   H   A   T
S P I N N E R   S P U D S
    K   D   P   O
C A B I N   T R E L L I S
H   I   P   A   E   S
O   O R A L L Y   M O S S
P I T   U   I   U
P   I   M O N O C L E S
Y A C H T S   G   S   S
```